Pure Maths For A-Level

Forthcoming titles of related interest

GCSE Mathematics
Owen Elbourn

Pure Maths
For A-Level

Owen Elbourn

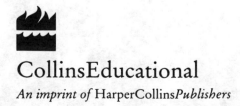

CollinsEducational
An imprint of HarperCollins*Publishers*

Published by
CollinsEducational
77–85 Fulham Palace Road
Hammersmith
London W6 8JB
UK

10 East 53rd Street
New York, NY 10022
USA

First published in 1992

British Library Cataloguing in Publication Data
Elbourn, Owen
  Pure mathematics.
  I. Title   II. Series
  510

  ISBN 0-00-322259-4

Library of Congress Cataloging in Publication Data
Available from the Library of Congress

Typeset in $9\frac{1}{2}$ on 12 point Times by
MS Filmsetting Limited, Frome, Somerset
and printed in Great Britain by
Butler & Tanner Ltd, Frome, Somerset

Contents

x

A note from the author

I have been teaching A level mathematics for 30 years and this book reflects that experience, and the approach that has worked for my students. I have tried to write it in an informal style and to make the book as easy to use as possible. Advanced mathematics is a difficult course and it can be the cause of much frustration, but I hope you will find it is a subject which offers much satisfaction and enjoyment.

Using this book

If you are to obtain the maximum benefit from this book you should use it in the way it was intended when it was written. So please, read this introduction carefully.

The book is aimed at all A level students, including those whose achievement so far is a GCSE grade C pass obtained at the intermediate level. It covers the pure mathematics content of the single subject A level examination for all examining boards.

The book is presented in the recommended working order, and full solutions are given to most of the questions. All discussions on theory have been kept to a minimum. The outstanding feature is the principle of teaching by example. Generally, a problem is presented, solved and then the relevant theory is explained. In each case it is essential that you read all the solutions carefully, however confident you feel, because often new theory or routine is introduced in the questions. Hence the book is of particular value to those students working alone or with minimal tuition. It is especially useful to teachers who are teaching A level mathematics for the first time.

At the end of the book there are 26 worksheets, some of which contain new material. These are intended to be used as you progress through the book and are designed to be tackled at specific stages. There is a table on page 313 showing when they should be done. There are also reminders at the ends of the relevant chapters. The purpose of these worksheets is constantly to review the work you have already done. This approach may seem harder than leaving all the revision until the end of the book, but it helps you to understand the whole course as you work through it.

Once you have completed the book you will be ready to start working through past A level examination papers. You will need to do as many of these as possible. If your course starts in September (usual) you should be through the book by December, 16 months later. You can use time from Christmas onwards to work through every A level paper you can get hold of. Papers are readily available from the examination boards. The book covers all the A level courses, except SMP, and you will need past papers for the particular syllabus you are doing. All questions set in the book prepare you for tackling examination papers. To help you with these – and indeed any problems you must solve through the course of this book – read the section on study skills and examination preparation on page xiii.

Study skills and examination preparation

Advanced level mathematics is a difficult course but it is also a very rewarding one. Mathematics is a most frustrating and a most satisfying subject to study, probably more so than any other subject. There is a popular belief that mathematics is a subject for the privileged few; that you must have some sort of extraordinary gift before you can do it. How often have you heard people say, 'I wasn't bad at school, but I couldn't do maths'?

More than any other subject, A level mathematics tests and develops your ability to persevere. It is important that you approach your study of the subject in an atmosphere of enterprise and initiative. Often you may read a question and feel at a loss to answer it, but don't give in! Spend some time thinking about the problem and don't be afraid to write something down, no matter how little confidence you have in its accuracy. Only when you have had a thorough try should you turn to the solution. Compared to other subjects mathematics is one which demands little memory work but much reasoning. Logic, deduction, and forming the maximum number of conclusions from the minimum of information are all hallmarks of mathematics. You will find advanced level mathematics very different from GCSE work. The advanced level is often based on rather simple information but the complexity of its problems is manifold.

Ideally the time allocation required to study A level mathematics should be two hours per day, five days per week, for two years. The two hours should be separated by at least one hour, and if one hour each day is a taught lesson you will be very fortunate indeed. For many students there is opportunity only for one or two lessons per week. In these circumstances this book will be of considerable help due to two important factors. One, the theory is kept to a minimum while still covering all that is necessary. Two, all but the simplest questions are provided with full solutions, and not just the final answers.

The idea is that you should have a go; write something down and play about with it – struggle, in fact. Mathematics is a mentally adventurous subject in which you have to be prepared to experiment and try out all ideas. Only after you have tried your hardest will you appreciate the full value of the solution. Working in this way builds up your mathematical expertise and knowledge, and you will learn how to present solutions.

Mathematics does not lend itself to frantic last minute study before an examination. It must be learnt slowly, and thoroughly, over a long period of time. 'Little and often' is by far the best method of study. As you study mathematics you will become aware of a strong element of pattern in the work, and it is the observation of these patterns which will help you to remember the basic materials and techniques.

There is a certain amount which you must be prepared to learn. Most examinations today provide reference leaflets, but too many students console themselves, thinking that because the information is on the leaflet it does not have to be learnt. This is a mistake. You cannot mentally manipulate information if you do not know it – it must be in your head, not on a piece of paper. The real purpose of leaflets is for you to check whether a plus sign in a formula is indeed a plus sign, and if it is $\dot{x}\ddot{y} - \ddot{x}\dot{y}$ or $\dot{x}\ddot{y} - \dot{x}\ddot{y}$, for example.

Similarly, notebooks are of doubtful value. Many students feel secure with a well-filled notebook, but it is a false security. In the head, not on paper. A key feature of this book is the block of worksheets. They should be started after you complete chapter 6. Working through them makes you repeatedly revise the course from an early stage. It is important to work through the book in the order it is written if you are to gain the maximum benefit from it. The book has wide margins in which to make brief personal comments or notes. The book is self sufficient if you use it this way.

Advanced level examiners, whilst upholding standards, are in the business of trying to be as helpful as possible to the candidates. Their working brief is to look for all possible reasons for giving you marks. Examiners do not look for reasons to deduct marks. Nevertheless, every mark has to be earned. Mathematics is about pursuing an argument from beginning to end, so complete solutions to fewer questions will gain more marks than partial answers to many questions.

In an exam, always work neatly and cross out mistakes, including whole or part answers, with a single straight line. If you have some correction fluid throw it away – examiners and teachers detest the stuff. An examiner can read what you have crossed out if he wishes and decide whether it was worth any credit.

Mathematics, as I have said earlier, can be very frustrating but it is undoubtedly immensely satisfying. If you have at least a grade C GCSE obtained at the intermediate level and you think you can meet the demands of the subject then get on with it! By the time you are through this book, in fact long before you are through it, you will be enjoying the pleasure and satisfaction that only this subject can give.

Chapter 1

FACTORISATION

Aims and objectives

Having worked through this chapter you will be able to factorise:

common factors	$ax + ay = a(x + y)$
including **'grouping' examples**	$ax + ay + bx + by = (a + b)(x + y)$
quadratic expressions	$x^2 + 11x + 30 = (x + 6)(x + 5)$
more complicated harder quadratics	$6x^2 - 5x - 6 = (3x + 2)(2x - 3)$
the difference of two squares.	$x^2 - y^2 = (x - y)(x + y)$

Splitting into factors

We have to be able to factorise quickly and efficiently to make progress in mathematics. A mathematician does it as commonly as a mechanic takes wheels off cars. Just as the mechanic learns how to take wheels off without looking at the instruction book, so we must be able to factorise without having to refer to notes etc.

Factorise means break up into factors.

$6 = 2 \times 3$

the factors of 6

$5 = 2 + 3$

2 and 3 are not factors of 5
∴ they have a + sign between them.

the sign which must be between factors

> **Remember**
>
> e.g. = *exempli gratia* which means for example. In this chapter these have been worked out for you.

Factors multiply together — they do not add together.

Number or expression	Factorised	Factors
15	3×5	3, 5
77	7×11	7, 11
9	3×3	3, 3
ab	$a \times b$	a, b
$5x$	$5 \times x$	$5, x$
$* \triangledown$	$* \times \triangledown$	$*, \triangledown$

> **Remember**
>
> ∵ = because
> ∴ = therefore
> Both signs will be used frequently in this book.

Note that 1 is a factor of all numbers but there is usually little point in writing, for example, $5 = 5 \times 1$ so it is often left out. However, although it is omitted in straightforward examples like these, it will be used frequently in later work.

Common factors

Brackets often occur in mathematics and they play an important part in factorising. Remember the rule:

> **When multiplying a bracket multiply everything inside the bracket.**

Remember

in algebra the $\times$ sign is usually left out.
$5 \times (x + y)$ would be written as $5(x + y)$.

e.g.

$5 \times (x + y) = 5 \times x + 5 \times y$ which is written $5x + 5y$

The reverse process of saying $5x + 5y = 5(x + y)$ is **factorising**.

$5x + 5y$ has been split into two quantities, 5 and $(x + y)$, which when multiplied together give $5x + 5y$.

e.g.

$3a + 6c = 3(a + 2c)$ i.e.   3 and $(a + 2c)$ are factors of $3a + 6c$

$x^2 + xy = x(x + y)$ i.e. x and $(x + y)$ are factors of $x^2 + xy$

$3k + 6p + 2h$ has no factors

$3k + 6k^2 + 9k^3 = 3k(1 + 2k + 3k^2)$

   i.e. 3, k and $(1 + 2k + 3k^2)$ are the factors of $3k + 6k^2 + 9k^3$

$a + ax = a \times 1 + a \times x = a(1 + x)$

Remember

a means $a \times 1$.

There now follows an exercise on factorising. It consists of 40 questions divided into eight groups. Do group A and check. If your answers are correct leave out the rest, otherwise do group B and check. Go on until it is not necessary to do any more.

Really there is no excuse for getting a factorising question wrong. Remember that if you multiply out your answer you should get what you started with.

EXERCISE 1.1

(*Answers on page 11*)

Factorise these as completely as possible.

e.g.

$2xy + 4xz$ $=$ $x(2y + 4z)$ $=$ $2x(y + 2z)$
partially factorised   *completely factorised*
(two factors)   *(three factors, impossible to make any more)*

Group A
1. 105
2. $ax + az$
3. $6a^2b + 3ab^2$
4. $x^2 + 2xy + 3xz$
5. $4a^2 - 8ab + 12ac$

Group B
1. 42
2. $c + cd$
3. $abc - bcd$
4. $a^2px - p^2x^2 + p^2y^2$
5. $2xy - 4x^2 + 6xz - 8xz^2$

Group C
1. 28
2. $2x + 6y$
3. $8pq - 12qr$
4. $x^3 - 2x^2y + 3xy^2$
5. $6c^3 - 4c^2 + 2c$

Group D
1. 72
2. $5k - 15l$
3. $20xy - 15xz$
4. $apx^2 - p^2x^2 + apx$
5. $6pq - 3p^2 + 12pr - 9qr$

Group E
1. 57
2. $wk - vk$
3. $5x^2y + 20xy^2$
4. $2(a + b) - x(a + b)$
5. $3ur^2 - 21u^2r + 15ur$

Group F
1. 210
2. $ax - a$
3. $pqr + qrs$
4. $x^2yz - xy^2z + rst$
5. $4a^2 - 16b^2$

Group G
1. 320
2. $3t - 12$
3. $abc^2 + ab^2c + a^2bc$
4. $8k^2lm - 4klm^2 + 6l^2mk$
5. $9p^2qr - 81pq^2r + 27pqr^3$

Group H
1. 132
2. $2x + 4y$
3. $wrv - vrx$
4. $\frac{1}{4}ut^2 - \frac{1}{2}ut$
5. $4x(a + b) - 8y(a + b) - (a + b)(k + l)$

So much for the basic version of factors. By now you should understand what factors are.

It is necessary to be efficient at recognising and factorising different types of algebraic expressions. You will have met these before but do not assume you are efficient with them: if you think you are, try the short test which follows.

EFFICIENCY TEST ON FACTORISING

Time allowed $2\frac{1}{2}$ minutes. No reference or calculator allowed.

(*Answers on page 11*)

1. Evaluate $51^2 - 49^2$
2. Factorise $x^2 - 5x - 6$
3. Factorise $12x^2 - 10x - 12$
4. Factorise $8x^2 + 6xy - 9y^2$
5. Factorise $2ac + 4am + 3kc + 6km$
6. Factorise $16k^4 - 1$

If you got at least five correct in the time allowed then your factorising ability is good and you can leave out the rest of this chapter, but use the exercises for occasional revision and practice.

If you did not get five correct – even if you did not get *one* correct – do not worry. The test is a guide to the pace of working of a good A-level student. Following this chapter through will help you develop that pace.

What are quadratic expressions?

e.g. Consider $(a + b)(x + y)$

$$(a + b)(x + y) \underset{factorising}{\overset{expanding}{\longleftrightarrow}} ax + by + bx + ay \qquad the\ name\ for\ removing\ brackets$$

e.g. Consider $(x + a)(x + b)$.

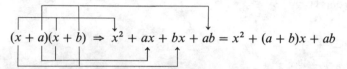

$$(x + a)(x + b) \Rightarrow x^2 + ax + bx + ab = x^2 + (a + b)x + ab$$

multiply everything in one bracket by everything in the other bracket

Now we shall look for some pattern or links.

$(x + \star)(x + \oplus)$ will always produce

(1) an x^2 term

(2) an x term

(3) a constant term (one without x in it)

Such an expression is a quadratic expression. Note that the sum of $\star$ and $\oplus$ gives the number of x's and the product of $\star$ and $\oplus$ gives the constant term.

$$(x + a)(x + b) = x^2 + (a + b)x + ab$$

sum

product

Now factorise $\qquad x^2 + 5x - 6$

	Step 1 *this tells you*	Step 2 *this tells you*
	$(x \quad)(x \quad)$	$(x - 6)(x + 1)$
		or $(x + 6)(x - 1)$
		or $(x - 3)(x + 2)$
		or $(x + 3)(x - 2)$

Checking, by expanding.

$(x - 6)(x + 1) = x^2 - 5x - 6$

$(x + 6)(x - 1) = x^2 + 5x - 6$ ←———————————— *the correct one*

$(x - 3)(x + 2) = x^2 - x - 6$

$(x + 3)(x - 2) = x^2 + x - 6$

So factorising $x^2 + 5x - 6$ gives $(x + 6)(x - 1)$.

EXAMPLE

Now try factorising $x^2 - 7x + 12$.

You should get $(x - 3)(x - 4)$ and in finding these factors you could have written, or considered

$$(x + 1)(x + 12)$$

or $(x + 2)(x + 6)$

or $(x + 3)(x + 4)$

or $(x - 1)(x - 12)$

or $(x - 2)(x - 6)$

or $(x - 3)(x - 4)$

or even other versions with the signs mixed.

    We need to find a more organised way of factorising a quadratic expression. For the next ten minutes confusion will reign but persevere, it will be well worth it!

Methods for factorising quadratic expressions

EXAMPLE

Consider the same expression as above.

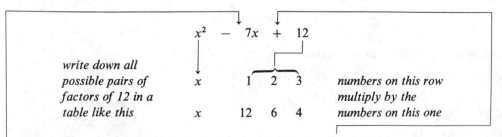

Now we have to decide what we are looking for: this 'plus' sign tells us we need the same sign in each bracket i.e. an addition to give the answer -7.

In the table we now work on diagonals.

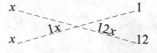

x 1   *no*   ∵ *1x and 12x do not*
       add to give 7x
x 12

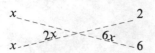

x 2   *no*   ∵ *2x and 6x do not*
       add to give 7x
x 6

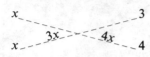

x 3   *yes*   ∵ *3x + 4x = 7x*

x 4

∴ factors are   (top row)(bottom row)

         i.e. $(x - 3)(x - 4)$

Finally these minus signs are inserted because $-7x$ is required.

> At this point you may be a bit dizzy but keep going and follow through the next one!

EXAMPLE

Factorise $x^2 + 6x - 16$

$$x^2 + 6x - 16$$

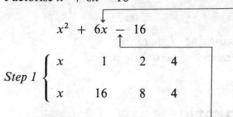

Step 1 $\begin{cases} x & 1 & 2 & 4 \\ x & 16 & 8 & 4 \end{cases}$

Step 2   Look at   and

        which tell us we want factors of 16 with a difference of 6.

Step 3   From the table: x 1

                      ⟹ $16x - x = 15x$ *no*

             x 16

             x 2

                      ⟹ $8x - 2x = 6x$ *yes*

             x 8

Step 4   Brackets are $(x \quad 2)(x \quad 8)$ at this stage.

        We now have to choose between $(x - 2)(x + 8)$
                                    and $(x + 2)(x - 8)$

           $(x - 2)(x + 8) \Rightarrow \ldots + 6x \ldots$

       and $(x + 2)(x - 8) \Rightarrow \ldots - 6x \ldots$

∴ factors are $(x - 2)$ and $(x + 8)$.

$x^2 + 6x - 16 = (x - 2)(x + 8)$

EXERCISE 1.2

(*Answers on page 12*)

In each question, factorise the expression into two brackets.

Group A
1. $x^2 - x - 12$
2. $x^2 - 9x + 14$
3. $x^2 - 5x + 4$
4. $x^2 - 4x - 32$
5. $x^2 - x - 72$

Group B
1. $x^2 - 3x + 2$
2. $x^2 + 6x + 5$
3. $x^2 - 11x + 18$
4. $x^2 + 7x + 12$
5. $x^2 + 17x + 60$

Group C
1. $x^2 + 4x - 5$
2. $x^2 - 15x - 16$
3. $x^2 + 2x - 15$
4. $x^2 + 11x + 18$
5. $x^2 + x - 210$

Group D
1. $x^2 - 8x + 7$
2. $x^2 + 3x + 2$
3. $x^2 - 2x - 35$
4. $x^2 + 9x + 20$
5. $x^2 - 14x - 32$

Group E
1. $x^2 + 12x + 11$
2. $x^2 + 14x + 13$
3. $x^2 + 9x + 14$
4. $x^2 - 23x - 50$
5. $x^2 + 2x - 24$

Complicated quadratic expressions

And now for the most complicated quadratics: those where the coefficient of x^2 is not 1.

> coefficient of
> = number of.

EXAMPLE

Factorise $3x^2 + 11x - 4$

$$3x^2 \quad + \quad 11x \quad - \quad 4$$

Step 1 The table

x	1	2	4
$3x$	4	2	1

> **Investigation 1**
> This column is now necessary. Why, when it wasn't before?

Step 2   Subtraction to give 11

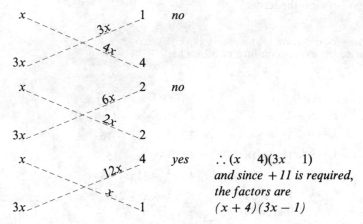

Investigation 2

Why is the table below too full?

x	3x	1	2	4
3x	x	4	2	1

$\therefore (x \quad 4)(3x \quad 1)$
and since $+11$ *is required,*
the factors are
$(x + 4)(3x - 1)$

We can now do the most complicated examples and all we need is practice!

EXERCISE 1.3

(*Answers on page 12*)

In each question, factorise the expression into two brackets.

Group A
1. $6x^2 + x - 12$
2. $6x^2 - 13x - 8$
3. $20x^2 - 29x - 36$
4. $4x^2 + 23x + 15$
5. $12x^2 - 37x - 30$

Group B
1. $2x^2 + 7x - 4$
2. $12x^2 - x - 1$
3. $12x^2 + 23x - 24$
4. $18x^2 - 9x - 2$
5. $24x^2 - 74x - 35$

Group C
1. $2x^2 + 11x + 12$
2. $15x^2 + x - 2$
3. $8x^2 + 14x - 15$
4. $24x^2 - 2x - 35$
5. $72x^2 + 17x - 72$

Group D
1. $3x^2 - 7x - 6$
2. $2x^2 + 5x - 7$
3. $20x^2 - x - 12$
4. $16x^2 - 34x - 15$
5. $30x^2 - 101x - 14$

Group E
1. $5x^2 - 19x - 4$
2. $5x^2 - 6x - 11$
3. $24x^2 + 55x - 24$
4. $50x^2 - 75x - 27$
5. $42x^2 + 103x - 24$

The difference of two squares

Finally we move to a special, though common, case.

Consider $(x - 3)(x + 3) = x^2 - 3x + 3x - 9 = x^2 - 9 = x^2 - 3^2$

There are three points to note about $x^2 - 3^2$.

(1) There is no x term; only x^2 and a constant.

(2) Both terms are squares; x^2 is a square, 3^2 is a square.

(3) There is a minus sign between the terms.

> **A minus sign between two quantities means that you are finding their difference.**

e.g. $11 - 7 = 4$ The difference between 11 and 7 is 4.
Look back to (2) and (3) above.

> **An expression like $x^2 - 3^2$ is called the difference of two squares.**

The pattern for factorising the difference of two squares is always

$$\square^2 - \triangle^2 = (\square + \triangle)(\square - \triangle)$$

> You will find use is made of this in later work, for example in surds and complex numbers. So learn it well.

e.g. $a^2 - b^2 \Rightarrow (a \quad)(a \quad) \Rightarrow (a \quad b)(a \quad b) \Rightarrow (a - b)(a + b)$

e.g. $25 - 16 = 5^2 - 4^2 \rightarrow (5 \quad)(5 \quad) \rightarrow (5 \quad 4)(5 \quad 4) \rightarrow (5 - 4)(5 + 4)$
$= 1 \times 9 = 9$

> You knew this at the start, but it helps to reinforce a point.

e.g. Look back to Exercise 1.1, F5.
$4(a^2 - 4b^2) = 4(a^2 - (2b)^2) = 4(a - 2b)(a + 2b)$

e.g. $(3p + 2q)^2 - (p - 4q)^2 \rightarrow \{(3p + 2q) \qquad \}\{(3p + 2q) \qquad \}$
$\rightarrow \{(3p + 2q) \quad (p - 4q)\}\{(3p + 2q) \quad (p - 4q)\}$
$\rightarrow \{(3p + 2q) + (p - 4q)\}\{(3p + 2q) - (p - 4q)\}$
$\rightarrow \{ 3p + 2q + p - 4q \}\{ 3p + 2q - p + 4q \}$

> Note the need for different shaped brackets.

$= (4p - 2q)(2p + 6q)$
$= 2(2p - q)2(p + 3q)$
$= 4(2p - q)(p + 3q)$

> Fancy brackets are no longer necessary.

e.g. Look again at the efficiency test on page 3, question 1.

Evaluate $51^2 - 49^2$
$51^2 - 49^2 = (51 - 45)(51 + 49)$
$= 2 \times 100$
$= 200$

EXERCISE 1.4

(*Answers on page 13*)

In each question, factorise the expression into brackets. When the question is purely numerical find the numerical answer.

Group A
1. $x^2 - y^2$
2. $a^2 - 1$
3. $4p^2 - 9$
4. $k^4 - 16$
5. $98.2^2 - 1.8^2$

Group B
1. $a^2 - b^2$
2. $4k^2 - 1$
3. $9a^2 - 25$
4. $t^4 - k^2$
5. $t^4 - 1$

Group C
1. $x^2 - 1$
2. $x^2 - 25$
3. $36t^2 - 1$
4. $16 - a^2$
5. $81k^4 - 16$

Group D
1. $76.8^2 - 23.2^2$
2. $x^2 - \frac{1}{4}$
3. $49t^2 - 36s^2$
4. $t^6 - k^2$
5. $(x - 1)^2 - 4$

Group E
1. $(2k + l)^2 - (4k - 3l)^2$
2. $\dfrac{x^2}{4} - \dfrac{1}{9}$
3. $998.8^2 - 1.2^2$
4. $y^{10} - x^6$
5. $y^2 - (x + 3)^2$

EXERCISE 1.5

(*Answers on page 14*)

In each question, factorise the expression fully.

Group A
1. $2x^2 - 2$
2. $x^2 + 3x - 10$
3. $5a^5 + 35a^3 + 50a$
4. $a^4 - 16$
5. $(a + 1)^2 - (b - 3)^2$

Group B
1. $3x^2 + 12$
2. $2 - 7y + 3y^2$
3. $(v - 3)^2 - 25$
4. $21x^3 + 6x^2 - 15x$
5. $(x + 2)^2 - y^2$

Group C
1. $5x^2 - 20$
2. $4k^2 - 6k - 18$
3. $\frac{9}{25} - a^2$
4. $k^8 - 1$
5. $x^4 - 10\,000$

Group D
1. $ac + ad + bc + bd$
2. $x^4 - x^2 - 12$
3. $81a^2 - 25b^2$
4. $18k^2 + 33k - 105$
5. $1 - 81k^4$

Answers to exercises

ANSWERS TO EXERCISE 1.1

Group A
1. $105 = 5 \times 21 = 5 \times 3 \times 7$
2. $a(x + z)$
3. $3ab(2a + b)$
4. $x(x + 2y + 3z)$
5. $4a(a - 2b + 3c)$ (†)

Group B
1. $2 \times 3 \times 7$
2. $c(1 + d)$
3. $bc(a - d)$
4. $p(a^2x - px^2 + py^2)$
5. $2x(y - 2x + 3z - 4z^2)$

Group C
1. $2 \times 2 \times 7$
2. $2(x + 3y)$
3. $4q(2p - 3r)$ (†)
4. $x(x^2 - 2xy + 3y^2)$
5. $2c(3c^2 - 2c + 1)$

Group D
1. $2 \times 2 \times 2 \times 3 \times 3 = 2^3 \times 3^2$
2. $5(k - 3l)$
3. $5x(4y - 3z)$
4. $px(ax - px + a)$
5. $3(2pq - p^2 + 4pr - 3qr)$

Group E
1. 3×19
2. $k(w - v)$
3. $5xy(x + 4y)$
4. $(a + b)(2 - x)$
5. $3ur(r - 7u + 5)$

Group F
1. $2 \times 3 \times 5 \times 7$
2. $a(x - 1)$
3. $qr(p + s)$
4. no factors
5. $4(a^2 - 4b^2)$ (†)(*)

Group G
1. $2^6 \times 5$
2. $3(t - 4)$
3. $abc(c + b + a)$
4. $2klm(4k - 2m + 3l)$
5. $9pqr(p - 9q + 3r^2)$

Group H
1. $2^2 \times 3 \times 11$
2. $2(x + 2y)$
3. $vr(w - x)$
4. $\frac{1}{2}ut(\frac{1}{2}t - 1)$ or $\frac{1}{4}ut(t - 2)$
5. $(a + b)(4x - 8y - (k + l)) = (a + b)(4x - 8y - k - l)$

(†) In these questions the factor 4 should appear as 2^2 but it is usual when factorising algebraic expressions to give the answer as shown.
(*) This will factorise further but you will have to wait until later in the chapter to find out how.

ANSWERS TO THE EFFICIENCY TEST ON FACTORISING

1. $(51 - 49)(51 + 49) = 2 \times 100 = 200$
2. $(x - 6)(x + 1)$
3. $2(6x^2 - 5x - 6) = 2(3x + 2)(2x - 3)$
4. $(4x - 3y)(2x + 3y)$
5. $2a(c + 2m) + 3k(c + 2m) = (c + 2m)(2a + 3k)$
6. $(4k^2 - 1)(4k^2 + 1) = (2k - 1)(2k + 1)(4k^2 + 1)$

ANSWERS TO EXERCISE 1.2

The answers to Group A are worked out in detail.

Group A

1. $x^2 - x - 12$ x   1 2 3 $\Rightarrow (x \quad 3)(x \quad 4) \Rightarrow (x + 3)(x - 4)$

        x   12 6 4

        ✓   ✓

2. $x^2 - 9x + 14$ x   1 2 $\Rightarrow (x \quad 2)(x \quad 7) \Rightarrow (x - 2)(x - 7)$

        x   14 7

        ✓   ✓

3. $x^2 - 5x + 4$ x   1 2 $\Rightarrow (x \quad 1)(x \quad 4) \Rightarrow (x - 1)(x - 4)$

        x   4 2

        ✓   ✓

4. $x^2 - 4x - 32$ x   1 2 4 $\Rightarrow (x \quad 4)(x \quad 8) \Rightarrow (x + 4)(x - 8)$

        x   32 16 8

        ✓   ✓

5. $x^2 - x - 72$ x   1 2 3 4 6 8 $\Rightarrow (x \quad 8)(x \quad 9) \Rightarrow (x + 8)(x - 9)$

        x   72 36 24 18 12 9

        ✓   ✓

Group B	Group C	Group D	Group E
1. $(x - 1)(x - 2)$	1. $(x + 5)(x - 1)$	1. $(x - 1)(x - 7)$	1. $(x + 1)(x + 11)$
2. $(x + 1)(x + 5)$	2. $(x - 16)(x + 1)$	2. $(x + 1)(x + 2)$	2. $(x + 1)(x + 13)$
3. $(x - 2)(x - 9)$	3. $(x + 5)(x - 3)$	3. $(x - 7)(x + 5)$	3. $(x + 2)(x + 7)$
4. $(x + 3)(x + 4)$	4. $(x + 2)(x + 9)$	4. $(x + 4)(x + 5)$	4. $(x + 2)(x - 25)$
5. $(x + 5)(x + 12)$	5. $(x + 15)(x - 14)$	5. $(x - 16)(x + 2)$	5. $(x + 6)(x - 4)$

ANSWERS TO EXERCISE 1.3

The answers to Group A are worked out in detail.

Group A

1. $6x^2 + x - 12$ 6x   3x   1 2 3 4 6 12

                       x   2x   12 6 4 3 2 1

                          ✓   ✓

$\left. \begin{array}{l} \text{looking for subtraction} \\ \text{answer to subtraction is } +1 \end{array} \right\} \Rightarrow$ *columns which are ticked*

∴ factors are $(3x - 4)(2x + 3)$

2. $6x^2 - 13x - 8$

x	$2x$		1	2	4	8
$6x$	$3x$		8	4	2	1
	✓		✓			

subtraction to give $-13 \Rightarrow$ *columns ticked*

$\Rightarrow (2x \quad 1)(3x \quad 8)$
$\Rightarrow (2x + 1)(3x - 8)$

3. $20x^2 - 29x - 36$

x	$2x$	$4x$		1	2	3	4	6	9	12	18	36
$20x$	$10x$	$5x$		36	18	12	9	6	4	3	2	1
	✓							✓				

$\Rightarrow (5x + 4)(4x - 9)$

4. $4x^2 + 23x + 15$

x	$2x$		1	3	5	15
$4x$	$2x$		15	5	3	1
✓				✓		

$\Rightarrow (x + 5)(4x + 3)$

5. $12x^2 - 37x - 30$

x	$2x$	$3x$		1	2	3	5	6	10	15	30
$12x$	$6x$	$4x$		30	15	10	6	5	3	2	1
	✓				✓						

$\Rightarrow (3x + 2)(4x - 15)$

Group B
1. $(2x - 1)(x + 4)$
2. $(4x + 1)(3x - 1)$
3. $(4x - 3)(3x + 8)$
4. $(6x + 1)(3x - 2)$
5. $(12x + 5)(2x - 7)$

Group C
1. $(x + 4)(2x + 3)$
2. $(5x + 2)(3x - 1)$
3. $(2x + 5)(4x - 3)$
4. $(6x + 7)(4x - 5)$
5. $(8x + 9)(9x - 8)$

Group D
1. $(x - 3)(3x + 2)$
2. $(2x + 7)(x - 1)$
3. $(4x + 3)(5x - 4)$
4. $(8x + 3)(2x - 5)$
5. $(15x + 2)(2x - 7)$

Group E
1. $(5x + 1)(x - 4)$
2. $(5x - 11)(x + 1)$
3. $(3x + 8)(8x - 3)$
4. $(10x + 3)(5x - 9)$
5. $(14x - 3)(3x + 8)$

ANSWERS TO EXERCISE 1.4

The answers to Group A are worked out in detail.

Group A

1. $x^2 - y^2 \xrightarrow{①} (\quad)(\quad) \xrightarrow{②} (x \quad)(x \quad) \xrightarrow{③} (x \quad y)(x \quad y) \xrightarrow{④} (x - y)(x + y)$

2. $a^2 - 1 = a^2 - 1^2 \xrightarrow{①} (\quad)(\quad) \xrightarrow{②} (a \quad)(a \quad) \xrightarrow{③} (a \quad 1)(a \quad 1) \xrightarrow{④} (a + 1)(a - 1)$

3. $4p^2 - 9 = (2p)^2 - 3^2 = (2p - 3)(2p + 3)$

4. $k^4 - 16 = k^4 - 2^4 = (k^2)^2 - (2^2)^2$

$\equiv (k^2 - 2^2)(k^2 + 2^2)$

but this is not the end $\because$ the 1st bracket, $k^2 - 2^2$, is also the difference of two squares.

$(x - y)(x + y)$
$= (x + y)(x - y)$
$\therefore$ It does not matter which brackets the signs are in.

Continuing,

$(k^2 - 2^2)(k^2 + 2^2) = (k - 2)(k + 2)(k^2 + 2^2)$

5. $98.2^2 - 1.8^2 = (98.2 - 1.8)(98.2 + 1.8) = 96.4 \times 100 = 9640$

You must now be thinking: what about the sum of two squares? Forget it!

$a^2 + b^2$

does not factorise.

Group B

1. $(a - b)(a + b)$

2. $(2k + 1)(2k - 1)$

3. $(3a - 5)(3a + 5)$

4. $(t^2 + k)(t^2 - k)$

5. $(t^2 + 1)(t - 1)(t + 1)$

Group C

1. $(x + 1)(x - 1)$

2. $(x - 5)(x + 5)$

3. $(6t + 1)(6t - 1)$

4. $(4 - a)(4 + a)$

5. $(9k^2 + 4)(9k^2 - 4) = (9k^2 + 4)(3k - 2)(3k + 2)$

Group D

1. $(76.8 - 23.2)(76.8 + 23.2) = 53.5 \times 100 = 5360$

2. $(x + \frac{1}{2})(x - \frac{1}{2})$

3. $(7t - 6s)(7t + 6s)$

4. $(t^3 - k)(t^3 + k)$

5. $(x - 1 - 2)(x - 1 + 2) = (x - 3)(x + 1)$

Group E

1. $\{(2k + l) - (4k - 3l)\}\{(2k + l) + (4k - 3l)\} = (-2k + 4l)(6k - 2l)$
$$= 4(2l - k)(3k - l)$$

2. $\left(\dfrac{x}{2} - \dfrac{1}{3}\right)\left(\dfrac{x}{2} + \dfrac{1}{3}\right)$

3. $997\,600$

4. $(y^5 - x^3)(y^5 + x^3)$

5. $(y - x - 3)(y + x + 3)$

ANSWERS TO EXERCISE 1.5

Group A

1. $2(x - 1)(x + 1)$

2. $(x + 5)(x - 2)$

3. $5a(a^2 + 2)(a^2 + 5)$

4. $(a^2 + 4)(a - 2)(a + 2)$

5. $(a + b - 2)(a - b + 4)$

Group B

1. $3(x^2 + 4)$

2. $(2 - y)(1 - 3y)$

3. $(v + 2)(v - 8)$

4. $3x(x + 1)(7x - 5)$

5. $(x + 2 - y)(x + 2 + y)$

Investigation 3

Investigate the difference between

$(2 - y)(1 - 3y)$

and

$(y - 2)(3y - 1)$.

Group C

1. $5(x - 2)(x + 2)$
2. $2(k - 3)(2k + 3)$
3. $\left(\dfrac{3}{5} + a\right)\left(\dfrac{3}{5} - a\right)$
4. $(k - 1)(k + 1)(k^2 + 1)(k^4 + 1)$
5. $(x^2 + 100)(x + 10)(x - 10)$

Group D

1. $(a + b)(c + d)$
2. $(x - 2)(x + 2)(x^2 + 3)$
3. $(9a + 5b)(9a - 5b)$
4. $3(2k + 7)(3k - 5)$
5. $(1 + 9k^2)(1 + 3k)(1 - 3k)$

Chapter 2

ALGEBRAIC TECHNIQUES

Aims and objectives

Having worked through this chapter you will be familiar with:
the **symbols and notation** of algebra
the use of **terms and formulae** in algebra
You will be able to:

change the subject of a formula $\qquad y = 2x - 1 \;\Rightarrow\; x = \dfrac{y+1}{2}$

transform formulae $\qquad T = 2\pi \sqrt{\dfrac{l}{g}} \;\Rightarrow\; g = \dfrac{4\pi^2 l}{T^2}$

solve for ... $\qquad yx + c = 3x - a \;\Rightarrow\; x = \dfrac{a+c}{3-y}$

and you will have a basic understanding of the principle of **inversion**.

Algebraic shorthand

In mathematics, we need to handle algebraic expressions. By using symbols and some standard notations, a problem can be written concisely and is easily read. This aids logical deductions. The well-known formula for solving quadratic equations is

$$x = \frac{-b \pm \sqrt{b^2 - 4ac}}{2a}$$

> This is discussed more fully in the next chapter.

It would be unmanageable if every time you used it you had to write: *the solutions are the negative of the coefficient of the first degree term added to, in turn, the positive and the negative square root of the square of the coefficient of the first degree term less the product of 4, the coefficient of the second degree term and the coefficient of the zero degree term, the whole divided by the product of two and the coefficient of the second degree term.*

You may be able to make sense of this lot but need we say more about the power of mathematical shorthand – algebra?

Generally the GCSE courses are an improvement on the courses they replace but unfortunately algebraic understanding and facility are not covered as thoroughly as they were. If you work through this chapter carefully you will go far to putting matters right.

Terms

In an equation like $a + b = c$ there are three terms, a, b and c.

A more complex equation like $\underbrace{2(x + a)} + \underbrace{5(y + b)} = \underbrace{3c}$ has three terms which are $2(x + a)$, $5(y + b)$ and $3c$ ...

but in this case $(x + a)$ and $(y + b)$ also each consist of two terms which are x and a, and y and b.

If the equation is written with the brackets removed it becomes

$$2x + 2a + 5y + 5b = 3c$$

and this contains five terms.

> **A general guide is that terms are separated by plus ($+$) and minus ($-$) signs.**

Formulae

In the formula $v = u + at$, v is said to be the **subject** because the equation is written in the form $v = \ldots$

It can be arranged into the form $u = v - at$ and now we can say either:

u is the subject of the formula, or

the solution of $v = u + at$, for u, is $u = v - at$.

Let us consider some examples.

 $s = vt$ Solve for t.

$$t = \frac{s}{v}$$ *obtained by dividing both sides by v*

 $E = mgh$ Make h the subject.

$$\frac{E}{mg} = \frac{mgh}{mg}$$ *divide both sides by mg*

$$\therefore h = \frac{E}{mg}$$

 $T = 2\pi\sqrt{\dfrac{l}{g}}$ Solve for l.

We know that we have to finish with $l = \ldots$ but how do we get there? One way is to look at, and list, what has been done to l in making the formula.

$v = u + at$

from mechanics

v = velocity
u = initial velocity
a = constant
     acceleration
t = time

Remember

equations have sides:
the left – LHS
and the right – RHS
and these initials are
used frequently.

$T = 2\pi\sqrt{\dfrac{l}{g}}$

from mechanics

T = time of swing of
     simple pendulum
l = length of pendulum
g = acceleration due to
     gravity

When you are doing this you have to concentrate on l and work outwards from it.

The list reads

From nearest to farthest is another description.

(1) Divide by g $\Rightarrow \dfrac{l}{g}$

(2) Take the square root $\Rightarrow \sqrt{\dfrac{l}{g}}$

(3) Multiply by 2π $\Rightarrow 2\pi \sqrt{\dfrac{l}{g}}$

Now go through this list in reverse order, 3, 2, 1, doing the **opposites** and remembering to do it both sides.

opposite (3) $\quad \dfrac{T}{2\pi} = \dfrac{2\pi}{2\pi} \sqrt{\dfrac{l}{g}} = \sqrt{\dfrac{l}{g}}$ $\qquad$ *divide both sides by 2π*

opposite (2) $\quad \left(\dfrac{T}{2\pi}\right)^2 = \left(\sqrt{\dfrac{l}{g}}\right)^2 \Rightarrow \dfrac{l}{g} = \dfrac{T^2}{4\pi^2}$ $\qquad$ *square both sides*

opposite (1) $\quad g \times \dfrac{l}{g} = g \times \dfrac{T^2}{4\pi^2}$ $\qquad$ *multiply by g*

$\therefore l = \dfrac{gT^2}{4\pi^2}$

Remember:

for an equation to remain true, whatever you do to one side, you must do to the other.

e.g. $\quad s = ut + \dfrac{1}{2}at^2$ $\quad$ Make a the subject.

(1) Divide by 2 $(\div 2)$ $\quad$ *things done*
(2) Multiply by t^2 $(\times t^2)$
(3) Add ut $(+ut)$

$\therefore -ut \Rightarrow s - ut = ut + \dfrac{1}{2}at^2 - ut = \dfrac{1}{2}at^2$

$\div t^2 \Rightarrow \dfrac{s - ut}{t^2} = \dfrac{1}{2}\dfrac{at^2}{t^2} = \dfrac{1}{2}a$

$\times 2 \Rightarrow \dfrac{2(s - ut)}{t^2} = 2.\dfrac{1}{2}a = a$

$\therefore a = \dfrac{2(s - ut)}{t^2}$

$s = ut + \frac{1}{2}at^2$
from mechanics

$s =$ distance
$u =$ initial velocity
$a =$ constant
$\quad$ acceleration
$t =$ time

Remember:
when multiplying, especially with numbers, we often use a dot ($\cdot$) to separate the things we are multiplying together.

You will have noticed that some questions are worded 'Solve for ...' and others 'Make ... the subject' or 'Transform the formula'. These all mean the same and there is no difference in the solution.

The process of changing the subject is fundamental to all the work you will do and mastery at this stage is essential.

EXERCISE 2.1

(*Answers on page 23*)

Group A

1. $P = Q + aW$ Solve for W.

2. $y = a + cx^2$ Solve for x.

3. $x = \dfrac{(a + bT)}{(c + dP)}$ Solve for T.

4. $C = a(1 + r^n)$ Solve for r.

5. $\dfrac{1}{v} + \dfrac{1}{u} = \dfrac{1}{f}$ Solve for v.

Group B

1. $C = PV^\gamma$ Solve for V.

2. $f = \dfrac{9c}{5} + 32$ Solve for c.

3. $V = \dfrac{\pi r^2 h}{3}$ Solve for r.

4. $A = \dfrac{(a + b)h}{2}$ Solve for a.

5. $S = \dfrac{n}{2}\{2a + (n - 1)d\}$ Solve for d.

Inverse

Inverse is a word used frequently in mathematics and is the correct one for 'doing the opposite' or 'undoing what has been done'.

If a quantity a is subject to various mathematical operations – which together constitute a **function** – and ends up with the value k, then the collection of operations which change k into a are called the **inverse function** of the original function.

> This definition is not very rigorous but it will suffice for now; there is much detailed work on functions and inverses later.

Now we shall consider this question.

$$T = \frac{(a + CW)}{(p + qW)}$$ Solve for W.

Do you see the problem? We can't list the 'things done' to the intended subject, W, because we don't know which W to look at.

Clearly, the method we have used so far has its limitation, namely, that we can use it only if the new subject appears just once.

A different technique is required.

Step 1   Get rid of fractions by multiplying through by any denominators.

$$\Rightarrow T(p + qW) = a + cW$$

Step 2   Get rid of brackets.

$$\Rightarrow Tp + TqW = a + cW$$

These first two steps have changed the equation to one with separate single terms. This is always the aim we start with, but we may sometimes have to vary steps 1 and 2 a little.

Step 3 Rearrange to get all terms containing the required subject to one side, with all other terms on the other side.

$$\Rightarrow TqW - cW = a - Tp$$

Step 4 Factorise, taking out W as a common factor.

$$\Rightarrow W(Tq - c) = a - Tp$$

This is the first time the new subject, W, has been written only once – we are getting there!

Step 5 Divide by $(Tq - c)$.

$$\Rightarrow W = \frac{a - Tp}{Tq - c} \qquad \textit{the required result}$$

 $x = \sqrt{\dfrac{a + b\cos\theta}{(c - d\cos\theta)}}$ Make $\cos\theta$ the subject.

Square both sides (to remove $\sqrt{}$) $\qquad\qquad\qquad x^2 = \dfrac{a + b\cos\theta}{c - d\cos\theta}$

Multiply by $(c - d\cos\theta)$ (to remove fractions) $x^2(c - d\cos\theta) = a + b\cos\theta$

Remove brackets $\qquad\qquad\qquad\qquad\quad x^2c - x^2d\cos\theta = a + b\cos\theta$

Rearrange $\qquad\qquad\qquad\qquad\qquad x^2c - a = x^2d\cos\theta + b\cos\theta$

Factorise $\qquad\qquad\qquad\qquad\qquad x^2c - a = \cos\theta(x^2d + b)$

Divide by $(x^2d + b)$ $\qquad\qquad\qquad\qquad \dfrac{x^2c - a}{x^2d + b} = \cos\theta$

EXERCISE 2.2

(*Answers on page 25*)

Group A

1. $\dfrac{y - y_1}{y_2 - y_1} = \dfrac{x - x_1}{x_2 - x_1}$ Make y_1 the subject.

2. $w = \dfrac{x + t^2}{y - t^2}$ Solve the equation for t.

3. $ax + abxy + by = pz$ Solve for a.

4. $\sqrt{1 + x^3} = y$ Make x the subject.

5. $a(1 + \sin\theta)^2 = b + d$ Make $\sin\theta$ the subject.

Group B

1. $x^2 + y^2 = a^2$ Solve for x.
2. $v^2 = u^2 + 2as$ Solve for u.
3. $a(x + y + z) = b(x - y - z)$ Solve for y.
4. $T = 2\pi \sqrt{\dfrac{l}{g}}$ Solve for g.
5. $S = \dfrac{n}{2}\{2a + (n - 1)d\}$ Solve for a.

Group C

1. $c = 2\pi r$ Solve for r.
2. $2y = 3(x - 1)$ Solve for x.
3. $S = \dfrac{a}{1 - r}$ Solve for r.
4. $3(x + a) = 5(x + c)$ Solve for x.
5. $\dfrac{2}{k + t} = \dfrac{5}{k - t}$ Solve for t.

Group D

1. $T = \dfrac{2\pi}{w}$ Solve for w.
2. $a + k = 3r$ Solve for k.
3. $R = \sqrt{(aP + bQ)}$ Solve for Q.
4. $(t + k)^2 = as$ Solve for t.
5. $R = \sqrt{\dfrac{c + aW}{b + dW}}$ Solve for W.

Group E

1. $n = 3l + 2k$ Solve for l.
2. $a^2 = b^2 + c^2 - 2px$ Solve for x.
3. $\dfrac{x^2}{a^2} + \dfrac{y^2}{b^2} = 1$ Solve for y.
4. $a(p + q - s) = p(a + b - c)$ Solve for a.
5. $t = \dfrac{a - b}{1 + ab}$ Solve for b.

Group F

1. $a = bc$ Solve for c.
2. $a + x = b - x$ Solve for x.
3. $kq^2 = pr^2$ Solve for q.
4. $\sqrt{a + b + c} = 1$ Solve for b.
5. $pq^n = 1$ Solve for q.

Group G

1. $k = 2h + l$ Solve for h.
2. $2t - k = 5t + 2k$ Solve for t.
3. $\sqrt{(ct)} = x + y$ Solve for t.
4. $\dfrac{1}{v} - \dfrac{1}{u} = \dfrac{1}{f}$ Solve for u.
5. $wt^3 = a - ut^3$ Solve for t.

Group H

1. $2q = 3r + 4s$ Solve for r.
2. $ay - bx = 0$ Solve for y.
3. $V = \dfrac{2\pi r^3}{3} + \pi a^2 h$ Solve for a.
4. $\dfrac{1}{(ax + b)} = \dfrac{2}{(cx + d)}$ Solve for x.
5. $\sqrt{\dfrac{ax + y}{c}} = \left(\dfrac{k}{px + qy}\right)$ Solve for a.

Group I

1. $ax + y = bz$ Solve for x.
2. $s(v + w) = t(v - u)$ Solve for v.
3. $\sqrt{1 + x^3} = y$ Solve for x.
4. $\dfrac{x + a}{x - b} = \dfrac{x + c}{x - d}$ Solve for x.
5. $c = p(1 + at^2)$ Solve for t.

Group J

1. $5p - 3q = 7r$ Solve for q.
2. $5(x - y) + 3(y - z) + 2(z - x) = 0$ Solve for x.
3. $\sqrt{a + x^2} = kx$ Solve for x.
4. $\sqrt{\dfrac{a + b}{x}} = ty^2$ Solve for a.
5. $\sqrt{\dfrac{a}{c + x}} = \sqrt{\dfrac{b}{d - x}}$ Solve for x.

Answers to exercises

ANSWERS TO EXERCISE 2.1

Group A

1. $P = Q + aW$ (1) $\times a$
              (2) $+ Q$

$\therefore - Q \Rightarrow P - Q = aW$

$\div a \Rightarrow \dfrac{P - Q}{a} = W$

2. $y = a + cx^2$ (1) $(\ )^2$
            (2) $\times c$
            (3) $+ a$

$\therefore - a \Rightarrow y - a = cx^2$

$\div c \Rightarrow \dfrac{y - a}{c} = x^2$

$\sqrt{\ } \Rightarrow \sqrt{\dfrac{y - a}{c}} = x$

3. $x = \dfrac{(a + bT)}{(c + aP)}$ (1) $\times b$
                 (2) $+ a$
                 (3) $\div (c + dP)$

$\therefore \times (c + dP) \Rightarrow x(c + aP) = a + bT$

$- a \Rightarrow x(c + dP) - a = bT$

$\div b \Rightarrow \dfrac{x(c + dP) - a}{b} = T$

4. $C = a(1 + r^n)$ (1)$(\ )^n$
                (2) $+ 1$
                (3) $\times a$

$\therefore \div a \Rightarrow \dfrac{C}{a} = 1 + r^n$

$- 1 \Rightarrow \dfrac{C}{a} - 1 = r^n$

$\sqrt[n]{\ } \Rightarrow \sqrt[n]{\dfrac{C}{a} - 1} = r$

5. $\dfrac{1}{v} + \dfrac{1}{u} = \dfrac{1}{f}$ (1) $\dfrac{1}{v}$

                (2) $+ \dfrac{1}{u}$

$\therefore - \dfrac{1}{u} \Rightarrow \dfrac{1}{v} = \dfrac{1}{f} - \dfrac{1}{u}$

$\dfrac{1}{1/v} \Rightarrow v = \dfrac{1}{\dfrac{1}{f} - \dfrac{1}{u}}$ (†) $= \dfrac{uf}{u - f}$

> † See notes overleaf on this bit!

Notes on solution 5

(a) $\dfrac{1}{\square}$ is called the **reciprocal** of $\square$. The reciprocal of 3 is $\dfrac{1}{3}$.

To 'undo' reciprocal is to **reciprocate**.

The reciprocal of $3 = \dfrac{1}{3}$.

The reciprocal of the reciprocal of $3 = \dfrac{1}{1/3} = 3$ *i.e. back where you started*

(b) You may think if you reciprocate $\dfrac{1}{v} = \dfrac{1}{f} - \dfrac{1}{u}$

you should get $v = f - u$ *a very popular mistake*

Proof of mistake:
$$5 = 2 + 3 \qquad \textit{is correct}$$

$$\text{but} \quad \frac{1}{5} = \frac{1}{2} + \frac{1}{3} \qquad \textit{is incorrect, obviously!}$$

And hence the clumsy looking arrangement at †.

$$\dfrac{1}{\dfrac{1}{f} - \dfrac{1}{u}} = \dfrac{1}{\dfrac{u-f}{fu}} = \dfrac{uf}{u-f}$$

Group B

1. $V = \sqrt[\gamma]{\dfrac{C}{P}}$

2. $c = \dfrac{5}{9}(f - 32)$

3. $r = \sqrt{\dfrac{3v}{\pi h}}$

4. $a = \dfrac{2A}{h} - b$

5. $d = \left(\dfrac{2S}{n} - 2a\right)\dfrac{1}{(n-1)}$

ANSWERS TO EXERCISE 2.2

Group A

1. $\dfrac{y - y_1}{y_2 - y_1} = \dfrac{x - x_1}{x_2 - x_1}$

y_1 appears twice

$\therefore (y - y_1)(x_2 - x_1) = (y_2 - y_1)(x - x_1)$ *fractions removed*

$yx_2 - yx_1 - y_1x_2 + y_1x_1 = y_2x - y_2x_1 - y_1x + y_1x_1$ *brackets removed*

$- y_1x_2 + y_1x_1 + y_1x - y_1x_1 = y_2x - y_2x_1 - yx_2 + yx_1$ *y_1 terms to LHS*

$\therefore y_1(x - x_2) = y_2x - y_2x_1 - yx_2 + yx_1$ *y_1 written once only*

$y_1 = \dfrac{y_2x - y_2x_1 - yx_2 + yx_1}{x - x_2}$ *y_1 on its own*

2. $w = \dfrac{x + t^2}{y - t^2}$ *t appears twice $\therefore$*

$w(y - t^2) = x + t^2$ *fractions removed*

$wy - wt^2 = x + t^2$ *brackets removed*

$wy - x = wt^2 + t^2$ *t terms to RHS (it does not matter which side but in this case they remain $+$)*

$wy - x = t^2(w + 1)$ *t once only*

$\dfrac{wy - x}{w + 1} = t^2$

$\sqrt{\dfrac{wy - x}{w + 1}} = t$

3. $ax + abxy + by = pz$ *a appears twice $\therefore$*

$ax + abxy = pz - by$ *a terms to LHS (no fractions, no brackets to deal with)*

$a(x + bxy) = pz - by$ *a once only*

$a = \dfrac{pz - by}{x + bxy}$ *a on its own*

4. $\sqrt{1 + x^3} = y$ *x once only $\therefore$*

$\left.\begin{array}{l}(1)\ (\ )^3 \\ (2)\ +1 \\ (3)\ \sqrt{}\end{array}\right\} \Rightarrow \begin{array}{l}(\ )^2 \\ -1 \\ \sqrt[3]{}\end{array} \begin{array}{l}1 + x^3 = y^2 \\ x^3 = y^2 - 1 \\ x = \sqrt[3]{(y^2 - 1)}\end{array}$

5. $a(1 + \sin\theta)^2 = b + d$ *$\sin\theta$ once only*

$$\div a \quad (1 + \sin\theta)^2 = \frac{b+d}{a}$$

$$\left.\begin{array}{l} (1) \ +1 \\ (2) \ (\ )^2 \\ (3) \ \times a \end{array}\right\} \Rightarrow \qquad \sqrt{} \quad 1 + \sin\theta = \sqrt{\frac{b+d}{a}}$$

$$-1 \qquad \sin\theta = \sqrt{\frac{b+d}{a}} - 1$$

Group B

1. $x = \pm\sqrt{a^2 - y^2}$

2. $u = \pm\sqrt{v^2 - 2as}$

3. $y = \dfrac{bx - bz - ax - az}{a + b}$

4. $g = \dfrac{4\pi^2 l}{T^2}$

5. $a = \dfrac{1}{2}\left\{\dfrac{2S}{n} - (n-1)d\right\}$

Group C

1. $r = \dfrac{c}{2\pi}$

2. $x = \dfrac{2y + 3}{3}$

3. $r = 1 - \dfrac{a}{S}$

4. $x = \dfrac{3a - 5c}{2}$

5. $t = -\dfrac{3k}{7}$

Group D

1. $W = \dfrac{2\pi}{T}$

2. $k = 3r - a$

3. $Q = \dfrac{R^2 - aP}{b}$

4. $t = -k \pm \sqrt{as}$

5. $w = \dfrac{c - bR^2}{R^2 d - a}$

Group E

1. $l = \dfrac{n - 2k}{3}$

2. $x = \dfrac{b^2 + c^2 - a^2}{2p}$

3. $y = \pm b\sqrt{1 - \dfrac{x^2}{a^2}}$

4. $a = \dfrac{p(b - c)}{(q - s)}$

5. $b = \dfrac{a - t}{at + 1}$

Group F

1. $c = \dfrac{a}{b}$

2. $x = \dfrac{b - a}{2}$

3. $q = \pm r\sqrt{\dfrac{p}{k}}$

4. $b = 1 - a - c$

5. $q = \sqrt[n]{\dfrac{1}{p}}$

Group G

1. $h = \dfrac{k - l}{2}$

2. $t = -k$

3. $t = \dfrac{(x + y)^2}{c}$

4. $u = \dfrac{fv}{f - v}$

5. $t = \sqrt[3]{\dfrac{a}{w + u}}$

Group H

1. $r = \dfrac{2q - 4s}{3}$

2. $y = \dfrac{bx}{a}$

3. $a = \pm\sqrt{\dfrac{3V - 2\pi r^3}{3\pi h}}$

4. $x = \dfrac{2b - d}{c - 2a}$

5. $a = \dfrac{1}{x}\left\{\dfrac{ck^2}{(px + qy)^2} - y\right\}$

Group I

1. $x = \dfrac{bz - y}{a}$

2. $v = \dfrac{sw + tu}{t - s}$

3. $x = \sqrt[3]{(y^2 - 1)}$

4. $x = \dfrac{ad - bc}{a + b - c - d}$

5. $t = \pm\sqrt{\dfrac{1}{a}\left(\dfrac{c}{p} - 1\right)} = \pm\sqrt{\dfrac{c - p}{ap}}$

Group J

1. $q = \dfrac{5p - 7r}{3}$

2. $x = \dfrac{2y + z}{3}$

3. $x = \pm\sqrt{\dfrac{a}{k^2 - 1}}$

4. $a = xt^2y^4 - b$

5. $x = \dfrac{ad - bc}{a + b}$

Chapter 3

INDICES

Aims and objectives

Having worked through this chapter you will understand and be able to use index notation, including:

the basic rules	$a \times a \times a = a^3$
	$a^4 \times a^2 = a^6$
	$a^5 \div a^2 = a^3$
a negative index	$3^{-2} = \frac{1}{9}$
a zero index	$5^0 = 1$
a fractional index	$27^{2/3} = 9$
and **any combination of these.**	$9^{-1/2} = \frac{1}{3}$

Index notation

In chapter 2 we referred to the use of shorthand in mathematics, in notations and symbols. Index notation is one of these.

We are familiar with the simplest form.

$$3 \times 3 \times 3 \times 3 \times 3 = 3^5$$

This is read and spoken as, 'three to the power five' or 'three to the fifth (power)'.

> **In the term 3^5 3 is the *base***
> **5 is the *index* or *power* or *exponent*.**

You need to know all four of these words.

Basic rules

Now $3^2 \times 3^3 = 3^5$ $\therefore$ $3^2 \times 3^3 = 3 \times 3 \times 3 \times 3 \times 3$

$3^1 \times 3^4 = 3^5$ $\therefore$ $3^1 \times 3^4 = 3 \times 3 \times 3 \times 3 \times 3$

Rule 1   When multiplying, add the indices.

Symbolically

$$x^k \times x^m = x^{k+m}$$

Investigation

Explain in the same way as above $x^0 \times x^5 = ?$ and try to decide the value of x^0. You will meet this again soon.

Rule 2   When dividing, subtract the indices.

For both rules, the following conditions apply.

1. Use only for operations of multiplication and division.
2. Quantities must all have the same base.

Important, remember these rules **and** the conditions.

Some examples of very popular mistakes will emphasise the importance of these conditions.

EXAMPLES

In arithmetic:
1. $3^2 + 3^3 = 3^5$ *wrong $\because$ not multiplication or division*
2. $3^5 \times 2^3 = 6^8$ *wrong $\because$ different bases*
3. $3^5 \times 2^3 = 6^{15}$ *wrong $\because$ different bases and indices multiplied*

In algebra:
4. $x^2 + x^3 = x^5$ *wrong $\because$ not multiplication or division*
5. $x^5 \times y^3 = xy^8$ *wrong $\because$ different bases*

The correct answers are listed below.

1. $3^2 + 3^3 = 9 + 27 = 36$
2. $3^5 \times 2^3 = 243 \times 8 = 1944$
3. $3^5 \times 2^3 = 243 \times 8 = 1944$ (as above)
4. $x^2 + x^3$ *You can do nothing with this except factorise to $x^2(1 + x)$.*
5. $x^5 \times y^3 = x^5 y^3$

EXERCISE 3.1

(*Answers on page 34*)

Ten questions have been worked out below, but some are wrong. Which ones? Correct them.

1. $a^2 \times c^3 \times a \div c = a^3c^2$ 2. $3x^2 \times 2y^3 = 6xy^5$

3. $a^2(b + c^3) = a^2b + a^2c^3$ 4. $5p^4 \times 6p \div 10p^2 = 3p^3$

5. $5x^3 + 2y^2 - 2x^2 = 3x + 2y^2$ 6. $9x^2 \times 3x = (3x)^3$

7. $4xy^2 \times 3x^3y = 12x^4y^3$ 8. $12a^3b \div 2a^2b = 6ab$

9. $5a^3 \times 2a^4 = 10a^{12}$ 10. $8ab^5 \div 4a^3b = 2a^{-2}b^4$

Negative indices

The answer to question 10 in Exercise 3.1 is correct. It does include a^{-2} i.e. a **negative** index. To make sense of this consider these examples.

$$x^5 \qquad \times \qquad \frac{1}{x^2} \qquad = \qquad x^3$$

| e.g. | and | x^5 | $\times$ | x^{-2} | $=$ | x^3 |

Now compare: *the same   the same* $\qquad$ *the same   the same*

$\therefore$ *must be the same*

$$\text{So} \quad x^{-2} = \frac{1}{x^2}$$

| **Rule 3 – for negative indices** $\qquad a^{-n} = \dfrac{1}{a^n}$ | Learn this. |

To remove the minus sign from the index the term goes from top to bottom or *vice versa*.

Mathematically speaking, the term crosses the *solidus* or *vinculum* (the line separating the top from the bottom in a fraction).

Hence: $3^{-2} \neq -6$

A load of rubbish!

but $3^{-2} = \dfrac{1}{3^2} = \dfrac{1}{9}$

(*Answers on page 34*)

EXERCISE 3.2

This is a short exercise to practice a simple rule. Evaluate or express with positive indices as appropriate. Use your calculator only as a check.

1. 5^{-1} 2. 10^{-3} 3. a^{-x} 4. $\dfrac{k^{-2}}{m^{-3}}$ 5. $\dfrac{2^{-4}}{8^{-2}}$

Zero indices

We now know how to deal with positive indices and negative indices but how about the one in between them, i.e. zero?

Consider $9^3 \times 9^0 = 9^{3+0} = 9^3$

and $x^5 \times x^0 = x^5$

and $k^t \times k^0 = k^t$

In each case a term has been multiplied by something to the power 0 and it has remained unaltered. Now the only factor we can multiply by and not change the original is 1. So the conclusion is that anything to the power 0 is equal to 1.

Rule 4 – for zero indices
$a^0 = 1$
for any value of a.

$$(\text{anything})^0 = 1$$
$$9^0 = 1$$
$$x^0 = 1$$
$$\left(\frac{73x^7y^3 + 17a^2b^5}{3p^9q^2}\right)^0 = 1$$

We now know the value of x^0 which was mentioned in the investigation at the beginning of this chapter.

Fractional indices

We have considered whole number indices. To round off the story we now consider fractional indices.

The statement $2 \times 2 \times 2 = 8$ leads to two possible statements.

8 is the cube of 2

and 2 is the cube (third) root of 8.

Similarly 5 is the square (second) root of 25

and 3 is the fourth root of 81.

Since $7^5 = 16\,807$ then 7 is the fifth root of $16\,807$ and this is written

$\sqrt[5]{16\,807} = 7$

and if $p^x = q \Rightarrow \sqrt[x]{q} = p$

> The second root and the third root have the names **square** and **cube** roots ∵ of their connection with areas and volumes respectively: all others are known just by the number.

> $\sqrt[5]{}$ means fifth root
> $5\sqrt{}$ means $5 \times$ square root

Consider these examples carefully.

e.g.

$2^{1/3} \times 2^{1/3} \times 2^{1/3} = 2^1$

$\Rightarrow 2^{1/3}$ is the third root of 2.

$2^{1/3} = \sqrt[3]{2^1}$

e.g.

$7^{2/5} \times 7^{2/5} \times 7^{2/5} \times 7^{2/5} \times 7^{2/5} = 7^{10/5} = 7^2$

$\Rightarrow 7^{2/5}$ is the fifth root of 7^2.

$7^{2/5} = \sqrt[5]{7^2}$

These two examples are sufficient to establish the rule for dealing with fractional indices.

> **Rule 4 – for fractional indices –** $a^{p/q} = \sqrt[q]{a^p}$

This will make more sense in the examples which follow the next exercise.

EXERCISE 3.3

(*Answers on page 34*)

Group A

Rewrite each of these, using the $\sqrt{}$ sign.

1. $5^{3/4}$ 2. $7^{2/3}$ 3. $x^{3/5}$ 4. $x^{k/5}$ 5. $x^{k/m}$

Group B

Rewrite each of these, using a fractional index.

1. $\sqrt[3]{11^2}$ 2. $\sqrt{x^5}$ 3. $5\sqrt{y^3}$ 4. $\sqrt[7]{x^2y^5}$ 5. $\sqrt[4]{\dfrac{a}{b}}$

Here is another problem to consider: evaluate $27^{2/3}$ without using your calculator.

$$27^{2/3} = \sqrt[3]{729}$$

We now have a choice of two methods.

Method 1 $\sqrt[3]{27^2} = \sqrt[3]{729}$

$\qquad\qquad = 9 \qquad\qquad$ *found by trial and error*

e.g. $1 \times 1 \times 1 \quad no$

$\qquad 2 \times 2 \times 2 \quad no$

etc.

Method 2 $\sqrt[3]{27^2} = \sqrt[3]{(3^3)^2} = 3^2 = 9$

In other words we can either deal with the power first and then the root, (Method 1), or deal with the root first and then the power, (Method 2). Method 2 is much the preferred one.

EXERCISE 3.4

(Answers on page 35)

Simplify and evaluate these without using a calculator.

1. $81^{1/4}$ 2. $16^{3/4}$ 3. $32^{3/5}$ 4. $4^{1/2}$ 5. $27^{-1/3}$

Below are some miscellaneous exercises. Only do as many as you need to now, until you are confident. Save the rest for later revision.

EXERCISE 3.5

(Answers on page 35)

Simplify each of these as much as possible. Evaluate numerical examples without using a calculator.

Group A

1. 7^2
2. $2^{-1} \times 4^2$
3. $x^{2/3} \div x^{1/2}$
4. $\dfrac{p^{11}}{p^2 q^7}$
5. $(x^2 + y)(y^2 + x)$

Group B

1. 2^{-3}
2. $4^{12} \div 4^{10}$
3. $81^{1/4} \times 8^{1/3}$
4. $\dfrac{s^3 y^2}{y x s^2}$
5. $(x^{1/2} + y^{1/2})(x^{1/2} - y^{1/2})$

Group C

1. $(5^{17})^0$
2. $2^9 \times 2^{-7} - 2^2$

Group D

1. $3^0 \times 5^2$
2. $81^{1/2} \times 36^{1/2}$

3. $\dfrac{x^5y^3z}{x^2yz^4}$

4. $\dfrac{xy^{1/2}}{x^{1/2}y} \times \sqrt{\dfrac{y}{x}}$

5. $(x^{1/3} + y^{2/3})(x^{2/3} - y^{1/3})$

3. $a^2(a + b)$

4. $xy(x^{1/2} + y^{1/2} - x^{1/2}y^{1/2})$

5. $(k^{1/2} - t^{1/2})^2$

Group E

1. $36^{-1/2}$

2. $9^{1/2} \times 4^2 \times 7^{-2}$

3. $(3x^3)^2 \div (2x^2)^3$

4. $(a^4b^6)^{1/2} \times (a^2b^3)^{-1}$

5. $(x^{1/3} + y^{1/3})(x^{2/3} - x^{1/3}y^{1/3} + y^{2/3})$

Answers to exercises

ANSWERS TO EXERCISE 3.1

All are correct except 2, 5, 8 and 9 which should be:

2. $3x^2 \times 2y^3 = 6x^2y^3$

5. $5x^3 + 2y^2 - 2x^2 = 5x^3 + 2y^2 - 2x^2$ *does not simplify*

8. $12a^3b \div 2a^2b = 6a$

9. $5a^3 \times 2a^4 = 10a^7$

ANSWERS TO EXERCISE 3.2

1. $5^{-1} = \dfrac{1}{5} = 0.2$ 2. $10^{-3} = \dfrac{1}{10^3} = \dfrac{1}{1000} = 0.001$ 3. $a^{-x} = \dfrac{1}{a^x}$

4. $\dfrac{k^{-2}}{m^{-3}} = \dfrac{m^3}{k^2}$ 5. $\dfrac{2^{-4}}{8^{-2}} = \dfrac{8^2}{2^4} = \dfrac{64}{16} = 4$

ANSWERS TO EXERCISE 3.3

Group A

1. $\sqrt[4]{5^3}$ 2. $\sqrt[3]{7^2}$ 3. $\sqrt[5]{x^3}$ 4. $\sqrt[5]{x^k}$ 5. $\sqrt[m]{x^k}$

Group B

1. $11^{2/3}$ 2. $x^{5/2}$ 3. $5y^{3/2}$ 4. $x^{2/7}y^{5/7}$ 5. $\left(\dfrac{a}{b}\right)^{1/4}$

ANSWERS TO EXERCISE 3.4

1. $81^{1/4} = \sqrt[4]{81^1} = 3$
2. $16^{3/4} = \sqrt[4]{16^3} = 2^3 = 8$
3. $32^{3/5} = \sqrt[5]{32^3} = 2^3 = 8$
4. $4^{1/2} = \sqrt{4} = 2$

5. $27^{-1/3} = \dfrac{1}{27^{1/3}} = \dfrac{1}{\sqrt[3]{27^1}} = \dfrac{1}{3}$

ANSWERS TO EXERCISE 3.5

Group A

1. $7^2 = 49$
2. $2^{-1} \times 4^2 = \frac{1}{2} \times 16 = 8$
3. $x^{2/3} \div x^{1/2} = x^{2/3 - 1/2} = x^{1/6}$

4. $\dfrac{p^{11}}{p^2 q^7} = \dfrac{p^9}{q^7}$

5. $(x^2 + y)(y^2 + x) = x^2 y^2 + x^3 + y^3 + xy$

Group B

1. $2^{-3} = \dfrac{1}{2^3} = \dfrac{1}{8}$

2. $4^{12} \div 4^{10} = 4^{12-10} = 4^2 = 16$

3. $81^{1/4} \times 8^{1/3} = \sqrt[4]{81^1} \times \sqrt[3]{8^1} = 3 \times 2 = 6$

4. $\dfrac{s^3 y^2}{yxs^2} = \dfrac{sy}{x}$

5. $(x^{1/2} + y^{1/2})(x^{1/2} - y^{1/2}) = x - y$

   difference of two squares! – see chapter 1

Group C

1. 1
2. 1

3. $\dfrac{x^3 y^2}{z^3}$

4. 1
5. $x - (xy)^{1/3} + (xy)^{2/3} - y$

Group D

1. 25
2. 54
3. $a^3 + a^2 b$
4. $x^{3/2}y + xy^{3/2} - (xy)^{3/2}$
5. $k - 2(kt)^{1/2} + t$

Group E

1. $\dfrac{1}{6}$

2. $\dfrac{48}{49}$

3. $\dfrac{9}{8}$

4. 1
5. $x + y$

Chapter 4

QUADRATICS

Aims and objectives

Having worked through this chapter, you will be efficient at all aspects of the work on quadratic functions, including:

the definition of a quadratic equation

solving quadratic equations by factorising

$$x^2 + 5x + 6 = 0 \Rightarrow (x + 2)(x + 3) = 0$$
$$\Rightarrow x = -2, x = -3$$

'lost' solutions

$$x^2 - 2x = 0 \Rightarrow x = 0, x = 2$$

graphical representations of quadratics

completing the square

$$x^2 + 6x + 7 = (x + 3)^2 - 2$$

solving equations by completing the square

the quadratic formula

$$x = \frac{-b \pm \sqrt{b^2 - 4ac}}{2a}$$

the definition of function, f(x)

sketching quadratics by transforming f(x) = x^2

complex roots

$$x^2 - 4x + 5 = 0 \Rightarrow x = 2 \pm i$$

equal roots

$$x^2 - 4x + 4 = 0 \Rightarrow x = 2, x = 2$$

simultaneous linear, quadratic equations

$$\left. \begin{array}{l} x^2 + y^2 = 20 \\ y = 2x \end{array} \right\} \Rightarrow x = 2, y = 4 \text{ and } x = -2, y = -4$$

and the **sum and product of roots**.

$$ax^2 + bx + c = 0 \Rightarrow \alpha + \beta = -b/a, \alpha\beta = c/a$$

What are quadratics?

In chapter 1 we spent some time on factorising quadratic expressions. We now look at quadratic equations. These are equations formed when a quadratic expression is equal to zero.

> **The general quadratic expression is represented by**
> $ax^2 + bx + c$ **where a, b and c are constants.**

a is the number of x^2 and is called the **coefficient** of x^2.

b is the number of x^1 and is called the **coefficient** of x.

QUADRATICS

c is the number of x^0 and is called the **constant term**.

The general quadratic equation is written $ax^2 + bx + c = 0$.

e.g.

Solve $x^2 + 5x + 6 = 0$

We can use our factorising ability to solve this.

$$\therefore x^2 + 5x + 6 = 0$$
$$\Rightarrow (x + 2)(x + 3) = 0$$

This says that we have a **product** (one bracket × another) which is zero. The only way we can get the answer zero to a product is if one of the factors is zero.

$$\therefore \textit{either} \quad x + 2 = 0 \qquad \textit{or} \qquad x + 3 = 0$$
$$\Rightarrow \qquad\qquad x = -2 \quad \textit{or} \qquad x = -3$$

This *does not* mean that we can please ourselves about which answer we choose. Usually both are acceptable and we would only ignore one of them if the conditions of the particular problem being solved eliminate it.

It *does* mean that substituting either $x = -2$ or $x = -3$ in the original equation will make it balance.

$$x^2 + 5x + 6 = 0 \qquad\qquad x^2 + 5x + 6 = 0$$
$$(-2)^2 + 5 \times {}^-2 + 6 = 0? \qquad (-3)^2 + 5 \times {}^-3 + 6 = 0?$$
$$4 - 10 + 6 = 0? \qquad\quad 9 - 15 + 6 = 0?$$
$$0 = 0 \quad \textit{a balance} \qquad\qquad 0 = 0 \quad \textit{a balance}$$

Thus the equation has two **answers** or **roots** or **solutions**.

These three words mean the same.

EXERCISE 4.1

(*Answers on page 56*)
Solve these equations:

Group A

1. $x^2 - x - 12 = 0$
2. $x^2 + 2x - 24 = 0$
3. $2x^2 + 5x - 3 = 0$
4. $3(x^2 + 1) = 10x$
5. $15x - 14 = \dfrac{8}{x}$

Group B

1. $x^2 - 5x + 6 = 0$
2. $x^2 + 20x + 64 = 0$
3. $5x^2 + 14x - 3 = 0$
4. $x^2 = 2(x + 12)$
5. $17 = 6x + \dfrac{12}{x}$

37

Lost solutions

Now is the time to point out the source of a very common mistake.

Consider this question.

Solve $4x - 6 = 0$.

Simplify by dividing throughout by 2.

$$\Rightarrow \frac{4x}{2} - \frac{6}{2} = \frac{0}{2}$$

$$\Rightarrow 2x - 3 = 0 \qquad \Rightarrow x = \tfrac{3}{2} \qquad\qquad \textit{which is correct}$$

Now consider this question.

Solve $4x^2 - 6x = 0$.

Method 1   Simplify by dividing throughout by $2x$.

$$\Rightarrow \frac{4x^2}{2x} - \frac{6x}{2x} = \frac{0}{2x}$$

$$\Rightarrow 2x - 3 = 0 \Rightarrow x = \tfrac{3}{2} \qquad \textit{which is only partially correct}$$

We could tackle this by another method.

Method 2 $4x^2 - 6x = 0 \Rightarrow 2x(2x - 3) = 0$

$$\Rightarrow \underset{\substack{\uparrow \\ daft}}{2 = 0} \quad \text{or} \quad x = 0 \quad \text{or} \quad 2x - 3 = 0$$

$$\therefore x = \tfrac{3}{2}$$

> a second solution which is
> 'lost' when method 1 is used

Losing a solution like this happens frequently and, of course, it should not. It will not if we develop the habit of looking carefully at the equation before we start to solve it.

The first equation $4x - 6 = 0$ is **linear** and we should only expect *one* solution.

The second equation $4x^2 - 6x = 0$ is **quadratic** and we should expect *two* solutions.

$$4x^2 - 6x = 0 \quad \times \frac{1}{2} \quad \Rightarrow 2x^2 - 3x = 0 \quad \textit{same equation}$$

$$4x^2 - 6x = 0 \quad \times \frac{1}{2x} \quad \Rightarrow 2x - 3 = 0 \quad \textit{different equation}$$

> The moral is that we must be very careful whenever we multiply throughout by a term which includes the variable.

Graphical representation

Throughout our work we should, whenever possible, try to visualise the shape of the functions we are working with. All of the functions which we meet can be represented graphically and for many of them, with a little practice, it will not be difficult to visualise the graph in the mind's eye and consequently draw a sketch.

> Giving real meaning to algebraic expressions.

If the equation is linear the graph is a straight line. If it is quadratic it takes the shape of a letter U, approximately.

Consider the equation $x^2 - x - 12 = 0$. First consider the graph of $y = x^2 - x - 12$. When drawn it looks like this.

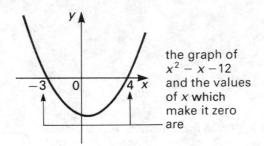

the graph of $x^2 - x - 12$ and the values of x which make it zero are

> **Investigation**
>
> Draw and remember the shapes of these curves.
> $y = x^2$ $y = -x^2$
> $x = y^2$ $x = -y^2$

Now if we put $y = 0$ we have the original question and we can see that the solutions are $x = -3$ or $x = 4$.

Check with your answer to Exercise 3.1, A1.

An alternative way of solving graphically is shown below.

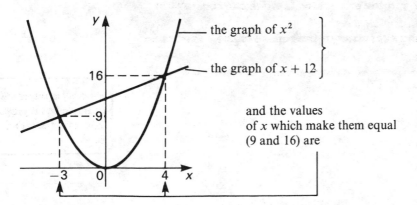

the graph of x^2

the graph of $x + 12$

and the values of x which make them equal (9 and 16) are

$x^2 - x - 12 = 0$ has been rewritten as $x^2 = x + 12$ and two graphs have been drawn, $y = x^2$ and $y = x + 12$. The solution lies in finding the values of x which make x^2 and $x + 12$ equal.

> We shall return to graphical work after we have considered some more algebra.

Completing the square

The expression **perfect square** applies in algebra just as it does in numerical work.

Numbers which are perfect squares are $1(1^2)$, $4(2^2)$, $9(3^2)$, $16(4^2)$, ...
Here are some examples of quadratic expressions which are perfect squares.

e.g. $x^2 - 2x + 1$ is the square of $x - 1$ i.e. $(x - 1)^2 = x^2 - 2x + 1$

e.g. $x^2 + 8x + 16$ is the square of $x + 4$

e.g. $x^2 - 10x + 25$ is the square of $x - 5$

e.g. $x^2 + x + \frac{1}{4}$ is the square of $x + \frac{1}{2}$

e.g. $x^2 - 2px + p^2$ is the square of $x - p$

e.g. $x^2 + 2px + p^2$ is the square of $x + p$

Check these and study them carefully. Try to find a pattern. If you cannot find it then consider the expression

$x^2 + 2ax + a^2$ and its square root which is $x + a$.

Look at and .

This is only another way of saying what has been said in the examples above.

> **The coefficient of x in the expression is twice the constant in the square root.**
> **The constant in the expression is the square of the constant in the square root.**

So, to square $(x + 87)$
write down x^2 x
then $x^2 + (2 \times 87)x + 87^2$
$= x^2 + 174x + 7569$

Possibly a rather silly example but it illustrates how easy the technique is.

EXERCISE 4.2

(*Answers on page 57*)

Group A
Which of the following quadratic expressions are perfect squares?
1. $x^2 + 6x + 9$

2. $x^2 - 12x - 36$

3. $x^2 + 10x + 25$

4. $1 - 2x + x^2$

5. $x^2 - x + \frac{1}{4}$

Group B

What must be added to each of the following to complete the square, i.e. make it into a perfect square?

1. $x^2 + 8x$

2. $x^2 + 6x + 6$

3. $x^2 + 4x + 7$

4. $x^2 - x - 1$

5. $x^2 + 14x + 48$

What if your quadratic is more complicated?

Consider $2x^2 + 10x + 8$

First, factorise to the form $2(x^2 + 5x + 4)$. Now concentrate on the bracket. To complete the square we need to add $2\frac{1}{4}$ inside the bracket to make

$$2(x^2 + 5x + 6\tfrac{1}{4}) = 2(x + 2\tfrac{1}{2})^2$$

Hence we need to add $2 \times 2\frac{1}{4} = 4\frac{1}{2}$ to $2x^2 + 10x + 8$ to complete the square.

| e.g. |

What needs to be added to $3x^2 + 12x + 8$ to complete the square?

Change to $3(x^2 + 4x + \frac{8}{3})$

half of this = 2, $2^2 = 4$, ∴ 4 needed here
∴ necessary to add $\frac{4}{3}$ (to make $\frac{12}{3} = 4$)

Hence $3 \times \frac{4}{3} = 4$ needs to be added to $3x^2 + 12x + 8$ to complete the square.

i.e. $3x^2 + 12x + 12 = 3(x + 2)^2$

> **Important**
>
> Although the expression 'complete the square' is used, $2(x + 2\frac{1}{2})^2$ is *not* a perfect square ∴ it does not have an exact square root.

EXERCISE 4.3

(*Answers on page 57*)

Complete the square in each case, remembering the note above about perfect squares.

Group A	Group B
1. $2x^2 + 12x + 8$	1. $2x^2 + 6x + 2$
2. $5x^2 - 15x + 10$	2. $4x^2 - 20x + 12$

3. $3x^2 + 9x - 6$ 3. $7x^2 + 21x + 14$

4. $4x^2 + 10x + 14$ 4. $2x^2 + 10x - 5$

5. $3x^2 - 7x + 5$ 5. $6x^2 + 15x + 12$

Now we have mastered the idea of completing the square we can use it in two areas, solving quadratic equations and sketching quadratic functions.

Solving quadratics by completing the square

Consider these equations:

$$x^2 = 1, \quad \text{roots} \quad x = \pm 1$$
$$x^2 = a, \quad \text{roots} \quad x = \pm\sqrt{a}$$
$$\text{and} (x + d)^2 = k \Rightarrow x + d = \pm\sqrt{k} \Rightarrow \text{roots } x = -d \pm \sqrt{k}$$

With this last one in mind let us now solve $x^2 + 6x - 7 = 0$.

Rearranging: $x^2 + 6x = 7$

Completing the square on LHS $\Rightarrow$ LHS $= x^2 + 6x + 9$

and adding the same to RHS $\Rightarrow$ RHS $= 7 + 9$

$\therefore x^2 + 6x + 9 = 7 + 9$

$\therefore \quad (x + 3)^2 = 16$

$\therefore \quad\quad x + 3 = \pm\sqrt{16} = \pm 4$

$\therefore \quad\quad\quad x = -3 \pm 4$

i.e. $x = -3 + 4 \quad \text{or} \quad x = -3 - 4$

            $x = 1 \quad\quad \text{or} \quad x = -7$

This answer could be confirmed by using the factorising method.

| e.g. | Solve $x^2 + 7x - 1 = 0$ by completing the square.

$$x^2 + 7x = 1$$

$$x^2 + 7x + \left(\frac{7}{2}\right)^2 = 1 + \left(\frac{7}{2}\right)^2$$

$$\left(x + \frac{7}{2}\right)^2 = 1 + \frac{49}{4} = \frac{53}{4}$$

$\therefore \quad\quad\quad x + \frac{7}{2} = \pm\sqrt{\frac{53}{4}}$

$$x = \frac{-7}{2} \pm \frac{7.3}{2}$$

$$\therefore \qquad x = \frac{0.3}{2} \quad \text{or} \quad x = \frac{-14.3}{2}$$

$$x = 0.15 \quad \text{or} \quad x = -7.15$$

This one is more complicated.

e.g. Solve $3x^2 + 4x - 2 = 0$

$$x^2 + \frac{4x}{3} - \frac{2}{3} = 0 \qquad \textit{divide by 3}$$

$$x^2 + \frac{4x}{3} = \frac{2}{3}$$

$$x^2 + \frac{4x}{3} + \left(\frac{2}{3}\right)^2 = \frac{2}{3} + \left(\frac{2}{3}\right)^2$$

$$\left(x + \frac{2}{3}\right)^2 = \frac{2}{3} + \frac{4}{9} = \frac{10}{9}$$

$$x + \frac{2}{3} = \pm\sqrt{\frac{10}{9}}$$

$$x = \frac{-2}{3} \pm \frac{3.2}{3}$$

$$\therefore \qquad x = \frac{1.2}{3} \quad \text{or} \quad x = \frac{-5.2}{3}$$

$$x = 0.4 \quad \text{or} \quad x = -1.7$$

> **Useful:**
> $$\sqrt{10} = 3.162$$
> and $\quad \pi = 3.142$
> $\therefore \qquad \pi^2 \approx 10$
>
> is a very good approximation.

EXERCISE 4.4

(*Answers on page 58*)

Solve each of these by completing the square.

Group A

1. $x^2 + 4x + 2 = 0$
2. $x^2 - 7x - 3 = 0$
3. $2x^2 + 6x + 3 = 0$
4. $5x^2 - 3x - 2 = 0$
5. $\dfrac{x^2}{2} - \dfrac{2x}{3} - 1 = 0$

Group B

1. $x^2 + 6x + 3 = 0$
2. $x^2 - 9x + 2 = 0$
3. $3x^2 + 12x + 4 = 0$
4. $2.3x^2 + 3.7x - 1.6 = 0$
5. $\left(\dfrac{x}{3}\right)^2 = \dfrac{2x}{9} + 1$

The quadratic formula

We can now tackle the standard notation quadratic equation using the method of completing the square.

$$ax^2 + bx + c = 0$$

$$x^2 + \frac{bx}{a} = -\frac{c}{a}$$

adding $\left(\frac{b}{2a}\right)^2$ *to complete the square on the LHS*

$$x^2 + \frac{bx}{a} + \left(\frac{b}{2a}\right)^2 = -\frac{c}{a} + \left(\frac{b}{2a}\right)^2$$

$$\left(x + \frac{b}{2a}\right)^2 = -\frac{c}{a} + \frac{b^2}{4a^2} = -\frac{4ac + b^2}{4a^2}$$

taking $\sqrt{}$ *of both sides*

$$x + \frac{b}{2a} = \pm\sqrt{\frac{b^2 - 4ac}{4a^2}} = \pm\frac{\sqrt{b^2 - 4ac}}{2a}$$

$$\therefore \ x = -\frac{b}{2a} \pm \frac{\sqrt{b^2 - 4ac}}{2a}$$

$$\text{i.e. } x = \frac{-b \pm \sqrt{b^2 - 4ac}}{2a}$$

This is the formula mentioned at the beginning of chapter 2.

e.g. Solve $7x^2 + 5x - 3 = 0$ using the formula.

now $a = 7, b = 5, c = -3$ and

$$x = \frac{-b \pm \sqrt{b^2 - 4ac}}{2a}$$

$$= \frac{-5 \pm \sqrt{5^2 - 4 \times 7 \times -3}}{2 \times 7}$$

$$= \frac{-5 \pm \sqrt{25 + 84}}{14}$$

$$= \frac{-5 \pm \sqrt{109}}{14}$$

$$= \frac{-5 \pm 10.4}{14}$$

$$\therefore x = 0.4 \text{ or } -1.1$$

If, in your working out, the quantity inside the square root sign is negative then you have made a mistake. You cannot realistically find the square root of a negative number. It is possible to have equations where the quantity inside the square root is negative and we shall deal with them shortly but it does mean that they do not have any real roots.

A cautionary note.

EXERCISE 4.5

(*Answers on page 59*)

Solve each of these by using the formula.

Group A

1. $3x^2 + 5x + 2 = 0$
2. $11x^2 + 7x - 9 = 0$
3. $x^2 - 6x + 3 = 0$
4. $\dfrac{x + 1}{x} = \dfrac{3x}{x + 2}$
5. $2x^4 - 5x^2 + 1 = 0$

Group B

1. $x^2 - 3x + 1 = 0$
2. $5x^2 + 7x - 4 = 0$
3. $2x^2 + 3x - 1 = 0$
4. $(x + 2)^2 = 3x + 7$
5. $3x^4 - 8x^2 + 4 = 0$

We now have four ways of solving quadratic equations.

(1) Factorising – this is not always possible but it is the way we should try firstly.

(2) Completing the square.

(3) The formula.

(4) Drawing a graph.

Further graphical considerations

If you carried out the investigation suggested on page 39 you should have got the four sketches shown below.

We are going to change our notation slightly now and instead of using $y = x^2$ we shall use $f(x) = x^2$.

We call $f(x)$ a **function**.

A function is a set of operations carried out on an independent variable.

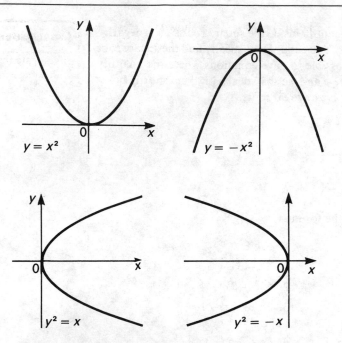

$y = x^2$

$y = -x^2$

$y^2 = x$

$y^2 = -x$

> The name given to all these curves is **parabola** – more later in chapter 18 on conics.

We read f(x) as 'function of x' and it means some algebraic operation into which is fed the basic, independent variable x. Out comes a value after it has been processed according to the operation.

e.g. f(x) = x^2 means that if x is fed in it has to be squared to make the output; if 3 goes in, out comes $3^2 = 9$.

e.g. f(x) = $2x + 5$ means that x must be doubled and 5 added; if 3 goes in, 11 comes out.

In mathematical notation this would be written

f(3) = 11

Now f(x) = x^2 is shown again here.

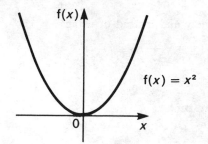

f(x) = x^2

Remember this one. If you do forget it, it is easy to draw and the others are all developed from it.

The effect of changing x to $x - 2$ i.e. $f(x) = (x - 2)^2$ is shown below.

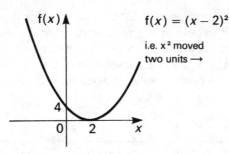

$f(x) = (x - 2)^2$

i.e. x^2 moved
two units $\longrightarrow$

> **Investigation**
>
> Investigate these effects with some examples of your own. You will then understand them fully.

The graph has moved 2 units right ($\longrightarrow$).

We now try a second effect of adding 3 to $(x - 2)^2$.

$f(x) = (x - 2)^2 + 3$ changes the graph like this.

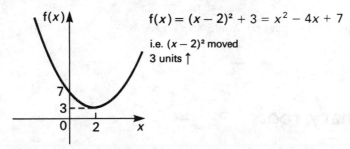

$f(x) = (x - 2)^2 + 3 = x^2 - 4x + 7$

i.e. $(x - 2)^2$ moved
3 units $\uparrow$

The graph has moved 3 units up ($\uparrow$).

e.g. Sketch $f(x) = x^2 + 4x + 3$.

$f(x) = x^2 + 4x + 2^2 - 1$

This has been added here to complete the square and this has been adjusted so that the constant term is 3, ($= 2^2 - 1$), as in the original function.

The function has not been altered in value, only appearance.

Now we can write $f(x) = (x + 2)^2 - 1$.

i.e. x^2 is moved 2 units to the left ($\longleftarrow$) and 1 unit down ($\downarrow$) to produce this curve:

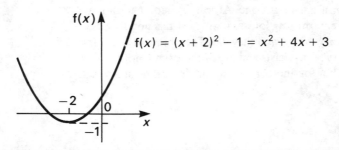

$f(x) = (x + 2)^2 - 1 = x^2 + 4x + 3$

Use of the computer

If you have access to a computer, spend an hour or so experimenting for yourself with the transformations such as the ones above. There are commercially produced programs available on disc which make this work easier, more interesting and consequently generate a better understanding.

EXERCISE 4.6

(*Answers on page 60*)

Sketch the following functions, making use of completing the square and transforming $f(x) = x^2$.

1. $f(x) = x^2 + 6x + 5$
2. $f(x) = x^2 - 7x + 3$
3. $f(x) = 3x^2 + 5x + 1$ (Referring to page 60 should help if need be.)
4. $f(x) = 2 + 2x - x^2$
5. $f(x) = 5 - 3x - 2x^2$

Real and imaginary roots

We have not finished with the quadratic formula yet. We now refer back to Exercise 3.5, page 33.

Let us now apply the formula $x = \dfrac{-b \pm \sqrt{b^2 - 4ac}}{2a}$ to two similar equations.

Firstly $\qquad 2x^2 + 3x - 3 = 0 \Rightarrow x = \dfrac{-3 \pm \sqrt{9 + 24}}{4} = \dfrac{-3 \pm \sqrt{33}}{4}$

and secondly $2x^2 + 3x + 3 = 0 \Rightarrow x = \dfrac{-3 \pm \sqrt{9 - 24}}{4} = \dfrac{-3 \pm \sqrt{-15}}{4}$

In the first we get two **distinct** or different real roots, 0.7 and -2.2.

In the second there is the problem of $\sqrt{-15}$. We cannot take the square root of a negative number, it hasn't got one. At least it hadn't until now. Mathematicians, being an enterprising lot, said, 'If $\sqrt{-1}$ has not got a real value let's give it an **imaginary** one,' – and they did. They called it i, the first letter of the word 'imaginary'. (Physicists and engineers call it j, not because they can't spell imaginary, but for another very sound, logical reason which will be explained later.)

Hence $\sqrt{-1} = i$

and $\quad \sqrt{-15} = \sqrt{15} \times \sqrt{-1} = \pm 3.9i$

A number which is made up of a real part and an imaginary part is called a *complex* number.

The roots of the second equation, $\dfrac{-3 \pm \sqrt{-15}}{4}$, are complex.

$$x = -\frac{3}{4} \pm \frac{3.9}{4} i$$

real   imaginary

Investigation

And how does all this appear on the graph? Investigate by sketching
$f(x) = 2x^2 + 3x - 3$
and
$f(x) = 2x^2 + 3x + 3$.

Finally, how about $x^2 + 8x + 16 = 0$?

$$x = \frac{-8 \pm \sqrt{64 - 64}}{2} = \frac{-8 \pm 0}{2} = -4$$

It seems to have only one answer. But if we look at the equation from a factorising angle we have

$x^2 + 8x + 16 = 0$

$(x + 4)(x + 4) = 0$

$\quad x + 4 = 0 \quad$ or $\quad x + 4 = 0$

$\quad\quad x = -4 \quad$ or $\quad x = -4$

Investigation

By referring to the diagrams on page 47, are the roots of
$x^2 - 4x + 7 = 0$ and
$x^2 + 4x + 3 = 0$ real or complex?

This gives the true picture, which is the same answer *twice*.

Quadratic discriminant

The results of the three investigative sketches are shown below.
Summary

If

Investigation

Investigate this by sketching.

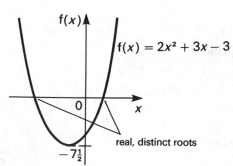

$f(x)$

$f(x) = 2x^2 + 3x - 3$

0

x

real, distinct roots

$-7\frac{1}{2}$

$b^2 > 4ac \quad$ real, distinct roots

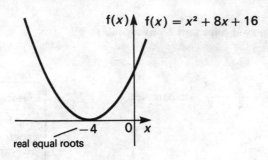

$b^2 = 4ac$ real, equal roots

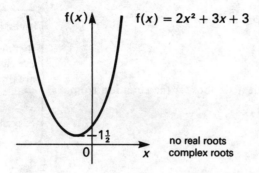

$b^2 < 4ac$ complex roots

Later in the book there is a whole chapter on complex numbers.

EXERCISE 4.7

(*Answers on page 61*)

Investigate the roots of the following equations.

1. $2x^2 + 3x + 2 = 0$

2. $x - \dfrac{2}{x} = 1$

3. $px^2 + qx + r = 0$ given that $p > 0$ and $r < 0$
4. $ax^2 + 4\sqrt{a}.x + 4 = 0$
5. $5(x + a)^2 + 5(x + a) + 1 = 0$

Simultaneous equations: one linear, one quadratic

Quite often in mathematics we meet situations where we need to solve simultaneously a linear and a quadratic equation, for example, finding where a straight line and a curve meet

e.g.

Find where $x^2 + y^2 = 4$ and $x + y = 2$ meet.

The problem could have been worded, 'Solve the simultaneous equations $x^2 + y^2 = 4$ and $x + y = 2$'. The wording chosen is more mathematical and it reminds us that these algebraic equations can take diagrammatic form, i.e. graphs.

As always, we can only find one unknown, x or y, at once and hence we are looking for a technique which will eliminate x or y whilst we find y or x.

From the linear equation we have $y = 2 - x$.

Substituting for y in the quadratic equation $\Rightarrow x^2 + (2 - x)^2 = 4$
Now we have an equation with only one unknown.

> **Remember**
>
> the routine of these two lines.

$$x^2 + (2 - x)^2 = x^2 + 4 - 4x + x^2 = 4$$
$$\therefore \quad 2x^2 - 4x = 0$$
$$\therefore \quad 2x(x - 2) = 0$$
$$\Rightarrow \qquad x = 0 \text{ or } \qquad x = 2$$

Substituting for these x values in the linear equation gives

$$x = 0, y = 2 \text{ and} \qquad x = 2, y = 0.$$

To follow up the problem we can show graphically what the solutions mean.

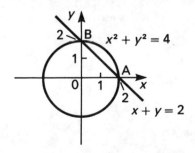

$x^2 + y^2 = 4$ is a circle of radius 2 units
$x + y = 2$ is a straight line
A and B are the points (2, 0) and (0, 2) where the line and the circle meet.

Solving equations of this type is necessarily routine and mechanical and it is important to set off on the right lines: those emphasised at the beginning of this solution.

Now for a more complicated case.

e.g. Solve the equations $x^2 - 2y^2 + 3x + 4 = 0$ and $3x + 4y + 2 = 0$.

From the linear equation $\quad y = \dfrac{-3x - 2}{4}$

Substitute in the quadratic $\quad x^2 - 2\left(\dfrac{-3x - 2}{4}\right)^2 + 3x + 4 = 0$

$\Rightarrow \qquad x^2 - \dfrac{{}^1\!\!\not{2}(9x^2 + 12x + 4)}{\not{16}_8} + 3x + 4 = 0$

$\therefore \qquad 8x^2 - 9x^2 - 12x - 4 + 24x + 32 = 0$

$$28 + 12x - x^2 = 0$$
$$(14 - x)(2 + x) = 0$$
$$\Rightarrow x = 14 \text{ or } x = -2$$

Substituting for x in the linear equation

$\Rightarrow y = \dfrac{-3 \times 14 - 2}{4} \qquad y = \dfrac{-3 \times -2 - 2}{4}$

$\qquad = -11 \qquad\qquad\qquad = 1$

$\therefore$ The line meets the curve in two points, $(14, -11)$ and $(-2, 1)$.

EXERCISE 4.8

(Answers on page 62)

Solve the following pairs of simultaneous equations.

Group A

1. $y^2 = 4x, y + x = 0$

2. $\dfrac{x^2}{9} + \dfrac{y^2}{16} = 1, 3y + 4x = 12$

3. $xy + 2x - y = 14, 3y + 2x = 14$
4. $x^2 + (y - 4)^2 = 169, y = x - 9$
5. $x^2 + y^2 - 4x - 2y - 20 = 0, 2y = x + 5$

Group B

1. $25y + x^2 = 0, 5y + x = 0$

2. $x^2 + \dfrac{y^2}{4} = 1, y + 2x + 2 = 0$

3. $xy + 3y - x = 23, 2y + x = 13$

4. $(x + 2)^2 + y^2 = 25, 7y = x + 27$
5. $x^2 + y^2 - 2x + 4y - 20 = 0, 4y + 3x + 5 = 0$

Sum and product of roots

Investigation

By looking at the five equations and their roots try to find a link between the coefficients and the roots.

Equation	Roots
1. $x^2 - 7x + 12 = 0$	$3, 4$
2. $x^2 + 7x + 10 = 0$	$-2, -5$
3. $x^2 + x - 6 = 0$	$-3, 2$
4. $x^2 - 8x + 15 = 0$	$3, 5$
5. $x^2 + 4x - 21 = 0$	$-7, 3$

Have you found the connections? If not you will find the explanation overleaf but don't give in too soon.

Now consider these:

6. $2x^2 + x - 15 = 0$	$2\frac{1}{2}, -3$
7. $3x^2 - 5x - 2 = 0$	$-\frac{1}{3}, 2$

Do your links still work? If not, concentrate on the basic difference between these equations and numbers 1–5.

Try two more:

8. $5x^2 - 2x - 3 = 0$	$-\frac{3}{5}, 1$
9. $8x^2 - 10x - 3 = 0$	$-\frac{1}{4}, 1\frac{1}{2}$

The links you should have found in your last investigation are:

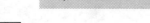

sum of roots $= -b/a$
product of roots $= c/a$

Remember

what a, b and c stand for. If you have forgotten, remind yourself by looking at page 36 at the beginning of this chapter.

e.g. Referring back to the equations in the investigation, and their roots:

1. $3 + 4 = -\dfrac{-7}{1} = 7 \qquad 3 \times 4 = \dfrac{12}{1} = 12$

5. $-7 + 3 = \dfrac{-4}{1} = -4 \qquad -7 \times 3 = \dfrac{-21}{1} = -21$

6. $2\frac{1}{2} - 3 = -\frac{1}{2} \qquad 2\frac{1}{2} \times -3 = \dfrac{-15}{2} = -7\frac{1}{2}$

The formal proof now follows.

Traditionally the Greek letters α and β are used to represent the roots of $ax^2 + bx + c = 0$ and there is no reason for us to do any differently.

We are now going to work backwards from the solutions.

$$x = \alpha \qquad \text{or} \qquad x = \beta$$
$$\therefore x - \alpha = 0 \qquad \text{or} \qquad x - \beta = 0$$
$$\therefore \quad (x - \alpha)(x - \beta) = 0$$
$$x^2 - (\alpha + \beta)x + \alpha\beta = 0 \qquad\qquad\qquad \textbf{A}$$

And, as we know, $ax^2 + bx + c = 0 \Rightarrow x^2 + \dfrac{bx}{a} + \dfrac{c}{a} = 0$ **B**

A and **B** are the same equation so we get, by comparison,

$$-(\alpha + \beta) = \frac{b}{a} \quad \text{and} \quad \alpha\beta = \frac{c}{a}$$

which is the result required.

The problems which follow, using these results, will test your algebraic ability considerably.

> Now you could continue your investigation and find a justification of these results algebraically.

e.g. Find $\alpha^2 + \beta^2$ if α and β are the roots of $2x^2 + 7x + 4 = 0$.

We may think here of using the formula for solving quadratic equations first, to find α and β separately, and then evaluate $\alpha^2 + \beta^2$. That is *not* the aim of the question! If we *had* been asked to find the exact value of $\alpha^2 + \beta^2$ we could not have used the formula since, at the square root stage, that only gives *approximate* values. Back to the question!

$$\alpha^2 + \beta^2 = \alpha^2 + \beta^2 + 2\alpha\beta - 2\alpha\beta$$
$$= (a + \beta)^2 - 2\alpha\beta$$

> $2\alpha\beta - 2\alpha\beta = 0$ which is what has been added.

and since we know that $\alpha + \beta = \dfrac{-7}{2}$ and $\alpha\beta = \dfrac{4}{2} = 2$

$$\alpha^2 + \beta^2 = \left(\frac{-7}{2}\right)^2 - 2 \times 2 = \frac{49}{4} - 4 = \frac{49}{4} - \frac{16}{4} = \frac{33}{4}.$$

e.g. Find $\dfrac{1}{\alpha} + \dfrac{1}{\beta}$ if α and β are the roots of $3x^2 + 4x - 2 = 0$.

$$\frac{1}{\alpha} + \frac{1}{\beta} = \frac{\beta + \alpha}{\alpha\beta} = \frac{-4/3}{-2/3} = 2$$

e.g. Form the equation with roots $\alpha + \dfrac{1}{\beta}$ and $\beta + \dfrac{1}{\alpha}$, where α and β are the roots of $3x^2 + 9x - 5 = 0$.

The new equation has the form $ax^2 + bx + c = 0$

$$\text{i.e. } x^2 + \frac{bx}{a} + \frac{c}{a} a = 0$$

where $\dfrac{b}{a} = -$ sum of new roots

$$\frac{b}{a} = -\left(\alpha + \frac{1}{\beta} + \beta + \frac{1}{\alpha}\right) = -\left(\alpha + \beta + \frac{\alpha + \beta}{\alpha\beta}\right)$$

and $\quad \dfrac{c}{a} = $ product of new roots

$$\frac{c}{a} = \left(\alpha + \frac{1}{\beta}\right)\left(\beta + \frac{1}{\beta}\right) = \alpha\beta + 1 + 1 + \frac{1}{\alpha\beta} = \alpha\beta + 2 + \frac{1}{\alpha\beta}$$

Now $\alpha + \beta = -\dfrac{9}{3} = -3 \quad$ and $\quad \alpha\beta = \dfrac{-5}{3}$

$$\therefore \frac{b}{a} = -\left(-3 + \frac{-3}{-\frac{5}{3}}\right) = -\left(-3 + \frac{9}{5}\right) = -\left(\frac{-15 + 9}{5}\right) = \frac{6}{5}$$

and $\dfrac{c}{a} = -\dfrac{5}{3} + 2 - \dfrac{3}{5} = \dfrac{-25 + 30 - 9}{15} = -\dfrac{4}{15}$

$\therefore$ new equation is $\quad x^2 + \dfrac{6x}{5} - \dfrac{4}{15} = 0$

$$\Rightarrow 15x^2 + 18x - 4 = 0$$

You should have realised by now that the aim in these questions is to express what you are being asked to find in terms of $(\alpha + \beta)$ and $(\alpha\beta)$ because these are the quantities you are usually given. If in doubt go back over the last three examples and establish the principle of the solutions rather than the algebraic or arithmetical details.

EXERCISE 4.9

(Answers on page 63)

Group A

1. Find the value of $\alpha - \beta$ if $\alpha + \beta = 5$ and $\alpha\beta = 3$.
2. Given that α and β are the roots of $5x^2 + 8x - 3 = 0$ find the value of $\alpha^3 + \beta^3$. $(\alpha^3 + \beta^3 = (\alpha + \beta)(\alpha^2 + \beta^2 - \alpha\beta))$.
3. Form the equation with roots $\dfrac{1}{\alpha}, \dfrac{1}{\beta}$ given that α and β are the roots of $x^2 + 6x + 4 = 0$.

4. If α and β are the roots of $ax^2 + bx + c = 0$ find the value of

$$\left(\alpha^2 + \frac{1}{\beta^2}\right)\left(\beta^2 + \frac{1}{\alpha^2}\right).$$

5. If one root of $px^2 + qx + r = 0$ is double the other find a relation between p, q and r.

Group B

1. If α and β are the roots of $2x^2 + 6x - 1 = 0$ find the value of $\alpha^2 - \beta^2$.

2. Form the equation with roots which are double the roots of $ax^2 + bx + c = 0$.

3. α and β are the roots of $3x^2 + 4x - 2 = 0$. Find the equation with roots

$$\alpha + \frac{1}{\alpha} \text{ and } \beta + \frac{1}{\beta}.$$

4. Find the average of the roots of the equation $x^2 + kx + n = 0$.

5. One root of $kx^2 + lx + m = 0$ is three times the other. Show that $3l^2 = 16\,km$.

Answers to exercises

ANSWERS TO EXERCISE 4.1

Group A

1. $x^2 - x - 12 = 0 \Rightarrow (x - 4)(x + 3) = 0$
$$\Rightarrow x - 4 = 0 \quad \text{or} \quad x + 3 = 0$$
$$\Rightarrow x = 4 \qquad \text{or} \quad x = -3$$

2. $x^2 + 2x - 24 = 0 \Rightarrow (x + 6)(x - 4) = 0$
$$\Rightarrow (x + 6) = 0 \quad \text{or} \quad x - 4 = 0$$
$$\Rightarrow x = -6 \qquad \text{or} \quad x = 4$$

3. $2x^2 + 5x - 3 = 0 \Rightarrow (2x - 1)(x + 3) = 0$
$$\Rightarrow 2x - 1 = 0 \quad \text{or} \quad x + 3 = 0$$
$$\Rightarrow x = \tfrac{1}{2} \qquad \text{or} \quad x = -3$$

4. $3(x^2 + 1) = 10x \Rightarrow 3x^2 - 10x + 3 = 0 \Rightarrow (3x - 1)(x - 3) = 0$
$$\Rightarrow 3x - 1 = 0 \quad \text{or} \quad x - 3 = 0$$
$$\Rightarrow x = \tfrac{1}{3} \qquad \text{or} \quad x = 3$$

5. $15x - 14 = \dfrac{8}{x} \Rightarrow 15x^2 - 14x - 8 = 0 \Rightarrow (5x + 2)(3x - 4) = 0$

$$\Rightarrow 5x + 2 = 0 \quad \text{or} \quad 3x - 4 = 0$$
$$\Rightarrow x = -\tfrac{2}{5} \quad \text{or} \quad x = \tfrac{4}{3}$$

Group B

1. $x = 2, x = 3$
2. $x = -4, x = -16$
3. $x = \tfrac{1}{5}, x = -3$
4. $x = -4, x = 6$
5. $x = \tfrac{4}{3}, x = \tfrac{3}{2}$

ANSWERS TO EXERCISE 4.2

Group A

1. *Yes* $\quad x^2 + 6x + 9 = (x + 3)^2$

2. *No* $\quad x^2 - 12x - 36$ *needs a $+$ here before it could be written as* $(x - 6)^2$
3. *Yes* $\quad x^2 + 10x + 25 = (x + 5)^2$
4. *Yes* $\quad 1 - 2x + x^2 = (1 - x)^2$
5. *Yes* $\quad x^2 - x + \tfrac{1}{4} = (x - \tfrac{1}{2})^2$

Group B

1. $x^2 + 8x$ *halve this* $\Rightarrow 4,$ *square it* $\Rightarrow 16$
   Add 16 to make $x^2 + 8x + 16 = (x + 4)^2$
2. *Add 3 to make* $x^2 + 6x + 9 = (x + 3)^2$
3. *Add -3 to make* $x^2 + 4x + 4 = (x + 2)^2$
4. *Add $\tfrac{5}{4}$ to make* $x^2 - x + \tfrac{1}{4} = (x - \tfrac{1}{2})^2$
5. *Add 1 to make* $x^2 + 14x + 49 = (x + 7)^2$

ANSWERS TO EXERCISE 4.3

Group A

1. $2x^2 + 12x + 8 \Rightarrow 2(x^2 + 6x + 4)$
   Add 5 inside the bracket to make $2(x^2 + 6x + 9) = 2(x + 3)^2$

   Add $2 \times 5 = 10$ to the expression.

2. $5x^2 - 15x + 10 = 5(x^2 - 3x + 2)$

   $\left(\dfrac{3}{2}\right)^2 = \dfrac{9}{4} = 2\tfrac{1}{4} \quad \therefore$ add $\tfrac{1}{4}$ inside the bracket.

   Add $5 \times \dfrac{1}{4} = \dfrac{5}{4}$ to the expression.

3. $3x^2 + 9x - 6 = 3(x^2 + 3x - 2)$

$\left(\dfrac{3}{2}\right)^2 = \dfrac{9}{4} = 2\tfrac{1}{4}$ $\therefore$ add $4\tfrac{1}{4}$ inside the bracket.

Add $3 \times 4\tfrac{1}{4} = 12\tfrac{3}{4}$ to the expression.

4. $4x^2 + 10x + 14 = 4\left(x^2 + \dfrac{5x}{2} + \dfrac{7}{2}\right)$

$\left(\dfrac{5}{4}\right)^2 = \dfrac{25}{16}$ $\dfrac{7}{2} = \dfrac{56}{16}$ $\therefore$ add $-\dfrac{31}{16}$ inside the bracket.

Add $4 \times \dfrac{-31}{16} = \dfrac{-31}{4} = -7\tfrac{3}{4}$ to the expression.

5. $3x^2 - 7x + 5 = 3\left(x^2 - \dfrac{7x}{3} + \dfrac{5}{3}\right)$

$\left(\dfrac{7}{6}\right)^2 = \dfrac{49}{36}$ $\dfrac{5}{3} = \dfrac{60}{36}$ $\therefore$ add $-\dfrac{11}{36}$ inside the bracket.

Add $3 \times \dfrac{-11}{36} = -\dfrac{11}{12}$ to the expression.

Group B

1. $2 \times \dfrac{5}{4} = \dfrac{5}{2}$ 2. $4 \times \dfrac{13}{4} = 13$ 3. $7 \times \dfrac{1}{4} = \dfrac{7}{4}$ 4. $2 \times \dfrac{35}{4} = \dfrac{35}{2}$ 5. $6 \times \dfrac{-7}{16} = \dfrac{-21}{8}$

ANSWERS TO EXERCISE 4.4

Group A

1. $x^2 + 4x + 2 = 0 \Rightarrow x^2 + 4x + 2^2 = -2 + 2^2 \Rightarrow (x+2)^2 = 2 \Rightarrow x + 2 = \pm\sqrt{2} \Rightarrow x = -2 \pm \sqrt{2}$
$\Rightarrow x = -0.6$ or -3.14

2. $x^2 - 7x - 3 = 0 \Rightarrow x^2 - 7x + \left(\dfrac{7}{2}\right)^2 = 3 + \left(\dfrac{7}{2}\right)^2 \Rightarrow \left(x - \dfrac{7}{2}\right)^2 = \dfrac{61}{4} \Rightarrow x - \dfrac{7}{2} = \pm\dfrac{\sqrt{61}}{2} \Rightarrow x = \dfrac{7}{2} \pm \dfrac{7.8}{2}$

$\Rightarrow x = 7.4$ or -0.4

3. $2x^2 + 6x + 3 = 0 \Rightarrow x^2 + 3x = -\dfrac{3}{2} \Rightarrow x^2 + 3x + \left(\dfrac{3}{2}\right)^2 = -\dfrac{3}{2} + \left(\dfrac{3}{2}\right)^2 \Rightarrow \left(x + \dfrac{3}{2}\right)^2 = \dfrac{3}{4} \Rightarrow x + \dfrac{3}{2} = \pm\sqrt{\dfrac{3}{4}}$

$\Rightarrow x = -\dfrac{3}{2} \pm \dfrac{\sqrt{3}}{2} \Rightarrow x = -0.65$ or -2.35

4. $5x^2 - 3x - 2 = 0 \Rightarrow x^2 - \dfrac{3x}{5} + \left(\dfrac{3}{10}\right)^2 = \dfrac{2}{5} + \left(\dfrac{3}{10}\right)^2 \Rightarrow \left(x - \dfrac{3}{10}\right)^2 = \dfrac{49}{100} \Rightarrow x - \dfrac{3}{10} = \pm\dfrac{7}{10}$

$\Rightarrow x = \dfrac{3}{10} \pm \dfrac{7}{10} \Rightarrow x = 1$ or -0.4

5. $\dfrac{x^2}{2} - \dfrac{2x}{3} - 1 = 0 \Rightarrow x^2 - \dfrac{4x}{3} + \left(\dfrac{2}{3}\right)^2 = 2 + \left(\dfrac{2}{3}\right)^2 \Rightarrow \left(x - \dfrac{2}{3}\right)^2 = \dfrac{22}{9} \Rightarrow x - \dfrac{2}{3} = \pm\sqrt{\dfrac{22}{9}} \Rightarrow x = \dfrac{2}{3} \pm \dfrac{4.7}{3}$

$\Rightarrow x = 2.2$ or -0.9

Group B

1. -0.6 or -5.4 2. 8.75 or 0.25 3. -0.4 or -3.6 4. 0.35 or -1.96 5. 4.2 or -2.2

ANSWERS TO EXERCISE 4.5

Group A

1. $a = 3, b = 5, c = 2$ so $x = \dfrac{-5 \pm \sqrt{25 - 24}}{6} = \dfrac{-5 \pm 1}{6}$

$x = -\dfrac{2}{3}$ or -1

2. $a = 11, b = 7, c = -9$ so $x = \dfrac{-7 \pm \sqrt{49 + 396}}{22} = \dfrac{-7 \pm 21.1}{22}$

$x = -1.3$ or 0.6

3. $a = 1, b = -6, c = 3$ so $x = \dfrac{6 \pm \sqrt{36 - 12}}{2} = \dfrac{6 \pm 4.9}{2}$

$x = 5.45$ or 0.55

4. $\dfrac{x + 1}{x} = \dfrac{3x}{x + 2} \Rightarrow (x + 1)(x + 2) = 3x^2 \Rightarrow x^2 + 3x + 2 = 3x^2 \Rightarrow 2x^2 - 3x - 2 = 0$

$a = 2, b = -3, c = -2$ so $x = \dfrac{3 \pm \sqrt{9 + 16}}{4} = \dfrac{3 \pm \sqrt{25}}{4}$

$x = 2$ or $-\tfrac{1}{2}$

5. This is not a quadratic equation. It has four roots, but it does have the quadratic pattern $2(x^2)^2 - 5(x^2) + 1 = 0$ and it can be solved with the help of the formula.

$a = 2, b = -5, c = 1$ so $x^2 = \dfrac{+5 \pm \sqrt{25 - 8}}{4} = \dfrac{5 \pm \sqrt{17}}{4} = \dfrac{5 \pm 4.1}{4}$

$\therefore x^2 = \dfrac{9.1}{4}$ or $\dfrac{0.9}{4}$ i.e. $x^2 = 2.3$ or 0.23

$\therefore x = \pm\sqrt{2.3}$ or $\pm\sqrt{0.23}$

$\therefore x = 1.5$ or -1.5 or 0.5 or -0.5

Group B
1. 2.6 or 0.4
2. 0.44 or -1.84

3. 0.28 or -1.78

4. 1.3 or -2.3

5. $x^2 = 2$ or $\frac{2}{3} \Rightarrow x = \pm 1.4$ or ± 0.8

ANSWERS TO EXERCISE 4.6

1. $f(x) = x^2 + 6x + 5 = (x + 3)^2 - 4$

When $x = 0$, $f(x) = 5$.

minimum value of $f(x)$ and it

occurs where $(x + 3) = 0$ i.e. $x = -3$

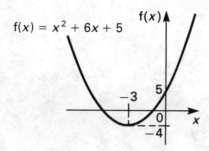

$$f(x) = x^2 + 6x + 5$$

2. $f(x) = x^2 - 7x + 3 = \left(x - \dfrac{7}{2} \right)^2 - \dfrac{37}{4}$

When $x = 0$ $f(x) = 3$.

minimum value of $f(x)$ and it

occurs where $\left(x - \dfrac{7}{2} \right) = 0$ i.e. $x = \dfrac{7}{2}$

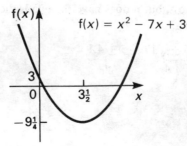

$$f(x) = x^2 - 7x + 3$$

3. $f(x) = 3x^2 + 5x + 1 = 3\left(x^2 + \dfrac{5}{3}x + \dfrac{1}{3} \right) = 3\left\{ \left(x + \dfrac{5}{6} \right)^2 - \dfrac{13}{36} \right\}$

Firstly sketch $\left(x + \dfrac{5}{6} \right)^2 - \dfrac{13}{36}$ and you will get the dotted graph shown.

The effect of the factor 3 is to increase all the y values by a factor of 3, to produce the graph shown – quite a significant change.

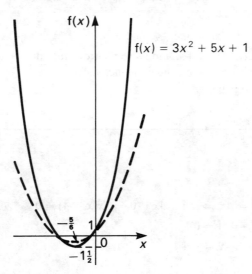

$f(x) = 3x^2 + 5x + 1$

4. $f(x) = 2 + 2x - x^2 = -\{x^2 - 2x - 2\} = -\{(x-1)^2 - 3\}$

This – sign inverts the graph of $(x - 1)^2 - 3$ to produce the graph shown.

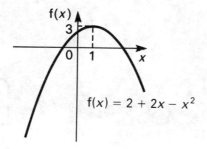

$f(x) = 2 + 2x - x^2$

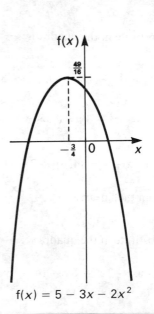

$f(x) = 5 - 3x - 2x^2$

5. $f(x) = 5 - 3x - 2x^2 = -2\left\{x^2 + \dfrac{3x}{2} - \dfrac{5}{2}\right\} = -2\left\{\left(x + \dfrac{3}{4}\right)^2 - \dfrac{49}{16}\right\}$

ANSWERS TO EXERCISE 4.7

1. Compare b^2 and $4ac$ $\Rightarrow$ $9 < 16$ i.e. $b^2 < 4ac$ $\therefore$ imaginary roots

2. $x - \dfrac{x}{2} = 1$ $\Rightarrow$ $x^2 - x + 1 = 0$

Compare b^2 and $4ac$ $\Rightarrow$ $1 > -8$ i.e. $b^2 > 4ac$ $\therefore$ real distinct roots

3. $px^2 + qx + r = 0$

Compare b^2 and $4ac \Rightarrow q^2 > 0, 4pr < 0 \because r < 0$ so $b^2 > 4ac \therefore$ real distinct roots

4. $ax^2 + 4\sqrt{a}.x + 4 = 0$

Compare b^2 and $4ac \Rightarrow 16a = 16a$ i.e. $b^2 = 4ac \therefore$ equal roots

5. $5(x + a)^2 + 5(x + a) + 1$ is a quadratic in $x + a$ and its roots are values of $x + a$.

Compare b^2 and $4ac \Rightarrow 25 > 20$ i.e. $b^2 > 4ac \therefore$ real distinct roots

So it has real roots for x provided a is real.

ANSWERS TO EXERCISE 4.8

Group A

1. $y^2 = 4x, y + x = 0$

From the linear: $y = -x$

Substitute in the quadratic: $(-x)^2 = 4x \Rightarrow x^2 - 4x = 0 \Rightarrow x(x - 4) = 0$

$\therefore x = 0$ Substitute in the linear: $\Rightarrow y = 0$

or $x = 4$ Substitute in the linear: $\Rightarrow y = -4$

$\therefore$ solutions are $(0, 0)$ and $(4, -4)$.

NB Having found $x = 4$ if we substitute back in the quadratic we get $y^2 = 16 \Rightarrow y = \pm 4$ i.e. two answers, only one of which is correct. To make sure you get the correct result always substitute back in the linear.

Investigation

Why is this so?

2. $\dfrac{x^2}{9} + \dfrac{y^2}{16} = 1, 3y + 4x = 12$

From the linear: $y = \dfrac{12 - 4x}{3}$

Substitute in the quadratic: $\Rightarrow \dfrac{x^2}{9} + \dfrac{(12 - 4x)^2}{9.16} = 1$

9.16 means 9×16. Note the position of the dot.

$\therefore 16x^2 + (12 - 4x)^2 = 9.16 \Rightarrow 32x^2 - 8.12x + 12^2 - 9.16 = 0$

$\Rightarrow 32x^2 - 96x = 0$

$\Rightarrow x^2 - 3x = 0 \Rightarrow x = 0$ Substitute in the linear: $y = 4 \therefore (0, 4)$

$x = 3$ Substitute in the linear: $y = 0 \therefore (3, 0)$

3. $xy + 2x - y = 14, 3y + 2x = 14$

From the linear: $y = \dfrac{14 - 2x}{3}$

Substitute in the quadratic: $\dfrac{x(14 - 2x)}{3} + 2x - \dfrac{(14 - 2x)}{3} = 14$

$\Rightarrow 14x - 2x^2 + 6x - 14 + 2x = 42 \Rightarrow x^2 - 11x + 28 = 0$

$\Rightarrow (x - 4)(x - 7) = 0$

$x = 4 \Rightarrow y = \dfrac{14 - 8}{3} = 2 \quad \therefore \quad (4, 2)$

$x = 7 \Rightarrow y = \dfrac{14 - 14}{3} = 0 \quad \therefore \quad (7, 0)$

4. $x^2 + (y - 4)^2 = 169, y = x - 9$

$\therefore x^2 + (x - 13)^2 = 169 \Rightarrow x^2 + x^2 - 26x + 169 = 169 \Rightarrow x^2 - 13x = 0$

$x = 0, \quad y = 0 - 9 = -9 \quad \therefore \quad (0, -9)$

$x = 13, \quad y = 13 - 9 = 4 \quad \therefore \quad (13, 4)$

5. $x^2 + y^2 - 4x - 2y - 20 = 0, 2y = x + 5$

Substitute from the linear in the quadratic for x:

$\Rightarrow (2y - 5)^2 + y^2 - 4(2y - 5) - 2y - 20 = 0$

$\Rightarrow 5y^2 - 30y + 25 = 0 \Rightarrow y^2 - 6y + 5 = 0 \Rightarrow (y - 1)(y - 5) = 0$

$y = 1 \Rightarrow x = 2 - 5 = -3 \therefore \quad (-3, 1)$

$y = 5 \Rightarrow x = 10 - 5 = 5 \therefore (5, 5)$

> Substituting for x is better than for y in this case $\because$ substituting for y would have involved fractions $\left(y = \dfrac{x + 5}{2} \right)$.

Group B

1. $(0, 0), (5, -1)$ 2. $(-1, 0), (0, -2)$ 3. $(7, 3), (1, 6)$ 4. $(1, 4), (-6, 3)$ 5. $(5, -5), (-3, 1)$

ANSWERS TO EXERCISE 4.9

Group A

1. $\alpha - \beta = \sqrt{(\alpha - \beta)^2} = \sqrt{(\alpha^2 + \beta^2 - 2\alpha\beta)} = \sqrt{(\alpha^2 + \beta^2 + 2\alpha\beta - 4\alpha\beta)}$

$\qquad = \sqrt{(\alpha + \beta)^2 - 4\alpha\beta} = \sqrt{(5^2 - 4 \times 3)}$

$\qquad = \sqrt{25 - 12} = \sqrt{13}$

2. $\alpha^3 + \beta^3 = (\alpha + \beta)(\alpha^2 + \beta^2 - \alpha\beta) = (\alpha + \beta)(\alpha^2 + \beta^2 + 2\alpha\beta - 3\alpha\beta)$

$\qquad = (\alpha + \beta)\{(\alpha + \beta)^2 - 3\alpha\beta\} = -\dfrac{8}{5}\left(\dfrac{64}{25} - 3 \times -\dfrac{3}{5} \right)$

$\qquad = -\dfrac{8}{5}\left(\dfrac{64}{25} + \dfrac{9}{5} \right) = -\dfrac{8}{5} \times \dfrac{109}{25} = -\dfrac{872}{125}$

3. $\dfrac{b}{a} = -\left(\dfrac{1}{\alpha} + \dfrac{1}{\beta} \right) = -\left(\dfrac{\beta + \alpha}{\alpha\beta} \right) = -\left(-\dfrac{6}{4} \right) = \dfrac{3}{2}$

$\dfrac{c}{a} = \dfrac{1}{\alpha} \cdot \dfrac{1}{\beta} = \dfrac{1}{\alpha\beta} = \dfrac{1}{4}$

$\therefore$ equation is $x^2 + \dfrac{3x}{2} + \dfrac{1}{4} = 0 \quad$ i.e. $4x^2 + 6x + 1 = 0$

4. $\left(\alpha^2 + \dfrac{1}{\beta^2}\right)\left(\beta^2 + \dfrac{1}{\alpha^2}\right) = \alpha^2\beta^2 + 1 + 1 + \dfrac{1}{\alpha^2\beta^2} = (\alpha\beta)^2 + 2 + \dfrac{1}{(\alpha\beta)^2} = \dfrac{c^2}{a^2} + 2 + \dfrac{a^2}{c^2} = \left(\dfrac{c}{a} + \dfrac{a}{c}\right)^2$

5. $px^2 + qx + r = 0.$ Roots are α, 2α.

Then $3\alpha = -\dfrac{q}{p} \Rightarrow 9\alpha^2 = \dfrac{q^2}{p^2} \Rightarrow \alpha^2 = \dfrac{q^2}{9p^2}$

and $2\alpha^2 = \dfrac{r}{p} \Rightarrow \alpha^2 = \dfrac{r}{2p}$

$\therefore \dfrac{r}{2p} = \dfrac{q^2}{9p^2} \Rightarrow 9pr = 2q^2$

Group B

1. $-3\sqrt{11}$ 2. $ax^2 + 2bx + 4c = 0$ 3. $6x^2 - 4x - 41 = 0$ 4. $-\dfrac{k}{2}$

Chapter 5

SURDS

Aims and objectives

Having worked through this chapter you will be competent to

know what surds are	$\sqrt{3}, \sqrt{7}$ but not $\sqrt{4}, \sqrt{9}$
rationalise simple denominators	$\dfrac{2}{\sqrt{3}} = \dfrac{2\sqrt{3}}{3}$
factorise	$\sqrt{18} = \sqrt{9} \times \sqrt{2} = 3\sqrt{2}$
evaluate	$\sqrt{18} + \sqrt{72} = 3\sqrt{2} + 6\sqrt{2} = 9\sqrt{2}$
further rationalise denominators.	$\dfrac{1}{\sqrt{5} - \sqrt{3}} = \dfrac{\sqrt{5} + \sqrt{3}}{2}$

Rational and irrational numbers

Rational numbers are those which are known exactly.

$$3 \qquad 57 \qquad -8 \qquad \tfrac{3}{4} \qquad \sqrt{9}$$

are all rational numbers.

Irrational numbers are those which are not known exactly.

$$\pi \qquad \sqrt{7}$$

$\sqrt{9}$ is rational, $\sqrt{7}$ is irrational.
What is the difference?

$\sqrt{9} = \pm 3 \qquad$ *exactly*

$\sqrt{7} = \pm 2.65 \quad$ *approximately*

> π is approximately 3.142
> or   3.1416
> or   3.14159
>
> It has been worked out to thousands of decimal places but it does not have an exact value.

Numbers like $\sqrt{7}$ are called *surds*.

Rationalising the denominator

In mathematics it is sometimes necessary to remove the square root without altering the value of the term it is in. The two favourite techniques for altering the appearance of a term without altering its value are to multiply by 1 or add 0. We have used the technique of adding 0 in work on roots of quadratic equations.

The way to make a square root sign disappear is to square the term except, obviously, in the case of square roots of perfect squares.

Now let's look at a common problem: remove the square roots from the bottom of the fraction $\dfrac{2}{\sqrt{3}}$.

$$\frac{2}{\sqrt{3}} = \frac{2}{\sqrt{3}} \times 1$$

$$= \frac{2}{\sqrt{3}} \times \frac{\sqrt{3}}{\sqrt{3}}$$

Secondly, fill this in so that we are multiplying the original by 1.

Firstly, pick this to get $\sqrt{3} \times \sqrt{3} = 3$ on the bottom.

$$= \frac{2\sqrt{3}}{3}$$

Now the formal name for what we have just done is **rationalising the denominator**, i.e. making the denominator into a rational number. This is especially useful if fractions need to be added, subtracted or compared.

> It does not matter at all that we finish up with roots on the top (**numerator**).

$$\frac{\sqrt{3}}{\sqrt{5}} = \frac{\sqrt{3}}{\sqrt{5}} \times \frac{\sqrt{5}}{\sqrt{5}} = \frac{\sqrt{15}}{5}$$

EXERCISE 5.1

(*Answers on page 70*)

Rationalise the denominator in each case, leaving your answer in surd form.

Group A

1. $\dfrac{1}{\sqrt{7}}$

2. $\dfrac{a}{\sqrt{x}}$

3. $\dfrac{a+2}{\sqrt{3}}$

4. $\dfrac{5}{2\sqrt{3}}$

5. $\dfrac{2}{\sqrt{3}} + \dfrac{1}{\sqrt{2}}$

Group B

1. $\dfrac{2}{\sqrt{17}}$

2. $\dfrac{1}{\sqrt{8}}$

3. $\dfrac{5}{\sqrt{3}}$

4. $\dfrac{3}{\sqrt{5}} - \dfrac{1}{\sqrt{2}}$

5. $\dfrac{a}{\sqrt{x}} + \dfrac{b}{\sqrt{y}}$

We should have a further look at question B2 above. The question and the answer both contain $\sqrt{8}$. It is unusual to leave $\sqrt{8}$ in that form.

$$\sqrt{8} = \sqrt{4} \times \sqrt{2} = 2 \times \sqrt{2} \quad \text{i.e. } 2\sqrt{2}$$
and $\sqrt{75} = \sqrt{25} \times \sqrt{3} = 5 \times \sqrt{3} \quad \text{i.e. } 5\sqrt{3}$

Query: if $\sqrt{27} = \sqrt{9} \times \sqrt{3}$

can we also say $\sqrt{27} = \sqrt{18} + \sqrt{9}$?

Investigation

You could investigate these statements for their validity before reading on.

Consider the statement $\sqrt{27} = \sqrt{9} \times \sqrt{3}$

$$\sqrt{27} = 27^{\frac{1}{2}} = (9 \times 3)^{1/2} = 9^{1/2} \times 3^{1/2} = \sqrt{9} \times \sqrt{3}$$

Clearly such a statement would be true whatever number is used.

Algebraically

$$\sqrt{ab} = (ab)^{1/2} = a^{1/2} \cdot b^{1/2} = \sqrt{a} \cdot \sqrt{b}$$

which is just as well otherwise the theory above using $\sqrt{8}$ and $\sqrt{75}$ would have been useless.

We could write QED here – Latin *quod erat demonstrandum* = what was to be proved has been.

Now for the statement $\sqrt{27} = \sqrt{18} + \sqrt{9}$.

Assume it is true and square both sides.

$$(\sqrt{27})^2 = (\sqrt{18} + \sqrt{9})^2$$
$$27 = 18 + 9 + 2\sqrt{18}\sqrt{9}$$
$$27 = 27 + 2\sqrt{18}\sqrt{9}$$

Remember

$(a+b)^2 = a^2 + b^2 + 2ab$

which is nonsense.

∴ the original statement is not true.

Another popular mistake and hence another occasion to make sure we are not in with the 'in' crowd!

This type of argument is known as *reductio ad absurdum* (Latin) = reduce to a nonsense.

The essential rules

The two simple rules are:

$$\sqrt{a} \times \sqrt{b} = \sqrt{ab}$$

and

$$\sqrt{a} + \sqrt{b} \neq \sqrt{a+b}$$

Strictly speaking, the sign for square root is $\sqrt{}$ and not $\sqrt{}$. In $\sqrt{}$ this bit is a bracket and means the same as ( ) or { } or [ ] ∴ $\sqrt{}$, $\sqrt{()}$, $\sqrt{\{\}}$, $\sqrt{[]}$ are all identical.

EXERCISE 5.2

(*Answers on page 70*)

Simplify each of these, leaving your answers in surd form.

Group A

1. $\sqrt{18} + 2\sqrt{8}$
2. $\sqrt{7} + \sqrt{28}$
3. $\sqrt{125} - \sqrt{72}$
4. $\sqrt{(x^6 y^3 \div x^4 y)}$
5. $\sqrt{50} + \sqrt{18} - \sqrt{128}$

Group B

1. $\sqrt{1000} + \sqrt{40}$
2. $\dfrac{\sqrt{288}}{\sqrt{32}}$
3. $\sqrt{81} - \sqrt{18} + 3\sqrt{2}$
4. $\sqrt{(x^{1/2} y^{5/3} \div x^{5/2} y)}$
5. $(\sqrt{x} - \sqrt{y})(\sqrt{x} + \sqrt{y})$

The question and answer for B5 reminds us of a well-known factorisation (difference of two squares). Look at it carefully. Notice particularly that there are no surds when the brackets have been removed. Hence, since

$$(A - B)(A + B) = A^2 - B^2$$

if there is a square root here and/or here they will disappear (because of the squaring).

e.g. $(\sqrt{5} - \sqrt{3})(\sqrt{5} + \sqrt{3}) = \sqrt{5}^2 - \sqrt{3}^2 = 5 - 3 = 2$

We make use of this in the next questions.

e.g. Rationalise the denominator of $\dfrac{1}{4 - \sqrt{3}}$.

$$\frac{1}{4 - \sqrt{3}} = \frac{1}{4 - \sqrt{3}} \times 1$$

$$= \frac{1}{(4 - \sqrt{3})} \times \frac{(4 + \sqrt{3})}{(4 + \sqrt{3})}$$

Secondly, choose this bracket to make the multiplying factor 1.

Firstly, decide on this bracket to complete the difference of two squares in the denominator.

$$= \frac{4 + \sqrt{3}}{4^2 - \sqrt{3}^2}$$

$$= \frac{4 + \sqrt{3}}{16 - 3} = \frac{4 + \sqrt{3}}{13}$$

Remember

that $\dfrac{1}{4 - \sqrt{3}}$ still equals $\dfrac{4 + \sqrt{3}}{13}$.

All we have done is alter the appearance so that there are no surds in the denominator.

e.g.

$$\frac{a}{\sqrt{x} - \sqrt{2}} = \frac{a}{(\sqrt{x} - \sqrt{2})} \times \frac{(\sqrt{x} + \sqrt{2})}{(\sqrt{x} + \sqrt{2})}$$

$$= \frac{a(\sqrt{x} + \sqrt{2})}{x - 2}$$

EXERCISE 5.3

(*Answers on page 71*)

Group A

1. Express $\sqrt{12}$ in its simplest form.

2. Express $\sqrt{30} \div \sqrt{54}$ in its simplest form.

3. Rationalise the denominator of $\dfrac{3}{\sqrt{5}}$.

4. Rationalise the denominator of $\dfrac{1}{\sqrt{2} - 1}$.

5. Rationalise the denominator of $\dfrac{2}{\sqrt{5} - \sqrt{3}}$.

Group B

1. Express $\sqrt{45}$ in its simplest form.

2. Express $\sqrt{98} - \sqrt{50}$ in its simplest form.

3. Rationalise the denominator of $\dfrac{x}{\sqrt{t}}$.

4. Rationalise the denominator of $\dfrac{3}{3 + \sqrt{3}}$.

5. Rationalise the denominator of $\dfrac{a}{\sqrt{t} - \sqrt{v}}$.

Group C

1. Express $\sqrt{72}$ in its simplest form.

2. Express $\sqrt{12} \div \sqrt{24}$ in its simplest form.

3. Rationalise the denominator of $\dfrac{\sqrt{3}}{\sqrt{7}}$.

4. Rationalise the denominator of $\dfrac{5}{7 - \sqrt{5}}$.

5. Rationalise the denominator of $\dfrac{1 + \sqrt{3}}{2\sqrt{2} - \sqrt{3}}$.

Group D

1. Express $\sqrt{28}$ in its simplest form.

2. Express $\sqrt{12} - \sqrt{48} + \sqrt{27}$ in its simplest form.

3. Rationalise the denominator of $\dfrac{2}{\sqrt{11}}$.

4. Rationalise the denominator of $\dfrac{1}{x + \sqrt{y}}$.

5. Rationalise the denominator of $\dfrac{\sqrt{k} + m}{a\sqrt{x} + \sqrt{y}}$.

Answers to exercises

ANSWERS TO EXERCISE 5.1

Group A

1. $\dfrac{1}{\sqrt{7}} = \dfrac{1}{\sqrt{7}} \times \dfrac{\sqrt{7}}{\sqrt{7}} = \dfrac{\sqrt{7}}{7}$

2. $\dfrac{a}{\sqrt{x}} = \dfrac{a}{\sqrt{x}} \times \dfrac{\sqrt{x}}{\sqrt{x}} = \dfrac{a\sqrt{x}}{x}$

3. $\dfrac{a+2}{\sqrt{3}} = \dfrac{a+2}{\sqrt{3}} \times \dfrac{\sqrt{3}}{\sqrt{3}} = \dfrac{(a+2)\sqrt{3}}{3}$

4. $\dfrac{5}{2\sqrt{3}} = \dfrac{5}{2\sqrt{3}} \times \dfrac{\sqrt{3}}{\sqrt{3}} = \dfrac{5\sqrt{3}}{2 \times 3} = \dfrac{5\sqrt{3}}{6}$

5. $\dfrac{2}{\sqrt{3}} + \dfrac{1}{\sqrt{2}} = \dfrac{2}{\sqrt{3}} \times \dfrac{\sqrt{3}}{\sqrt{3}} + \dfrac{1}{\sqrt{2}} \times \dfrac{\sqrt{2}}{\sqrt{2}} = \dfrac{2\sqrt{3}}{3} + \dfrac{\sqrt{2}}{2} = \dfrac{4\sqrt{3} \times 3\sqrt{2}}{6}$

Group B

1. $\dfrac{2\sqrt{17}}{17}$

2. $\dfrac{\sqrt{8}}{8}$

3. $\dfrac{5\sqrt{3}}{3}$

4. $\dfrac{6\sqrt{5} - 5\sqrt{2}}{10}$

5. $\dfrac{ay\sqrt{x} + bx\sqrt{y}}{xy}$

ANSWERS TO EXERCISE 5.2

Group A

1. $\sqrt{18} + 2\sqrt{8} = \sqrt{9}\sqrt{2} + 2\sqrt{4}\sqrt{2} = 3\sqrt{2} + 4\sqrt{2} = 7\sqrt{2}$

2. $\sqrt{7} + \sqrt{28} = \sqrt{7} + \sqrt{4}\sqrt{7} = \sqrt{7} + 2\sqrt{7} = 3\sqrt{7}$

3. $\sqrt{125} - \sqrt{72} = \sqrt{25}\sqrt{5} - \sqrt{36}\sqrt{2} = 5\sqrt{5} - 6\sqrt{2}$

4. $\sqrt{(x^6 y^3 - x^4 y)} = \sqrt{x^2 y^2} = xy$

5. $\sqrt{50} + \sqrt{18} - \sqrt{128} = \sqrt{25}\sqrt{2} + \sqrt{9}\sqrt{2} - \sqrt{64}\sqrt{2} = 5\sqrt{2} + 3\sqrt{2} - 8\sqrt{2} = 0$

Group B

1. $12\sqrt{10}$ 2. 3 3. 9 4. $\dfrac{y^{1/3}}{x}$ 5. $x - y$

ANSWERS TO EXERCISE 5.3

Group A

1. $\sqrt{12} = \sqrt{4} \times \sqrt{3} = 2\sqrt{3}$

2. $\dfrac{\sqrt{30}}{\sqrt{54}} = \dfrac{\sqrt{5} \times \sqrt{6}}{\sqrt{9} \times \sqrt{6}} = \dfrac{\sqrt{5}}{\sqrt{9}} = \dfrac{\sqrt{5}}{3}$

3. $\dfrac{3}{\sqrt{5}} = \dfrac{3}{\sqrt{5}} \times \dfrac{\sqrt{5}}{\sqrt{5}} = \dfrac{3\sqrt{5}}{5}$

4. $\dfrac{1}{\sqrt{2}-1} = \dfrac{1}{(\sqrt{2}-1)} \times \dfrac{(\sqrt{2}+1)}{(\sqrt{2}+1)} = \dfrac{\sqrt{2}+1}{2-1} = \sqrt{2}+1$

5. $\dfrac{2}{\sqrt{5}-\sqrt{3}} = \dfrac{2}{(\sqrt{5}-\sqrt{3})} \times \dfrac{(\sqrt{5}+\sqrt{3})}{(\sqrt{5}+\sqrt{3})} = \dfrac{2(\sqrt{5}+\sqrt{3})}{5-3} = \dfrac{2(\sqrt{5}+\sqrt{3})}{2} = \sqrt{5}+\sqrt{3}$

Group B

1. $3\sqrt{5}$

2. $2\sqrt{2}$

3. $\dfrac{x\sqrt{t}}{t}$

4. $\dfrac{3-\sqrt{3}}{2}$

5. $\dfrac{a(\sqrt{t}+\sqrt{v})}{t-v}$

Group C

1. $6\sqrt{2}$

2. $\dfrac{1}{\sqrt{2}} = \dfrac{\sqrt{2}}{2}$

3. $\dfrac{\sqrt{21}}{7}$

4. $\dfrac{5(7+\sqrt{5})}{44}$

5. $\dfrac{(1+\sqrt{3})(2\sqrt{2}+\sqrt{3})}{5}$

Group D

1. $2\sqrt{7}$

2. $\sqrt{3}$

3. $\dfrac{2\sqrt{11}}{11}$

4. $\dfrac{x-\sqrt{y}}{x^2-y}$

5. $\dfrac{(\sqrt{k}+m)(a\sqrt{x}-\sqrt{y})}{a^2x-y}$

Chapter 6

LOGARITHMS

Aims and objectives

Having worked through this chapter, you will:

know what logs are

know the basic manipulations $\qquad\qquad \log x + \log y = \log xy$

be able to change the base $\qquad\qquad \log_4 8 = \dfrac{\log_2 8}{\log_2 4}$

have done some investigation into the log function.

Definition of logarithms

From the work on indices we know that

$32 = 2^5$

which, in words, is 'thirty-two is two to the power five'.

An alternative form in words is 'the logarithm of thirty-two to the base two is five.'

Written mathematically this is:

$5 = \log_2 32$

In symbols:

> **If $p = r^q$ then $q = \log_r p$**

> **When one number is expressed as a power of another number then the power is the logarithm of the first number with the other number as base.**

Nobody ever says 'logarithm' and from now on we shall say log.

Concentrate on this statement. It does make sense!

$64 = 8^2 \Rightarrow 2 = \log_8 64$ *2 is log to the base 8 of 64*

$ = 4^3 \Rightarrow 3 = \log_4 64$ *3 is log to the base 4 of 64*

$ = 2^6 \Rightarrow 6 = \log_2 64$

Basic operations

We shall now develop six basic rules used in the manipulation of logs. They are not very difficult but we need to learn them well.

Suppose $\quad a = \log_n x \quad$ and $\quad b = \log_n y$

then $\qquad n^a = x \quad$ and $\quad n^b = y$

$\therefore \qquad xy = n^a \times n^b = n^{a+b}$

$\therefore \qquad \log_n(xy) = a + b$

Rule 1

$\quad \log_n(xy) = \log_n x + \log_n y$

Rule 2

We can use a similar argument to show that

$\quad \log_k\left(\dfrac{p}{q}\right) = \log_k p - \log_k q$

> **Remember**
>
> logs can only be combined in these ways if they are to the same base.

$\log_5 4 + \log_5 7 = \log_5(4 \times 7) = \log_5 28$

$\log_2 9 + \log_2 5 - \log_2 15 = \log_2\left(\dfrac{9 \times 5}{15}\right) = \log_2 3$

EXERCISE 6.1

(*Answers on page 77*)

Express each of these as a single log where possible.

1. $\log_3 8 + \log_3 2$
2. $\log_5 7 - \log_5 2$
3. $\log_7 8 + \log_7 3 - \log_7 12$
4. $\log_2 3 + \log_3 2$
5. $\log_2 12 - \log_2 3 - \log_2 4$

Now consider this sum.

$3\log_a x = \log_a x + \log_a x + \log_a x = \log_a x^3$

$\therefore 3\log_a x = \log_a x^3$

and from this we can state the third rule.

Rule 3

$\quad n\log x = \log x^n$

And now for two special cases.

If $\quad t = \log_n n$

then $\quad n^t = n = n^1 \quad$ *from the basic definition*

$\therefore \quad t = 1$

but $\quad t = \log_n n$

Rule 4

$\log_n n = 1 \quad \Rightarrow \quad$ **log to any base of the base number = 1**

If $\quad f = \log_d 1$ where d can take any value

then $d^f = 1$

and the only way this can be true is if $f = 0$.

Rule 5

$\log_d 1 = 0 \quad \Rightarrow \quad$ **log to any base of 1 is zero**

Now finally to a most powerful rule concerning logs.

Suppose $\quad x = \log_a y$

$\therefore \quad a^x = y \quad$ *using the basic definition*

Then $\quad \log_c a^x = \log_c y \quad$ *taking logs, to a new base, of both sides*

$\therefore \quad x \log_c a = \log_c y$

$\therefore \quad x = \dfrac{\log_c y}{\log_c a}$

Rule 6

log to old base equals log to new base over log to new base of old base.

$\log_a y = \dfrac{\log_c y}{\log_c a}$

The rule for changing bases: you need to know this.

Investigations

If done thoroughly, these will stand you in good stead later.

Use your calculator to find the shape of $y = \log_{10} x$. To help with your investigation: the ⬚log⬚ button on your calculator gives logs to the base 10.

You know that $10^3 = 1000$ but check.

Enter 1000, press $\boxed{\log}$, do you get 3?

i.e. $3 = \log_{10}1000$

Investigation 1

Now try these sequences.

$\boxed{3}$ $\boxed{\log}$ $\Rightarrow 0.477$ and

$\boxed{3}$ $\boxed{\pm}$ $\boxed{\log}$ $\Rightarrow$ error

Vary this number and try the sequences a few times. What conclusion can you come to?

You should now be able to sketch $y = \log_{10} x$.

A good conclusion to this investigation would be to sketch $y = 10^x$ on the same diagram. This should lead you to a definite conclusion.

Investigation 2

Now investigate $y = \log_{100} x$. You should be able to deduce what the curve will look like and how it compares with $y = \log_{10} x$.

Investigation 3

Before the electronic calculator many calculations were done using log tables; find out how they were used.

Investigation 4

The $\boxed{\ln}$ button gives logs to the base e where $e \approx 2.718$. There will be more on this later. Find out what you can about John Napier (1550–1617).

Now for some examples.

 Write as a single log: $\log_2 x - 2\log_2 y$.

$\log_2 x - 2\log_2 y = \log_2 x - \log_2 y^2$ *using rule 3*

$$= \log_2 \frac{x}{y^2} \qquad \textit{using rule 2}$$

 Evaluate $\log_5 125$.

$\log_5 125 = \log_5 5^3$

$\qquad\quad = 3 \log_5 5 \qquad\qquad \textit{using rule 3}$

$\qquad\quad = 3 \qquad\qquad\qquad\quad \textit{using rule 4}$

e.g. $\log_4 32 \times \log_8 4$

$\log_4 32 \times \log_8 4 = \log_4 2^5 \times \log_8 2^2$

$$= \frac{\log_2 2^5}{\log_2 4} \times \frac{\log_2 2^2}{\log_2 8} \quad \text{using rule 6}$$

$$= \frac{5}{\log_2 2^2} \times \frac{\log_2 2^2}{\log_2 2^3} \quad \text{using rules 6 and 7}$$

$$= \frac{5}{3\log_2 2} \quad \text{cancelling } \log_2 2^2$$

$$= \frac{5}{3}$$

e.g. $\log_x y \times \log_y z \times \log_z x = \log_x y \times \dfrac{\log_x z}{\log_x y} \times \dfrac{\log_x x}{\log_x z} \quad \text{using rule 6}$

$$= \log_x x = 1$$

e.g. $\log_{16} 2 = \dfrac{\log_2 2}{\log_2 16} \quad \text{or} \quad \log_{16} 2 = \log_{16} 16^{1/4}$

$$= \frac{\log_2 2}{\log_2 2^4} \qquad\qquad = \tfrac{1}{4}\log_{16} 16$$

$$= \frac{1}{4\log_2 2} \qquad\qquad = \tfrac{1}{4}$$

$$= \tfrac{1}{4}$$

EXERCISE 6.2

(*Answers on page 77*)

Group A

1. Find the value of $\log_3 81$ (without using a calculator).

2. Find the value of $\log_{25} 125$.

3. Express as a single log: $3\log 7 + \dfrac{1}{3}\log 27 - 6\log 2$.

4. Write $\log \dfrac{p^3 \sqrt{q}}{r}$ in terms of $\log p$, $\log q$ and $\log r$.

5. Solve the equation $2^x = 3$.

> When $\log x$ is written without the base being named, it is assumed to be to base 10.

Group B

1. Find the value of $\log_2 32$.
2. Evaluate $\log_{1.5}(\log_4 8)$.
3. Reduce $\log(x + 1) + \log(x - 1)^2 - \log(x^2 - 1)$ to a single term.
4. Solve the equation $\log_5 x - 1 = \log_5 4$.
5. Find x if $5^x = 4$.

Group C

1. Evaluate $\log_5\left(\dfrac{1}{125}\right)$.
2. Evaluate $\log_{\sqrt{2}} 16$.
3. If $\log_a(x + 1) = \log_a 4 + 2$, find x in terms of a.
4. Express in terms of $\log a$, $\log b$, and $\log c$ the term
$$\log\left(\frac{\sqrt[3]{a^2 b^3}}{\sqrt{c^{-3} b^7}}\right).$$
5. Prove that $\log_x \sqrt[3]{a} = \dfrac{1}{\log_a x^3}$.

Answers to exercises

ANSWERS TO EXERCISE 6.1

1. $\log_3 8 + \log_3 2 = \log_3(8 \times 2) = \log_3 16$

2. $\log_5 7 - \log_5 2 = \log_5\left(\dfrac{7}{2}\right) = \log_5 3.5$

3. $\log_7 8 + \log_7 3 - \log_7 12 = \log_7\left(\dfrac{8 \times 3}{12}\right) = \log_7 2$

4. $\log_2 3 + \log_3 2$ nothing can be done with these, as they are to different bases.

5. $\log_2 12 - \log_2 3 - \log_2 4 = \log_2\left(\dfrac{12}{3 \times 4}\right) = \log_2 1 = 0$

ANSWERS TO EXERCISE 6.2

Group A

1. $\log_3 81 = \log_3 3^4 = 4\log_3 3 = 4$

2. $\log_{25}125 = \dfrac{\log_5 125}{\log_5 25} = \dfrac{\log_5 5^3}{\log_5 5^2} = \dfrac{3\log_5 5}{2\log_5 5} = \dfrac{3}{2}$

3. $3\log 7 + \dfrac{1}{3}\log 27 - 6\log 2 = \log 7^3 + \log 27^{1/3} - \log 2^6 = \log\left(\dfrac{343 \times 3}{64}\right)$

4. $\log\dfrac{p^3\sqrt{q}}{r} = \log p^3 + \log\sqrt{q} - \log r = 3\log p + \tfrac{1}{2}\log q - \log r$

5. $2^x = 3 \Rightarrow \log 2^x = \log 3 \Rightarrow x\log 2 = \log 3 \Rightarrow x = \dfrac{\log 3}{\log 2} = 1.6$

Group B

1. 5

2. 1

3. $\log\dfrac{(x+1)(x-1)^2}{x^2-1} = \log(x-1)$

4. $\log_5 x - \log_5 5 = \log_5 4 \Rightarrow \dfrac{x}{5} = 4 \Rightarrow x = 20$

5. $x = \dfrac{\log 4}{\log 5} = 0.86$

Group C

1. -3

2. 8

3. $4a^2 - 1$

4. $\dfrac{2}{3}\log a - \dfrac{1}{2}\log b + \dfrac{3}{2}\log c$

Now try worksheets 1 and 2.

Chapter 7

INEQUALITIES

Aims and objectives

Having worked through this chapter, you will:

know the basic rules of inequalities

be able to apply them. $x(x-1)(x+2) > 0 \implies -2 < x < 0, x > 1$

Equations and inequalities

Mathematics is very much concerned with equations, or statements that things are equal. However, some work is concerned with statements that two things are *not* equal and these statements are **inequations** or **inequalities.** *A* may be **greater** than *B* (*A* > *B*), or **less** than *B* (*A* < *B*).

Inequalities occur constantly in everyday life. The maximum number of passengers on a bus would be written mathematically as

number of passengers $\leqslant$ 56

which is read as 'the number of passengers is less than or equal to 56'.

Before one large newspaper will admit a party to visit their printing works the party must have a minimum of ten members and a maximum of sixteen. This would be written

$10 \leqslant$ number in party $\leqslant 16$

and read as 'ten is less than or equal to the number of people which is less than or equal to 16'.

We have to be very careful when dealing with inequalities; they can be very misleading.

In the next exercise there are six true statements concerning equations and with each is the same statement applied to inequalities. Decide whether each is true or false.

EXERCISE 7.1

(*Answers on page 85*)

In each case, say whether the inequality is true or false.

Equation	Inequality
1. $x = a \implies x + c = a + c$	$x > a \implies x + c > a + c$
2. $x = k \implies 2x = 2k$	$x > k \implies 2x > 2k$
3. $x = k \implies ax = ak$	$x > k \implies ax > ak$

4. $x = 3 \Rightarrow -x = -3$ $x > 3 \Rightarrow -x > -3$

5. $\dfrac{1}{x} = \dfrac{1}{f} \Rightarrow x = f$ $\dfrac{1}{x} > \dfrac{1}{f} \Rightarrow x > f$

6. $\dfrac{1}{x} = x + 2 \Rightarrow 1 = x^2 + 2x$ $\dfrac{1}{x} > x + 2 \Rightarrow 1 > x^2 + 2x$

Number lines

Working with inequalities is often simplified by using a simple **number line**.

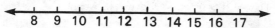

The inequality mentioned above, $10 \leqslant n \leqslant 16$ would be represented by this number line. Now consider

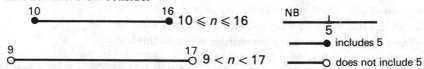

When n is a whole number or **integer**, these two statements are the same but if n could be a fraction they are not.

Think about it!

Let us consider the statement $xy > 0$. This says that the product of x and y has to be positive (>0). From basic algebra this can only be so if both x and y are positive or if they are both negative.

How about $xyz > 0$? This can only be true if x, y and z are all positive or if just two of x, y and z are negative.

We shall now use these ideas in some problems.

> Integer – the mathematical name for whole numbers, including negative.

> Digest this.

e.g.

Find the range of values of x for which $(x + 2)(x - 3) > 0$

We need to find values of x for which both brackets are positive or both are negative. On the number line it looks like this.

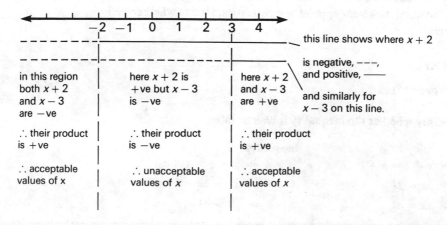

$\therefore (x+2)(x-3) > 0$ for $x < -2$ and $x > 3$.

e.g. Find the range of values of x for which $x(x-4) > 0$.

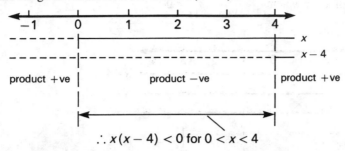

$\therefore x(x-4) < 0$ for $0 < x < 4$

e.g. Find the range of values of x for which $(x-2)(1-x) > 0$.

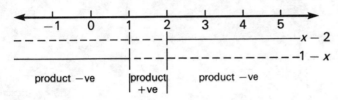

$\therefore (x-2)(1-x) > 0$ for $1 < x < 2$.

Representing each factor on the number line enables us to see at a glance when it is positive and when it is negative and to see the combinations required. The technique can be extended to any number of factors.

e.g. Find the range of values of x for which $x(x-1)(x+2)(x+3) > 0$.

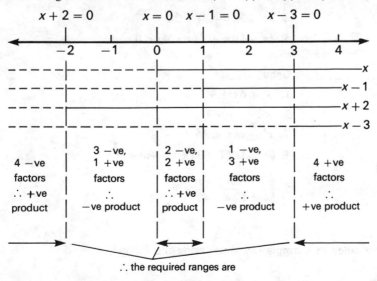

∴ the required ranges are $x < -2$, $0 < x < 1$ and $x > 3$.

e.g. Find the range of values of x for which $\dfrac{x+4}{(3-x)(x-1)} < 0$.

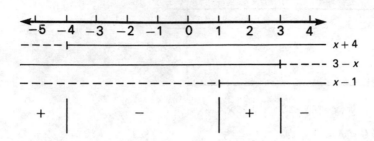

∴ $\dfrac{x+4}{(3-x)(x-1)} < 0$ for $-4 < x < 1$ and $x > 3$.

EXERCISE 7.2

(*Answers on page 85*)

Find the values of x which satisfy these inequalities.

Group A

1. $3x - 1 > > 7$
2. $-5x < 25$
3. $x(x + 2) > 0$
4. $(x - 3)^2 + 1 > 0$
5. $x^2 - 5x - 6 > 0$

Group B

1. $5x - 2 > 8$
2. $x(x - 5) < 0$
3. $x^2 + 7x + 12 < 0$
4. $(x - 3)(x + 2) > 24$
5. $(x - 1)(x + 2)(x - 4) < 0$

Group C

1. $6 - x < 3x + 5$
2. $(x + 5)(2x - 7) > 0$
3. $(2 - x)(x + 5) < 0$
4. $\dfrac{(1 - x)(3 - 2x)}{x + 2} > 0$
5. $\dfrac{(x + 5)(x - 2)}{(3 - x)(x + 1)} > 0$

Group D

1. $x^2 + 6x + 9 > 0$
2. $x(2 - x) > 0$
3. $x^2 - 16x < 36$
4. $(1 - 2x)(2 - 3x)(3 - 4x) < 0$
5. $\dfrac{(x - 2)(2 - x)}{(x + 1)(x - 4)} > 0$

We will now extend our range of examples by considering the following question.

EXAMPLE

Find the range of values of x for which

$$\frac{x+2}{x} > \frac{1}{2}.$$

A common mistake would be for the next line to read:

$2(x+2) > x$

What is the mistake?

Go back to the beginning. Writing for the first line

$\frac{2(x-2)}{x} > 1$ is OK. Why?

But then saying

$2(x+2) > x$ is not OK. Why?

Multiplying through is OK provided we know that we are multiplying by a positive quantity – refer to basic rules in Exercise 7.1.

Now for the correct approach!

$$\frac{x+2}{x} > \frac{1}{2}$$

$\therefore \quad \frac{2(x+2)}{x} > 1 \qquad\qquad \because 2\ is\ positive$

$\therefore \frac{x^2.2(x+2)}{x} > x^2 \qquad\qquad \because x^2\ is\ positive$

$\therefore\ x.2(x+2) > x^2$

$\therefore\quad 2x^2 + 4x > x^2$

$\therefore\quad\ x^2 + 4x > 0$

$\therefore\quad\ x(x+4) > 0$

i.e. $x > -4$ or $x > 0$

EXAMPLE

Find the range of values of x for which $\frac{1}{x} > \frac{1}{7}$.

Following the basic rules, if we reciprocate both sides and change the inequality we get

$x < 7$ – but is this the whole story?

Consider instead

$$\frac{1}{x} > \frac{1}{7}$$

$$\therefore \frac{7}{x} > 1$$

$$x^2 \cdot \frac{7}{x} > x^2$$

$$7x > x^2$$

$$0 > x^2 - 7x$$

$$0 > x(x - 7)$$

$\Rightarrow 0 < x < 7$ which is the true answer – see the diagram below.

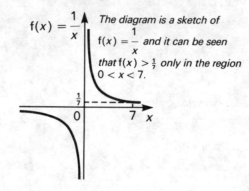

$$f(x) = \frac{1}{x}$$

The diagram is a sketch of $f(x) = \frac{1}{x}$ and it can be seen that $f(x) > \frac{1}{7}$ only in the region $0 < x < 7$.

EXERCISE 7.3

(*Answers on page 86*)

Find the range of values of x which satisfy these inequalities.

Group A

1. $\dfrac{1}{x} < 3$

2. $\dfrac{x - 1}{x} > 3$

3. $\dfrac{(x - 1)(x - 2)}{x} > -6$

Group B

1. $\dfrac{2}{x - 1} > \frac{1}{2}$

2. $\dfrac{x + 4}{x - 2} > \frac{3}{4}$

3. $\dfrac{(x + 2)(x + 4)}{(2x + 5)} > 1$

4. $x + 3 > \dfrac{20}{x + 2}$

4. $2x + 1 > \dfrac{30}{x - 5}$

5. $x + 7 > \dfrac{8}{x}$

5. $x - 4 < \dfrac{21}{x}$

Answers to exercises

ANSWERS TO EXERCISE 7.1

1. True   e.g. $3 > 2 \Rightarrow 3 + 5 > 2 + 5$ or $3 - 7 > 2 - 7$

2. True   e.g. $5 > 3 \Rightarrow 10 > 6$

3. True only if $a > 0$ e.g. $5 > 3 \Rightarrow 20 > 12$
   but $5 > 3 \nRightarrow -20 > -12$

4. False   e.g. $5 > 3 \nRightarrow -5 > -3$ *If you change $+/-$ signs throughout you must change the $>/<$ signs.*

5. False   e.g. $\frac{1}{2} > \frac{1}{4}$ but $2 \ngtr 4$ *If you turn both sides upside down (reciprocate) you must change the $>/<$ signs.*

6. True only if $x > 0$ – see number 4.   *This one is developed further later.*

ANSWERS TO EXERCISE 7.2

Group A

1. $3x - 1 > 7 \Rightarrow 3x > 8 \Rightarrow x > \frac{8}{3}$

2. $-5x < 25 \Rightarrow 5x > -25 \Rightarrow x > -5$

3. $x(x + 2) > 0 \Rightarrow$

$\Rightarrow x < -2$ or $x > 0$

4. $(x - 3)^2 + 1 > 0$ All values of x ∵ $(x - 3)^2 > 0$ whatever x value.

5. $x^2 - 5x - 6 > 0 \Rightarrow (x - 6)(x + 1) > 0 \Rightarrow x < -1$ or $x > 6$.

Group B

1. $x > 2$
2. $0 < x < 5$
3. $-4 < x < -3$
4. $x < -5$ and $x > 6$
5. $x < -2$ and $1 < x < 4$

Group C

1. $x > \frac{1}{4}$
2. $x < -5$ and $x > 3.5$
3. $x < -5$ and $x > 2$
4. $-2 < x < 1$ and $x > \frac{3}{2}$
5. $-5 < x < -1$ and $2 < x < 3$

Group D

1. All values of x
2. $0 < x < 2$
3. $-2 < x < 18$
4. $\frac{1}{2} < x < \frac{2}{3}$ or $x > \frac{3}{4}$
5. $-1 < x < 4$

ANSWERS TO EXERCISE 7.3

Group A

1. $\dfrac{1}{x} < \dfrac{1}{3}$ $\Rightarrow x^2.\dfrac{1}{x} < x^2.3 \Rightarrow x < 3x^2$

                    $\Rightarrow 0 < 3x^2 - x = x(3x - 1) \Rightarrow x < 0 \text{ or } x > \frac{1}{3}$

2. $\dfrac{x-1}{x} > 3$ $\Rightarrow x(x-1) > 3x^2 \Rightarrow 0 > 2x^2 + x$

                    $\Rightarrow 0 > x(2x + 1) \Rightarrow -\frac{1}{2} < x < 0$

3. $\dfrac{(x-1)(x-2)}{x} > -6 \Rightarrow x(x-1)(x-2) > -6x^2$

                    $\Rightarrow x\{(x-1)(x-2)+6x\} > 0$

                    $\Rightarrow x(x^2 + 3x + 2) > 0 \Rightarrow x(x+1)(x+2) > 0$

                    $\Rightarrow -2 < x < -1 \text{ or } x > 0$

4. $x + 3 > \dfrac{20}{x+2}$ $\Rightarrow (x+2)^2(x+3) > 20(x+2)$

                    $\Rightarrow (x+2)\{(x+2)(x+3) - 20\} > 0$

                    $\Rightarrow (x+2)(x^2 + 5x - 14) > 0$

                    $\Rightarrow (x+2)(x-2)(x+7) > 0$

                    $\Rightarrow -7 < x < -2 \text{ or } x > 2$

5. $x + 7 > \dfrac{8}{x}$ $\Rightarrow x^2(x+7) > 8x \Rightarrow x\{x(x+7) - 8\} > 0$

                    $\Rightarrow x(x^2 + 7x - 8) > 0 \Rightarrow x(x-1)(x+8) > 0$

                    $\Rightarrow -8 < x < 0 \text{ or } x > 1.$

Group B

1. $1 < x < 5$

2. $x < -22 \text{ or } x > 2$

3. $-3 < x < -\dfrac{5}{2} \text{ or } x > -1$

4. $-\dfrac{5}{2} < x < 5 \text{ or } x > 7$

5. $x < -3 \text{ or } 0 < x < 7$

Chapter 8

PARTIAL FRACTIONS

Aims and objectives

Having worked through this chapter you will be able to:

recognise partial fractions

distinguish between equations and identities

$$ax^2 + bx = 2x^2 + x$$
$$\text{and } ax^2 + bx \equiv 2x^2 + x$$

deal with linear denominators

$$\frac{1}{x^2 + 3x + 2} \equiv \frac{1}{x + 1} - \frac{1}{x + 2}$$

deal with quadratic and higher denominators

$$\frac{x^2 - x}{(x + 1)(x^2 + 1)} \equiv \frac{1}{x + 1} - \frac{1}{x^2 + 1}$$

sort out denominators with repeated factors

$$\frac{1}{(x - 1)(x + 2)^2} \equiv \frac{1}{9(x - 1)} - \frac{1}{9(x + 2)} - \frac{1}{3(x + 2)^2}$$

deal with cases where the numerator is of higher degree than the denominator

$$\frac{x^4 + 2x^3 - x^2 + 3x - 2}{x^2 + 5x + 6} = x^2 - 3x + 8 - \frac{12}{x + 2} - \frac{7}{x + 3}$$

including **algebraic long division**.

$$x^3 + x - 1 \div x + 2 = x^2 - 2x + 5 - \frac{11}{x + 2}$$

This will conclude the work on fundamental algebraic knowledge and techniques.

Definition

An important algebraic technique which will be needed in this course is **partial fractions**.

This is a way of splitting up a fraction into the component fractions from which it may have been formed.

e.g.

$$\frac{1}{6} = \frac{1}{2 \times 3} = \frac{1}{2} - \frac{1}{3}$$

$$\frac{8}{15} = \frac{8}{3 \times 5} = \frac{1}{3} + \frac{1}{5}$$

$$\frac{1}{(x-1)(x+2)} = \frac{1}{3(x-1)} - \frac{1}{3(x+2)}$$

> This question is the example worked out below.

On the right-hand side (RHS) of these examples we have the fractions which we would add or subtract to give the left-hand side (LHS). The fractions on the RHS are called the partial fractions of the fraction on the LHS.

Equations and identities

A further important principle is that when we create the partial fractions, we also create an **identity**. In GCSE work we came across the term **congruent** and we learnt that this meant 'identically equal to'. The most common examples we met were congruent triangles but we would also consider other shapes. In our work now, we extend the idea of congruency to algebra and trigonometry.

The difference between an **equation**, which uses an equals sign $(=)$, and an **identity**, which uses an identity sign $(\equiv)$, is that whereas equations are only true for certain values of the variable, the **solutions**, identities are true for **all** values of the variable. A bit heavy this and perhaps an example will help.

A common equation might be $x^2 = 5x - 6$ and for this there are only two values of x, 2 and 3, which satisfy it, i.e. make the LHS equal the RHS.

An equation like $3(x + 2) = (2x + 9) + (x - 3)$ is satisfied whatever value is given to x and it should be written:

$$3(x + 2) \equiv (2x + 9) + (x - 3)$$

Let us now work through an example

> $\equiv$ is the sign for 'is congruent to' or 'is identically equal to'.

e.g.

Express $\dfrac{1}{(x-1)(x+2)}$ in partial fractions.

Let
$$\frac{1}{(x-1)(x+2)} \equiv \frac{A}{x-1} + \frac{B}{x+2}$$

the problem now is to find A and B so that the identity is true

$$\frac{1}{(x-1)(x+2)}(x-1)(x+2) \equiv \frac{A}{(x-1)}(x-1)(x+2) + \frac{B}{(x+2)}(x-1)(x+2)$$

multiplying throughout by $(x-1)(x+2)$

$$\therefore \quad 1 \equiv A(x+2) + B(x-1)$$

We now find A by eliminating B:

Substitute $x = 1$: $1 = A.3 + B.0$ *this is why we chose x = 1*

$$\therefore A = \tfrac{1}{3}$$

And we find B by eliminating A.

Substitute $x = -2$: $1 = A.0 + B.-3$ *this is why we chose x = -2*

$$\therefore B = -\tfrac{1}{3}$$

and then we finally have

You can check this identity by putting in any values you like and seeing that LHS = RHS.

$$\frac{1}{(x-1)(x+2)} \equiv \frac{1}{3(x-1)} - \frac{1}{3(x+2)}$$

Now let's try another example.

e.g.

$$\frac{2x+1}{x^2-7x+10} \equiv \frac{2x+1}{(x-2)(x-5)} \equiv \frac{A}{x-2} + \frac{B}{x-5}$$

$$\therefore \quad 2x+1 \equiv A(x-5) + B(x-2)$$

$$x = 5 \Rightarrow 11 = 3B \qquad \therefore \quad B = \tfrac{11}{3}$$

$$x = 2 \Rightarrow 5 = -3A \qquad \therefore \quad A = -\tfrac{5}{3}$$

and hence $\dfrac{2x+1}{(x-2)(x-5)} \equiv -\dfrac{5}{3(x-2)} + \dfrac{11}{3(x-5)}$

A fair question at this point would be, 'Why are we doing these things?' The answer is, to make work which comes later on in calculus and algebra easier; the partial fractions are easier to deal with than the compound fraction.

EXERCISE 8.1

(*Answers on page 95*)

Express these as partial fractions.

Group A

1. $\dfrac{1}{x(x-2)}$

2. $\dfrac{5}{(x+1)(x-3)}$

Group B

1. $\dfrac{1}{(x-1)(x+3)}$

2. $\dfrac{4}{(x-2)(3-x)}$

3. $\dfrac{3}{(x-1)(x+4)(x-2)}$ 3. $\dfrac{1}{(x+2)(x-3)(x+6)}$

4. $\dfrac{3x+2}{(x+5)(x-2)}$ 4. $\dfrac{2x-5}{x(x+1)(x-4)}$

5. $\dfrac{2x}{x^2-x-12}$ 5. $\dfrac{x}{x^2+11x+30}$

> Similar method but find A, B and C.

Quadratic and higher degrees of denominators

And now we come to the complications, the first of which we shall consider by doing an example, explaining as we go.

 Express $\dfrac{1}{(x-1)(x^2+1)}$ in partial fractions.

$$\frac{1}{(x-1)(x^2+1)} \equiv \frac{A}{(x-1)} + \frac{Bx+C}{x^2+1}$$

this top, $Bx + C$, is like it is $\because$ of a further rule:

> **When setting up partial fractions the expression on the top must contain terms up to and including one of degree one less than the highest term on the bottom.**

> I make no apology for tackling this work by stating rules. The theory is too heavy and unnecessary. We are only learning a 'tool of the trade' at this stage.

A bottom (**denominator**) of

This power is 1 less than this. ⌐ $x^6 + 1$ would have a top (**numerator**) of

$Ax^5 + Bx^4 + Cx^3 + Dx^2 + Ex + F$

but we shall not meet any as complicated as this.

Continuing with the example:

$$1 \equiv A(x^2+1) + (Bx+C)(x-1)$$
$$x1 = 1 \Rightarrow 1 = 2A \quad \therefore \quad A = \tfrac{1}{2}$$

And now we hit a snag: there is no substitution we can make (using real numbers) which will make $x^2 + 1 = 0$. However, we get round this by remembering that we are dealing with an identity: the LHS is exactly the same as the RHS. This means that there are as many x^2 on one side as the other, as many x ... and so on.

So, comparing coefficients:

$$x^2 \Rightarrow \quad 0x^2 = Ax^2 + Bx^2 \quad \text{i.e. } 0 = A + B \quad \therefore B = -\tfrac{1}{2} \quad \because A = \tfrac{1}{2}$$

constants $\Rightarrow \quad 1 = A - C \quad \therefore C = A - 1 = \tfrac{1}{2} - 1 = -\tfrac{1}{2}$

hence $\dfrac{1}{(x-1)(x^2+1)} \equiv \dfrac{1}{2(x-1)} + \dfrac{-\tfrac{1}{2}x - \tfrac{1}{2}}{x^2+1} \equiv \dfrac{1}{2(x-1)} - \dfrac{1}{2}\dfrac{(x+1)}{(x^2+1)}$

Now one more example!

e.g.

$$\dfrac{x-2}{x^3+2x} \equiv \dfrac{x-2}{x(x^2+2)} \equiv \dfrac{A}{x} + \dfrac{Bx+C}{x^2+2}$$

$$\therefore x - 2 \equiv A(x^2+2) + (Bx+C)x$$

$$x = 0 \Rightarrow \quad -2 = 2A \quad \therefore A = -1$$

Comparing coefficients:

$$x^2 \Rightarrow \quad 0 = A + B \quad \therefore B = 1$$

$$x \Rightarrow \quad 1 = C$$

$$\therefore \dfrac{x-2}{x^3+2x} \equiv -\dfrac{1}{x} + \dfrac{x+1}{x^2+2}$$

EXERCISE 8.2

(*Answers on page 97*)

Express these in partial fractions.

Group A

1. $\dfrac{1}{x(x^2+1)}$

2. $\dfrac{2x}{(x-1)(x^2+2)}$

3. $\dfrac{5}{(x+1)(x^2+x+1)}$

4. $\dfrac{3x-1}{(x^3+2)(3-x)}$

5. $\dfrac{1}{(x-1)(x+2)(x^2+2)}$

Group B

1. $\dfrac{2}{x(x^2-2)}$

2. $\dfrac{x}{(x^2+1)(x-4)}$

3. $\dfrac{1}{(x-2)(2x^2-x+4)}$

4. $\dfrac{x+5}{(x^3-3)(x+1)}$

5. $\dfrac{3}{x(x+3)(x^2-3)}$

Repeated factors

A further variation is illustrated by the following example. The particular feature in this case is that the denominator of the original fraction contains a repeated factor but it is easily dealt with.

 Express $\dfrac{1}{(x-1)(x+2)^2}$ in partial fractions.

From what we have just done we might expect to start with

$$\frac{1}{(x-1)(x+2)^2} = \frac{A}{x-1} + \frac{Bx+D}{(x+2)^2}$$

However, although this would not be wrong there is an easier alternative.

$$\frac{1}{(x-1)(x+2)^2} = \frac{A}{x-1} + \underbrace{\frac{B}{x+2} + \frac{C}{(x+2)^2}}$$

↑
This is the repeated factor

↑
and it is dealt with like this.

$$\frac{B}{x+2} + \frac{C}{(x+2)^2}$$
$$= \frac{B(x+2) + C}{(x+2)^2}$$
$$= \frac{Bx + 2B + C}{(x+2)^2}$$
$$= \frac{Bx + D}{(x+2)^2}$$
– as above

From now on the method is as before.

$$1 \equiv A(x+2)^2 + B(x-1)(x+2) + C(x-1)$$

$$x = 1 \Rightarrow A = \tfrac{1}{9}$$
$$x = -2 \Rightarrow C = -\tfrac{1}{3}$$
$$\text{c.f. } x^2 \Rightarrow B = -\tfrac{1}{9}$$

$$\therefore \frac{1}{(x-1)(x+2)^2} = \frac{1}{9(x-1)} - \frac{1}{9(x+2)} - \frac{1}{3(x+2)^2}$$

There are some questions on this in Exercise 8.3 but before we try that exercise we must consider the last of the complications.

Numerator of higher degree than denominator

In all the questions we have been asked to do so far, in the original fraction the numerator has been of lower degree than the denominator. Sometimes, though, the top of a fraction can be of equal or higher degree than the bottom and since our technique for partial fractions applies only when it is of lower degree something has to be done! We need to carry out a long division. If we can do a numerical long division we shall find what follows easier than if we can only do one by calculator! Anyway it's got to be done so here goes.

 Divide $x^4 + 2x^3 - x^2 + 3x - 2$ by $x^2 + 5x + 6$.

Step 1   this → into → this — — — — → goes

      $x^2 + 5x + 6$) $x^4 + 2x^3 - \;\; x^2 + 3x - 2(x^2$

$x^4 \div x^2 = x^2$

Step 2 $x^2(x^2 + 5x + 6) \Rightarrow x^4 + 5x^3 + 6x^2$

Step 3   subtract $-3x^3 - 7x^2 + 3x$

We now rewrite the problem (to make it clearer) and then repeat steps 1, 2 and 3.

$x^2 + 5x + 6)x^4 + 2x^3 - \;\; x^2 + 3x - 2(x^2 - 3x$

          $x \;\; + 5x^3 + \;\; 6x^2$

Step 1   this into this
             goes $-3x^3 - \;\; 7x^2 + \;\; 3x$

Step 2 $-3x(x^2 + 5x + 6) \Rightarrow -3x^3 - 15x^2 - 18x$

Step 3   subtract $8x^2 + 21x - 2$

The whole process is repeated again until the final problem looks like this.

$x^2 + 5x + 6)x^4 + 2x^3 - \;\; x^2 + \;\; 3x - 2(x^2 - 3x + 8$

          $x^4 + 5x^3 + \;\; 6x^2$

          $-3x^3 - \;\; 7x^2 + \;\; 3x$

          $-3x^3 - 15x^2 - 18x$

          $8x^2 + 21x - 2$

          $8x^2 + 40x + 48$

          $-19x - 50$

Investigation

Compare this algebraic example with numerical ones. Remember for example,

$42\,951 = 4.10^4 + 2.10^3 + 9.10^2 + 5.10^1 + 1$

By now we could be forgiven for having forgotten what it was we set out to do in the first place. To clarify:

dividing 5 into 17 could be set out:

this into goes with a remainder of

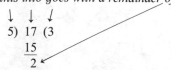
5) 17 (3
   15
    2

and similarly:

$x^2 + 5x + 6$ goes into $x^4 + 2x^3 - x^2 + 3x - 2$ a total of $x^2 - 3x + 8$ times with a remainder of $-19x - 50$.

Written in a more mathematical way:

$$\frac{x^4 + 2x^3 - x^2 + 3x - 2}{x^2 + 5x + 6} = x^2 - 3x + 8 + \frac{-19x - 50}{x^2 + 5x + 6}$$

Compared with the sum above:

$$\frac{17}{5} = 3 + \frac{2}{5}$$

And finally, the bit which goes into partial fractions is the fraction at the end.

So, carrying on, we have:

$$\frac{-19x - 50}{(x + 2)(x + 3)} \equiv \frac{A}{x + 2} + \frac{B}{x + 3}$$

$$\therefore -19x - 50 \equiv A(x + 3) + B(x + 2)$$

$x = -3 \Rightarrow \quad 7 = -B \quad B = -7$

$x = -2 \Rightarrow \quad -12 = \quad A$

$$\therefore \frac{x^4 + 2x^3 - x^2 + 3x - 2}{x^2 + 5x + 6} \equiv x^2 - 3x + 8 - \frac{12}{x + 2} - \frac{7}{x + 3}$$

Remember

This technique is only necessary when the numerator is of equal or higher degree than the denominator.

EXERCISE 8.3

(*Answers on page 98*)

This is an exercise on division only. Leave it out if your division is good.
1. $x^3 + x - 1 \div x + 2$
2. $2x^4 - x^3 + x - 1 \div x^2 + 3$
3. $5x - 3x^2 - x^3 + 2 \div 3x - 1 - x^2$
4. $2x^5 + 1 \div x^2 + 2$
5. $2x^3 + 3x^2 - 4x + 5 \div 3x^3 + 2x^2 - 3x + 2$

EXERCISE 8.4

(*Answers on page 99*)

Express these in partial fractions.

Group A

1. $\dfrac{2x + 1}{3x^2 + 5x - 2}$

Group B

1. $\dfrac{1 - x}{15x^2 - x - 2}$

2. $\dfrac{x^2}{x^2 + 2x + 1}$

2. $\dfrac{x^2}{x^2 - 1}$

3. $\dfrac{1}{x^3 + 7x^2 + 12x}$

3. $\dfrac{1}{x^4 - 16}$

4. $\dfrac{2 - x^2}{(x - 2)(x + 3)}$

4. $\dfrac{4}{(x + 1)(x^2 + 2x + 3)}$

5. $\dfrac{x^3 + x + 1}{x^2 - x - 12}$

5. $\dfrac{x^4 - 2x^2 + 2}{2x^3 + 3x^2 - 3x}$

> This one will test your basic algebraic manipulation.

Now try worksheets 3 and 4.

Answers to exercises

ANSWERS TO EXERCISE 8.1

Group A

1. $\dfrac{1}{x(x - 2)} \equiv \dfrac{A}{x} + \dfrac{B}{x - 2}$

$\therefore 1 \equiv A(x - 2) + Bx$

$x = 0 \Rightarrow \quad 1 = -2A \quad \therefore A = -\tfrac{1}{2}$

$x = 2 \Rightarrow \quad 1 = 2B \qquad \therefore B = \tfrac{1}{2}$

$\therefore \dfrac{1}{x(x - 2)} \equiv -\dfrac{1}{2x} + \dfrac{1}{2(x - 2)}$

2. $\dfrac{5}{(x + 1)(x - 3)} \equiv \dfrac{A}{x + 1} + \dfrac{B}{x - 3}$

$\therefore 5 \equiv A(x - 3) + B(x + 1)$

$x = 3 \Rightarrow \quad 5 = 4B \qquad \therefore B = \tfrac{5}{4}$

$x = -1 \Rightarrow \quad 5 = -4A \quad \therefore A = -\tfrac{5}{4}$

$\therefore \dfrac{5}{(x + 1)(x - 3)} \equiv -\dfrac{5}{4(x + 1)} + \dfrac{5}{4(x - 3)}$

3. $\dfrac{3}{(x-1)(x+4)(x-2)} \equiv \dfrac{A}{(x-1)} + \dfrac{B}{(x+4)} + \dfrac{C}{(x-2)}$

$\therefore 3 \equiv A(x+4)(x-2) + B(x-1)(x-2) + C(x-1)(x+4)$

$x = 2 \Rightarrow \quad 3 = C.1.6 \qquad \therefore C = \tfrac{1}{2}$

$x = -4 \Rightarrow \quad 3 = B.-5.-6 \quad \therefore B = \tfrac{1}{10}$

$x = 1 \Rightarrow \quad 3 = A.5.-1 \qquad \therefore A = -\tfrac{3}{5}$

$\therefore \dfrac{3}{(x-1)(x+4)(x-2)} \equiv -\dfrac{3}{5(x-1)} + \dfrac{3}{10(x+4)} + \dfrac{1}{2(x-2)}$

4. $\dfrac{3x+2}{(x+5)(x-2)} \equiv \dfrac{A}{(x+5)} + \dfrac{B}{(x-2)}$

$\therefore 3x + 2 \equiv A(x-2) + B(x+5)$

$x = 2 \Rightarrow \qquad 8 = 7B \qquad \therefore B = \tfrac{8}{7}$

$x = -5 \Rightarrow \quad -13 = -7A \quad \therefore A = \tfrac{13}{7}$

$\therefore \dfrac{3x+2}{(x+5)(x-2)} \equiv \dfrac{13}{7(x+5)} + \dfrac{8}{7(x-2)}$

5. $\dfrac{2x}{x^2 - x - 12} \equiv \dfrac{2x}{(x-4)(x+3)} \equiv \dfrac{A}{x-4} + \dfrac{B}{x+3}$

$\therefore 2x \qquad \equiv A(x+3) + B(x-4)$

$x = 4 \Rightarrow \qquad 8 = 7A \qquad \therefore A = \tfrac{8}{7}$

$x = -3 \Rightarrow \quad -6 = -7B \quad \therefore B = \tfrac{6}{7}$

$\therefore \dfrac{2x}{x^2 - x - 12} \equiv \dfrac{8}{7(x-4)} + \dfrac{6}{7(x+3)}$

Group B

1. $\dfrac{1}{4(x-1)} - \dfrac{1}{4(x+3)}$

2. $\dfrac{4}{x-2} + \dfrac{4}{3-x} \quad \text{or} \quad \dfrac{4}{x-2} - \dfrac{4}{x-3}$

3. $-\dfrac{1}{20(x+2)} + \dfrac{1}{45(x-3)} + \dfrac{1}{36(x+6)}$

4. $\dfrac{5}{4x} - \dfrac{7}{5(x+1)} + \dfrac{3}{20(x-4)}$

5. $-\dfrac{5}{x+5} + \dfrac{6}{x+6}$

ANSWERS TO EXERCISE 8.2

Group A

1. $\dfrac{1}{x(x^2 + 1)} \equiv \dfrac{A}{x} + \dfrac{Bx + C}{x^2 + 1}$

$\therefore 1 \equiv A(x^2 + 1) + (Bx + C)x$

$x = 0 \Rightarrow \quad 1 = A$

c.f. $x^2 \Rightarrow \quad 0 = A + B \quad \therefore B = -1$

c.f. $x \Rightarrow \quad 0 = C \qquad \therefore C = 0$

$\therefore \dfrac{1}{x(x^2 + 1)} \equiv \dfrac{1}{x} - \dfrac{x}{x^2 + 1}$

> We use c.f. as an abbreviation for 'compare'.

2. $\dfrac{2x}{(x - 1)(x^2 + 2)} \equiv \dfrac{A}{x - 1} + \dfrac{Bx + C}{x^2 + 2}$

$\Rightarrow \quad 2x \equiv A(x^2 + 2) + (Bx + C)(x - 1)$

$x = 1 \Rightarrow \quad 2 = 3A \qquad \therefore A = \frac{2}{3}$

c.f. $x^2 \Rightarrow \quad 0 = A + B \qquad \therefore B = -\frac{2}{3}$

c.f. $x \Rightarrow \quad 2 = C - B \qquad \therefore C = \frac{8}{3}$

$\therefore \dfrac{2x}{(x - 1)(x^2 + 2)} \equiv \dfrac{2}{3(x - 1)} + \dfrac{-\frac{2}{3}x + \frac{8}{3}}{x^2 + 2}$

$\therefore \dfrac{2x}{(x - 1)(x^2 + 2)} \equiv \dfrac{2}{3(x - 1)} + \dfrac{2(4 - x)}{3(x^2 + 2)}$

3. $\dfrac{5}{(x + 1)(x^2 + x + 1)} \equiv \dfrac{A}{x + 1} + \dfrac{Bx + C}{x^2 + x + 1}$

$\therefore 5 \equiv A(x^2 + x + 1) + (Bx + C)(x + 1)$

$x = -1 \Rightarrow \quad 5 = A$

c.f. $x^2 \Rightarrow \quad 0 = A + B \qquad \therefore B = -5$

c.f. $x \Rightarrow \quad 0 = A + B + C \quad \therefore C = 0$

$\therefore \dfrac{5}{(x + 1)(x^2 + x + 1)} \equiv \dfrac{5}{x + 1} - \dfrac{5x}{x^2 + x + 1}$

4. $\dfrac{3x - 1}{(x^3 + 2)(3 - x)} \equiv \dfrac{Ax^2 + Bx + C}{x^3 + 2} + \dfrac{D}{3 - x}$

$\Rightarrow \quad 3x - 1 \equiv (Ax^2 + Bx + C)(3 - x) + D(x^3 + 2)$

$x = 3 \Rightarrow \quad 8 = D.29 \qquad \therefore D = \frac{8}{29}$

c.f. $x^3 \Rightarrow \quad 0 = -A + D \quad \therefore A = \frac{8}{29}$

c.f. $x^2 \Rightarrow \quad 0 = 3A - B \qquad \therefore B = \frac{24}{29}$

c.f. $x \Rightarrow \quad 3 = 3B - C \quad \therefore C = -\frac{15}{29}$

$$\therefore \frac{3x - 1}{(x^3 + 2)(3 - x)} \equiv \frac{8x^2 + 24x - 15}{29(x^3 + 2)} + \frac{8}{29(3 - x)}$$

5. $\dfrac{1}{(x - 1)(x + 2)(x^2 + 2)} \equiv \dfrac{A}{x - 1} + \dfrac{B}{x + 2} + \dfrac{Cx + D}{x^2 + 2}$

$$\therefore \ 1 \equiv A(x + 2)(x^2 + 2) + B(x - 1)(x^2 + 2) + (Cx + D)(x - 1)(x + 2)$$

$x = 1 \Rightarrow \quad 1 = 9A \qquad\qquad \therefore A = \frac{1}{9}$

$x = -2 \Rightarrow \quad 1 = -18B \qquad\qquad \therefore B = -\frac{1}{18}$

c.f. $x^3 \Rightarrow \quad 0 = A + B + C \qquad \therefore C = -\frac{1}{18}$

c.f. const $\Rightarrow \quad 1 = 4A - 2B - 2D \quad \therefore D = -\frac{2}{9}$

$$\therefore \frac{1}{(x - 1)(x + 2)(x^2 + 2)} \equiv \frac{1}{9(x - 1)} - \frac{1}{18(x + 2)} - \frac{x + 4}{18(x^2 + 2)}$$

Group B

1. $\dfrac{x}{x^2 - 2} - \dfrac{1}{x}$

2. $\dfrac{1 - 4x}{17(x^2 + 1)} + \dfrac{4}{17(x - 4)}$

3. $\dfrac{1}{10(x - 2)} - \dfrac{2x + 3}{10(2x^2 - x + 4)}$

4. $\dfrac{x^2 - x + 2}{x^3 - 3} - \dfrac{1}{x + 1}$

5. $-\dfrac{1}{3x} - \dfrac{1}{6(x + 3)} + \dfrac{x - 1}{2(x^2 - 3)}$

ANSWERS TO EXERCISE 8.3

1. $x + 2)x^3 \qquad\quad + \quad x - 1(x^2 - 2x + 5$

$\qquad\quad \underline{x^3 + 2x^2}$

$\qquad\qquad -2x^2 + \ x$

$\qquad\qquad \underline{-2x^2 - 4x}$

$\qquad\qquad\qquad 5x - 1$

$\qquad\qquad\qquad \underline{5x + 10}$

$\qquad\qquad\qquad\quad -11$

$$\frac{x^3 + x - 1}{x + 2} = x^2 - 2x + 5 - \frac{11}{x + 2}$$

> Notice the space left for 'x^2' column.

2. $x^2 + 3\overline{)2x^4 - x^3 \qquad + \quad x \quad - 1}(2x^2 - x - 6$

$\qquad \underline{2x^4 \qquad\quad + 6x^2}$

$\qquad\qquad - x^3 - 6x^2 + \quad x$

$\qquad\qquad \underline{- x^3 \qquad\quad + 3x}$

$\qquad\qquad\qquad - 6x^2 - 2x \ - 1$

$\qquad\qquad\qquad \underline{- 6x^2 \qquad\quad - 18}$

$\qquad\qquad\qquad\qquad - 2x \ + 17$

$$\frac{2x^4 - x^3 + x - 1}{x^2 + 3} = 2x^2 - x - 6 + \frac{17 - 2x}{x^2 + 3}$$

3. $-x^2 + 3x - 1\overline{)- x^3 - 3x^2 + \ 5x + 2}(x - 6$

$\qquad\qquad \underline{- x^3 + 3x^2 - \quad x}$

$\qquad\qquad\quad - 6x^2 + \ 6x + 2$

$\qquad\qquad\quad \underline{- 6x^2 - 18x + 6}$

$\qquad\qquad\qquad\quad 24x - 4$

$$\frac{5x - 3x^2 - x^3 + 2}{3x - 1 - x^2} = x - 6 + \frac{24x - 4}{3x - 1 - x^2}$$

4. $x^2 + 2\overline{)2x^5 \qquad\qquad\qquad + 1}\ (2x^3 - 4x$

$\qquad\quad \underline{2x^5 + 4x^3}$

$\qquad\qquad - 4x^3$

$\qquad\qquad \underline{- 4x^3 - 8x}$

$\qquad\qquad\qquad 8x + 1$

$$\frac{2x^5 + 1}{x^2 + 2} = 2x^3 - 4x + \frac{8x + 1}{x^2 + 2}$$

5. $3x^3 + 2x^2 - 3x + 2\overline{)2x^3 + 3x^2 - 4x + 5}\ (\tfrac{2}{3}$

$\qquad\qquad\qquad \underline{2x^3 + \tfrac{4}{3}x^2 - 2x + \tfrac{4}{3}}$

$\qquad\qquad\qquad\qquad \tfrac{5}{3}x^2 - 2x + \tfrac{11}{3}$

$$\frac{2x^3 + 3x^2 - 4x + 5}{3x^3 + 2x^2 - 3x + 2} = \frac{2}{3} + \frac{\tfrac{5}{3}x^2 - 2x + \tfrac{11}{3}}{3x^3 + 2x^2 - 3x + 2}$$

ANSWERS TO EXERCISE 8.4

Group A

1. $\dfrac{2x + 1}{3x^2 + 5x - 2} = \dfrac{2x + 1}{(3x - 1)(x + 2)}$

$\qquad\qquad \equiv \dfrac{A}{3x - 1} + \dfrac{B}{x + 2}$

$\qquad \therefore 2x + 1 \equiv A(x + 2) + B(3x - 1)$

NB To find A don't bother substituting $x = \tfrac{1}{3}$ ∵ too messy. Consider coefficients of x instead.

$x = -2 \Rightarrow \quad \therefore B = \frac{3}{7}$

c.f. $x \Rightarrow \quad 2 = A + 3B \quad \therefore A = \frac{5}{7}$

$\therefore \dfrac{2x + 1}{3x^2 + 5x - 2} \equiv \dfrac{5}{7(3x - 1)} + \dfrac{3}{7(x + 2)}$

2. $\dfrac{x^2}{x^2 + 2x + 1}$ *top of same degree as bottom* $\therefore$ *division necessary*

$$
\begin{array}{r}
x^2 + 2x + 1 \overline{\smash{)}x^2} \qquad\qquad (1 \\
\underline{x^2 + 2x + 1} \\
- 2x - 1
\end{array}
$$

$\therefore \dfrac{x^2}{x^2 + 2x + 1} = 1 + \dfrac{-2x - 1}{x^2 + 2x + 1}$

Consider $\dfrac{-2x - 1}{x^2 + 2x + 1} = \dfrac{-2x - 1}{(x + 1)^2} \equiv \dfrac{A}{x + 1} + \dfrac{B}{(x + 1)^2}$

$\therefore -2x - 1 \equiv A(x + 1) + B$

$x = -1 \Rightarrow \quad B = 1$

c.f. $x \Rightarrow \quad A = -2$

$\therefore \dfrac{x^2}{x^2 + 2x + 1} \equiv 1 - \dfrac{2}{x + 1} + \dfrac{1}{(x + 1)^2}$

3. $\dfrac{1}{x^3 + 7x^2 + 12x} = \dfrac{1}{x(x^2 + 7x + 12)} = \dfrac{1}{x(x + 3)(x + 4)}$

$$\equiv \dfrac{A}{x} + \dfrac{B}{x + 3} + \dfrac{C}{x + 4}$$

$$\therefore 1 \equiv A(x + 3)(x + 4) + Bx(x + 4) + Cx(x + 3)$$

$x = \quad 0 \Rightarrow \quad A = \frac{1}{12}$

$x = -3 \Rightarrow \quad B = -\frac{1}{3}$

$x = -4 \Rightarrow \quad C = \frac{1}{4}$

$\therefore \dfrac{1}{x^3 + 7x^2 + 12x} \equiv \dfrac{1}{12x} - \dfrac{1}{3(x + 3)} + \dfrac{1}{4(x + 4)}$

4. $\dfrac{2 - x^2}{(x - 2)(x + 3)}$ Don't be fooled by the fact that the denominator looks as if it is not of 2nd degree: it is, and so is the top $\therefore$ division.

$$
\begin{array}{r}
x^2 + x - 6 \overline{\smash{)}- x^2} \qquad\qquad + 2 \,(-1 \\
\underline{- x^2 - x + 6} \\
x - 4
\end{array}
$$

$\therefore \dfrac{2 - x^2}{(x - 2)(x + 3)} = -1 + \dfrac{x - 4}{(x - 2)(x + 3)}$

> Note the space left for 'x' column and the rearranging so that top and bottom are in descending order.

Consider $\dfrac{x - 4}{(x - 2)(x + 3)} \equiv \dfrac{A}{x - 2} + \dfrac{B}{x + 3}$

$\therefore x - 4 \equiv A(x + 3) + B(x - 2)$

$x = \quad 2 \Rightarrow A = -\frac{2}{5}$

$x = -3 \Rightarrow B = \frac{7}{5}$

$\therefore \dfrac{2 - x^2}{(x - 2)(x + 3)} \equiv -1 - \dfrac{2}{5(x - 2)} + \dfrac{7}{5(x + 3)}$

5. $\dfrac{x^3 + x + 1}{x^3 - x - 12} \Rightarrow x^2 - x - 12)\overline{x^3 \qquad + \quad x + \ 1}(x + 1$

$$\underline{x^3 - x^2 - 12x}$$
$$x^2 + 13x + \ 1$$
$$\underline{x^2 - \quad x - 12}$$
$$14x + 13$$

Consider $\dfrac{14x + 13}{(x - 4)(x + 3)} \equiv \dfrac{A}{x - 4} + \dfrac{B}{x + 3}$

$\therefore 14x + 13 \equiv A(x + 3) + B(x - 4)$

$x = \quad 4 \Rightarrow A = \frac{69}{7}$

$x = -3 \Rightarrow B = \frac{29}{7}$

$\therefore \dfrac{x^3 + x + 1}{x^2 - x - 12} = x + 1 + \dfrac{69}{7(x - 4)} + \dfrac{29}{7(x + 3)}$

Group B

1. $\dfrac{3}{11(5x - 2)} - \dfrac{4}{11(3x + 1)}$

2. $1 + \dfrac{1}{2(x - 1)} - \dfrac{1}{2(x + 1)}$

3. $\dfrac{1}{32(x - 2)} - \dfrac{1}{32(x + 2)} - \dfrac{1}{8(x^2 + 4)}$

4. $\dfrac{2}{x + 1} - \dfrac{2x + 2}{x^2 + 2x + 3}$

5. $\dfrac{x}{2} - \dfrac{3}{4} - \dfrac{2}{3x} + \dfrac{37x - 3}{12(2x^2 + 3x - 3)}$

> If you got this answer –
> well done! – you won't
> get one anything like
> this in future work.

Chapter 9

FUNCTIONS

Aims and objectives

Having worked through this chapter you will understand:

basic terms used in graphical work

principles of curve sketching

different kinds of functions including

continuous and discontinuous functions

functions which are periodic

odd functions

even functions
composite functions,

the **modulus function**

the **reciprocal function**

the **inverse function.**

More thoughts about functions

We now turn our attention to some work which comes under the heading of functions, a word which seems to unsettle many students. When petrol is fed into a motor car it works, or functions, and the net result is power and distance travelled. A popular statistic concerning cars is to quote miles per gallon, m.p.g. and when you do this you are quoting a function; the miles covered is a function of the gallons of petrol used.

In mathematics we substitute a number into a formula or equation and out comes another number e.g. if x is made equal to 5 in the expression $3x$ then out comes 15. Here the function is to multiply the input by 3. In mathematical terms we would write:

$f(x) = 3x$

read as: a function of x is, or equals, $3x$.

The comparison with the car would be f(petrol) = miles.

In $f(x) = 3x$ the x here is known as the **independent** variable, it depends

on nothing else just as petrol is a basic independent (excluding oil tankers, wells etc) quantity needed for a car.

Domain and range

When we come to graphical work the x values are always plotted $\rightarrow$, i.e. across, they are called the **abscissae** (singular *abscissa*) and the spread of values is called the **domain**.

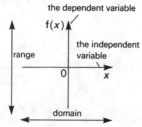

The values of f(x) are always plotted $\uparrow$, i.e. upwards. They are called the **ordinates** and the spread of values is called the **range**.

The best example of an independent variable is **time**. We cannot alter time, we can only measure it. Functions of time such as velocity and distance are always drawn with time as the abscissae.

EXERCISE 9.1

(*Answers on page 116*)

Complete the following table.

	Domain	Function	Range
1.	$-2 \leqslant x \leqslant 3$	$3x + 1$	-5 to 10
2.	$0 \leqslant x \leqslant$	$x^2 - 5$	$\leqslant f(x) \leqslant 95$
3.	$-6 \leqslant x \leqslant 2$	$1 - \dfrac{x}{2}$	
4.		$(x - 1)^3$	$-27 \leqslant f(x) \leqslant 64$
5.	$0 \leqslant x \leqslant$	$x^2 + x + 1$	$\leqslant f(x) \leqslant 43$
6.	$1, 2, 3, 4$		$2, 9, 28, 65$
7.	$1, 3, 5$		$3, 13, 31$
8.	$0 < x \leqslant 6$	$\dfrac{1}{x}$	
9.	$0 \leqslant x \leqslant 5$	$\pm\sqrt{25 - x^2}$	
10.	$1, 2, 3, 4$		$0, 1, 4, 9$

Sketch graphs

Graphical representation is an important part of work on functions. We must distinguish here between graph **drawing** and graph **sketching**. In GCSE work on drawing graphs, we made an accurate table of coordinates of points, plotted them very carefully on graph paper, on axes drawn to scale, and then drew an accurate graph. A sketch graph is one which is not accurately plotted but one which shows the salient features and at the same time bears a good likeness to the shape of the function. Important features are:

- where it crosses the axes
- any turning points ←
- any symmetry
- the tendency when $|x|$ is large
- any asymptotes.

> More on these in the next chapter:

> $|x|$ is the modulus of x, the numerical value ignoring whether it is $+$ or $-$.
> $|5| = 5$
> $|-5| = 5$

We have already met some curve sketching in chapter 4.

Odd and even functions

Firstly we will have a look at some symmetrical properties. These figures show two graphs, each with a type of symmetry.

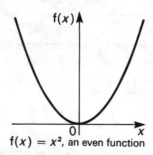

$f(x) = x^2$, an even function

The graph of $f(x) = x^2$ is symmetrical about the y-axis.

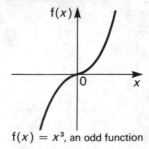

$f(x) = x^3$, an odd function

The graph of $f(x) = x^3$ has rotational symmetry, order 2, about the origin.

Because of the symmetry about the y-axis x^2 is said to be an **even** function.

Because of rotational symmetry, order 2, about the origin x^3 is an **odd** function. In algebraic form the definitions are:

> **A function is**
> **even if** $f(a) < f(-a)$ **i.e. changing the sign of x does not alter the sign of the function**
> **odd if** $f(a) = -f(-a)$ **i.e. changing the sign of x does alter the sign of the function.**

EXERCISE 9.2

(*Answers on page 116*)

Consider whether the following functions are odd, even or neither. Check your answers by making sketch graphs.

1. $x^2 + 2$
2. $(x + 2)^2$
3. $2x^2$
4. x
5. $x^3 + 2$
6. $(x + 2)^3$
7. $2x^3$
8. $-x$
9. $4 - x^4$
10. $5 - x^5$

Periodic functions

If we were to measure the height above the ground of Joe's head as he sits in a chair on the big wheel at the fair and draw a graph with the height as ordinates and time as abscissae we would get a graph like this one. (You will probably recognise this as the sine curve.)

Don't worry if your sines etc are rusty: they will be well covered soon, Chapter 11.

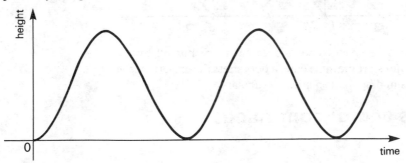

> **A curve of this type is said to be *periodic* because it repeats itself at regular intervals.**

Look at this question.

A periodic function has period 3 and it is defined by

$f(x) = 2x$ for $0 \leqslant x \leqslant 2$ and
$f(x) = x^2$ for $2 \leqslant x \leqslant 3$.

Sketch it for $-9 \leqslant x \leqslant 9$.

The wording is off-putting but it is easy to sort out.

A periodic function	*one which repeats itself*
has period 3	*every 3 units along the x-axis*
and it is defined by	*the rules for making it are*

$f(x) = 2x$ for $0 \leqslant x \leqslant 2$
and
$f(x) = x^2$ for $2 < x < 3$.

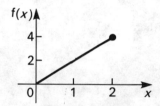 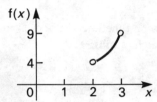

So much for the meaning of the question. Now, joining together the two segments (pieces) of graphs we have this.

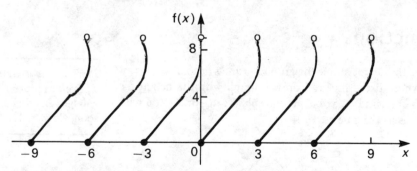

This example should have given us confidence not to be put off by the wording used in questions. At the same time, it does stress the importance of acquiring and understanding mathematical vocabulary.

Continuous and discontinuous functions

There is one obvious difference between the function shown in the last example and the sine curve. One is continuous and one is discontinuous: no prizes for deciding which is which! Nevertheless we must be aware of continuous and discontinuous functions.

FUNCTIONS

EXERCISE 9.3

(*Answers on page 119*)

Sketch the following functions, stating whether or not they are continuous, odd or even.

1. $f(x) = 3x$ for $0 \leqslant x < 1$ period 1, for $0 \leqslant x \leqslant 4$

2. $f(x) = x^2$ for $0 \leqslant x < 4$
   $f(x) = 16$ for $4 \leqslant x < 6$
   $f(x) = 64 - 8x$ for $6 \leqslant x < 8$ period 8, for $0 \leqslant x \leqslant 16$

3. $f(x) = 2$ for $0 \leqslant x < 2$
   $f(x) = 4$ for $2 \leqslant x < 4$
   $f(x) = 6$ for $4 \leqslant x < 6$ period 6, for $0 \leqslant x \leqslant 18$

4. $f(x) = -(x + 2)^2$ for $-2 \leqslant x \leqslant -1$
   $f(x) = x$ for $-1 < x \leqslant 1$
   $f(x) = (x - 2)^2$ for $1 \leqslant x \leqslant 2$ period 4, for $-8 \leqslant x \leqslant 8$

5. $f(x) = 1 - x$ for $0 \leqslant x < 2$
   $f(x) = x - 3$ for $2 \leqslant x < 4$ period 4, for $-4 \leqslant x \leqslant 4$

Composite functions

If we return to our analogy with the cars we can see that although the car was called a function which converted petrol into distance it is in fact a **composition** of many functions. The distance depends on the wheels which depend on the axle which depends on the gearbox which depends on the engine which depends on the petrol . . . are some of the many functions to be found in a car. And so in mathematics we have composite functions (but not as complex as the car!).

Consider the function $(x + 2)^2$.

This has been built up by starting with the basic variable x and:
Step 1   adding 2 $\Rightarrow$ $x + 2$ and then
Step 2   squaring $\Rightarrow$ $(x + 2)^2$

   The mathematical notation would be

Step 1 $f(x) = x + 2$ *Step 2* $g(x) = x^2$

             change this to this   *change this to this*

If we wish to use these notations for our original problem, we would write:

if $f(x) = x + 2$ and $g(x) = x^2$

then $gf(x) = (x + 2)^2$

107

$$gf(x) = g[f(x)]$$

this (g) tells us to square this [ ] and this (f) tells you to add 2 to this (x).

When building up the function, work from right to left.

> Four 'this's on one line but persevere.

> **Investigation**
>
> Verify that $fg(x) = x^2 + 2$.

EXERCISE 9.4

(*Answers on page 120*)

Form the composite functions, given

$$f(x) = x - 1 \qquad g(x) = x^3 \qquad h(x) = \frac{1}{x}$$

e.g.   1. $gh(x)$

Step 1   Find h(x) $h(x) = \frac{1}{x}$

The question now becomes 'form $g\left(\dfrac{1}{x}\right)$'.

Step 2   From the given information $g(x) = x^3$.

$$\therefore g\left(\frac{1}{x}\right) = \frac{1^3}{x^3} = \frac{1}{x^3}$$

e.g.   2. $g\,h\,f(x) = \dfrac{1}{x^3}$

> **Remember**
>
> Start here, then here and finally here.

Hence $ghf(x) = gh(x - 1)$

$$= g\left(\frac{1}{x - 1}\right)$$

$$= \frac{1}{(x - 1)^3}$$

3. $gf(x)$

4. $hg(x)$

5. hgf(x)
6. gfh(x)
7. gfg(x)
8. hff(x)
9. fgh(x)
10. fghgh(x)

A composite function like gf(x) is quite often referred to as **a function of a function of x.** Remember this wording; you will need it in the next chapter. What would you call fgh(x)? Yes; and now a serious answer!

The modulus of a function

We continue now by considering two functions which occur frequently. The first of these is to consider the modulus function. The basic idea of the modulus is explained on page 104.

> When we talk of the modulus of a function we are referring to its size or magnitude regardless of its sign, and the modulus is always taken as positive.

If Joe's bank account is in credit to £50 and Helen's is in debt to £50 both accounts have the same modulus, £50. A velocity of $10\,\text{km}\,\text{h}^{-1}$ north is different from a velocity of $10\,\text{km}\,\text{h}^{-1}$ east, but they both have the same modulus, $10\,\text{km}\,\text{h}^{-1}$ (this is called the speed). (Velocity is a vector quantity which takes into account both magnitude – speed – and direction.)

It follows then that if we sketch any modulus functions the graph will always be above the x-axis.

And it follows that $y = -|x|$ will always be below the x-axis.

 From the graphs of $y = x$ and $y = x^2 - 4$ deduce the graphs of $y = |x|$ and $y = |x^2 - 4|$.

$|x|$ reads modulus of x
$|x^2 - 4|$ reads modulus of $x^2 - 4$.

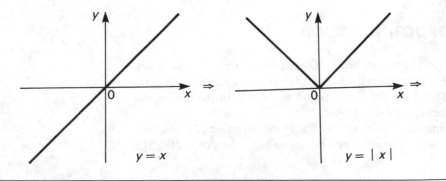

$$y = x \qquad\qquad y = |x|$$

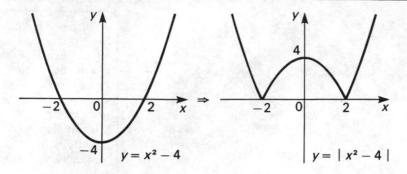

$y = x^2 - 4$ $\Rightarrow$ $y = |x^2 - 4|$

EXERCISE 9.5

(*Answers on page 121*)

Sketch the following functions and deduce the sketch of the modulus of the function as in examples given.

1. $y = 2x$ and $y = |2x|$

2. $y = x + 2$ and $y = |x + 2|$

3. $y = (x + 2)^2 - 3$ and $y = |(x + 2)^2 - 3|$

4. $y = x^3$ and $y = |x^3|$

5. $y^2 = x$ and $y = |\sqrt{x}|$

6. $y = \dfrac{1}{x}$ and $y = \left|\dfrac{1}{x}\right|$ ⟵

> **NB**
>
> There is an added complication in this question and it is developed in the next section, but have a go.

7. Look at the answers to Exercise 9.3. Consider the moduli of each of these compound functions.
   (a) In which cases would the graph not change?
   (b) In those in which it does change draw the new graph.

The reciprocal function

The second function to consider here is the **reciprocal** function. In the work we have just done sketching the moduli of functions it was easy to recognise the original function from the modulus and vice-versa. In the case of the reciprocal the effect is quite dramatic.

Consider the functions $y = x$ and $y = 1/x$. Draw the graph of $y = x$ and, using the reciprocal button on your calculator to find values of y, draw the graph of $1/x$.

You should have got these.

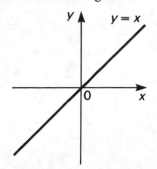

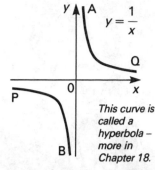

This curve is called a hyperbola – more in Chapter 18.

These graphs illustrate well two important features to look for when sketching reciprocals:

> **a large modulus on the original ⇒ a small modulus on the reciprocal.**

and the converse:

> **a small modulus on the original ⇒ a large modulus on the reciprocal.**

As $|x|$ increases then $\dfrac{1}{|x|}$ decreases.

The extreme cases are

$$y \to \infty \quad \Rightarrow \quad \frac{1}{\infty} = 0$$

and $y \to 0 \Rightarrow \dfrac{1}{0} = \infty$

> → – tends to, approaches.

Infinity obviously cannot be drawn and all we can do is as shown at A and B, and P and Q on the graph above. The meaning of the sketch at A is that the curve meets the positive y-axis at ∞.

In a situation like this the y-axis is said to be an **asymptote** to the curve at A and B, and the x-axis is an asymptote at P and Q.

> ∞ – infinity, immeasurably large, indefinite.

> **An asymptote is a straight line to which a curve gets closer the more it is drawn but the curve never crosses it.**

> Asymptotes defined.

EXERCISE 9.6

(*Answers on page 123*)

1. Draw the reciprocals of the graphs $y = x^2 - 4$ and $y = |x^2 - 4|$.
2. Draw the reciprocals of the functions in Exercise 9.3.

Inverse functions

The diagram shows a sketch of $y = x^3$ or $f(x) = x^3$.

x^3 is the function $f(x)$ which with input, or x values, of

$-2 \quad 0 \quad 1 \quad 3$ has output, or $f(x)$ values, of
$-8 \quad 0 \quad 1 \quad 27$ respectively.

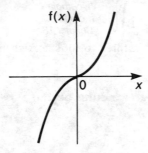

Our problem now is to consider which

function with inputs of $\quad -8 \quad 0 \quad 1 \quad 27$
would have outputs of $\quad -2 \quad 0 \quad 1 \quad 3$

In other words we wish to find the function which does the opposite. Now in this example this is not difficult

originally: input $x \to$ cube it $\to$ output x^3

so now: input $x \to$ cube root it $\to$ output $\sqrt[3]{x}$

Cube root is the opposite of cubing.

So the function which does the opposite is $f(x) = \sqrt[3]{x}$, and its graph looks like this.

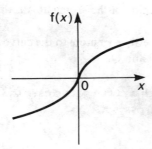

As has been mentioned earlier this use of the word 'opposite' is really not correct and we should use **inverse**. From now on we shall not use the word 'opposite' in this context again.

e.g. Consider the function, $f(x) = 2x + 1$. Its graph looks like this.

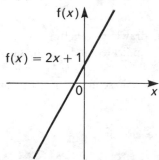

Notation

The inverse of $f(x)$ is written as $f^{-1}(x)$. By the laws of indices you may think

$$f^{-1}(x) = \frac{1}{f(x)}$$

but this is definitely not so.

Remember

inverse $f(x) = f^{-1}(x)$

We now wish to find the inverse function. To try and undo $f(x)$ (which is what finding the inverse is) we need to consider what has been done to x in $f(x)$.

Start with x.

Step 1 multiply by 2 ($\times 2$)
Step 2 add 1 ($+1$)

$\therefore$ for $f^{-1}(x)$ we start with x and

Step 1 subtract 1 (-1) $\quad$ ⎫ *These are steps 1 and 2 above taken in*
Step 2 divide by 2 ($\div 2$) $\quad$ ⎬ *reverse order and inversed in each case.*

$\therefore f^{-1}(x) = \dfrac{x-1}{2}$ and it looks like this.

We have seen this idea before in chapter 2.

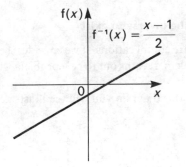

e.g. If $f(x) = 2 - 3x$ draw the graphs of both $f(x)$ and $f^{-1}(x)$.

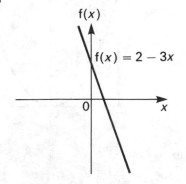

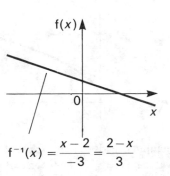

$$f^{-1}(x) = \frac{x-2}{-3} = \frac{2-x}{3}$$

Investigation

If $\dfrac{x-1}{2}$ is the inverse of $2x + 1$ what is the inverse of $\dfrac{x-1}{2}$?

Decide on your answer not by an algebraic routine but by thinking carefully about what inverses are.

EXERCISE 9.7

(*Answers on page 125*)

Find the inverses of the following functions drawing both function and inverse on the same graph. Use the range of x indicated and use the same scale on each axis.

Do not look at any answers until you are told to do so in the investigation after question 3.

1. $\dfrac{2x}{3} + 3 \quad -6 \leqslant x \leqslant 6 \quad 1\,\text{cm to 2 units on each axis}$

2. $2 - \dfrac{x}{2} \quad -6 \leqslant x \leqslant 6 \quad 1\,\text{cm to 1 unit on each axis}$

3. $\sqrt{x} \quad 0 \leqslant x \leqslant 2.25 \quad 2\,\text{cm to 1 unit on each axis}$

   (Only positive values of $\sqrt{x}$ to be used.)

If you cannot see the relationship you had better look at the answers now.

Investigation

After drawing your answers to these questions you should see a geometric property emerging. Can you describe it?

> **The geometric property is that a function and its inverse are a reflection of each other in the line $y = x$.**

Conditions for the inverse to exist

As always there are complications. If we consider the inverse of $f(x) = x^2$ we shall see the problem. It turns out to be a problem with the simplest possible answer.

If you look at this diagram you will see illustrated again the idea of the

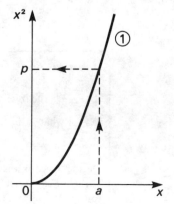 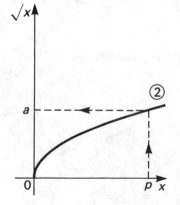 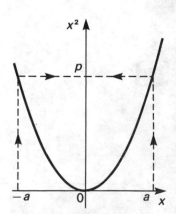

inverse. Looking at ①, an input a leads to the value p. Now ② gives us an input of p leading to the value a i.e. ② is the inverse of ①.

Now in this diagram, $f(x) = x^2$, a leads to p and $-a$ also leads to p. When we look for the inverse, for input of p, what do we want out, a or $-a$? Since there is no reason for one or the other, a or $-a$, the conclusion is that x^2 does not have an inverse. This is the simple answer referred to above: no inverse.

So which functions have inverses and which don't? We seem to have contradictions here. We are saying that x^2 does not have an inverse and yet in question 3 of Exercise 9.7, combined with the investigation on page 113, we are saying that x^2 does have an inverse. So what now? The answer lies in the graphs. In the diagram above x^2 is drawn for a domain of all x but in Exercise 9.7 it is drawn only for the domain $x > 0$. Above we have an example of a **many-to-one** function i.e. many (in this case two, anything more than 1 is many in this situation) values of x leading to one value of $f(x)$ whereas in Exercise 9.7 we have an example of a **one-to-one** function i.e. one value of x leads to one value of y, and vice versa.

The simple rule is that:

We can only have an inverse of a one-to-one function: one-to-many, many-to-one, many-to-many functions do not have inverses.

Examples of all these are shown below.

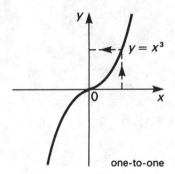

one-to-one

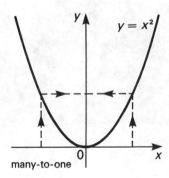

many-to-one

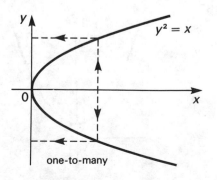

one-to-many

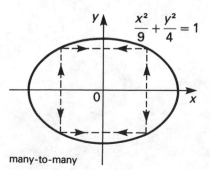

many-to-many

EXERCISE 9.8

(*Answers on page 126*)

Sketch the following functions and their inverses.

1. $f(x) = \dfrac{2x - 9}{3}$

2. $f(x) = (x - 3)^2$ for $x > 3$

3. $f(x) = 2x - 4$ for $0 \leqslant x \leqslant 2$, $f(x) = (x - 2)^2$ for $x > 2$

4. $f(x) = (x + 2)^3$

5. $f(x) = 5 - 3x$

Answers to exercises

ANSWERS TO EXERCISE 9.1

2. $x \leqslant 10,\ -5 \leqslant f(x)$

3. $0 \leqslant f(x) \leqslant 4$

4. $-2 \leqslant x \leqslant 5$

5. $x \leqslant 6,\ 1 \leqslant f(x)$

6. $x^3 + 1$

7. $x^2 + x + 1$

8. $f(x) \geqslant \frac{1}{6}$ $\left(x = 0 \Rightarrow \frac{1}{x} = \infty \quad \text{and} \quad x = 6 \Rightarrow \frac{1}{x} = \frac{1}{6} \quad \therefore\ \infty \geqslant f(x) \geqslant \frac{1}{6} \quad \text{or} \quad f(x) \geqslant \frac{1}{6}\right)$

9. $-5 \leqslant f(x) \leqslant 5$

10. $(x - 1)^2$

ANSWERS TO EXERCISE 9.2

1. Even $\because (-x)^2 + 2 = x^2 + 2$

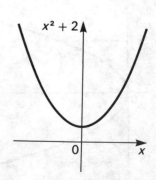

2. Neither $\because (-x + 2)^2 \neq (x + 2)^2$ and $(-x + 2)^2 \neq -(x + 2)^2$

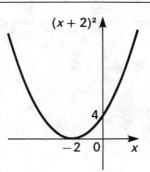

3. Even $\because 2(-x)^2 = 2x^2$

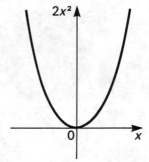

4. Odd $\because x = -(-x)$

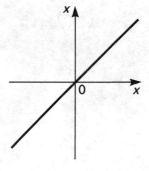

5. Neither $\because (-x)^3 + 2 \neq (-x)^3 + 2$ and $(-x)^3 + 2 \neq -(x^3 + 2)$

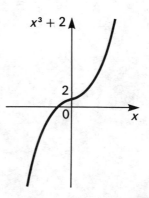

6. Neither $\because (-x+2)^3 \neq (x+2)^3$ and $(-x+2)^3 \neq -(x+2)^3$

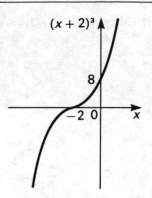

7. Odd $\because 2(-x)^3 = -2x^3$

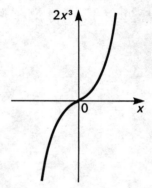

8. Odd $\because -(-x) = x$

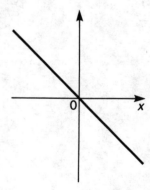

9. Even $\because 4 - (-x)^4 = 4 - x^4$

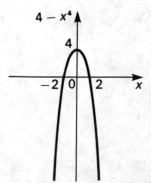

10. Neither $\because 5 - (-x)^5 = 5 + x^5$ i.e. neither $5 - x^5$ nor $-(5 - x^5)$

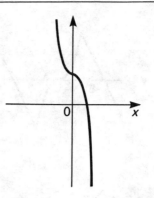

ANSWERS TO EXERCISE 9.3

1.

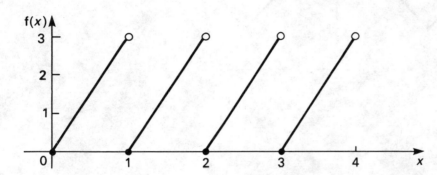

2.

continuous

3.

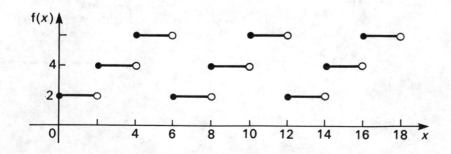

4.

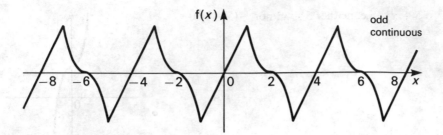

5.

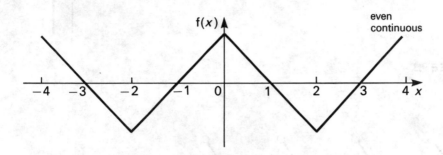

ANSWERS TO EXERCISE 9.4

3. $gf(x) = g(x - 1) = (x - 1)^3$

4. $hg(x) = h(x^3) = \dfrac{1}{x^3}$

5. $hgf(x) = hg(x - 1) = h((x - 1)^3) = \dfrac{1}{(x - 1)^3}$

6. $gfh(x) = gf\left(\dfrac{1}{x}\right) = g\left(\dfrac{1}{x} - 1\right) = \left(\dfrac{1}{x} - 1\right)^3$

7. $gfg(x) = gf(x^3) = g((x^3 - 1)) = (x^3 - 1)^3$

8. $hff(x) = hf(x - 1) = h(x - 2) = \dfrac{1}{x - 2}$

9. $fgh(x) = fg\left(\dfrac{1}{x}\right) = f\left(\dfrac{1}{x^3}\right) = \dfrac{1}{x^3} - 1$

10. $fghgh(x) = fghg\left(\dfrac{1}{x}\right) = fgh\left(\dfrac{1}{x^3}\right) = fg(x^3) = f(x^9) = x^9 - 1$

Answer
fgh(x) is a function of a function of a function of x.

ANSWERS TO EXERCISE 9.5

1.

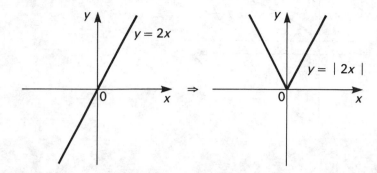

2.

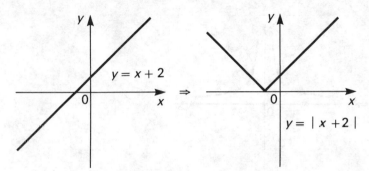

3.

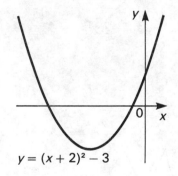

4.

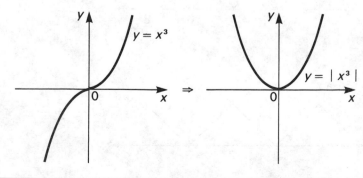

5.

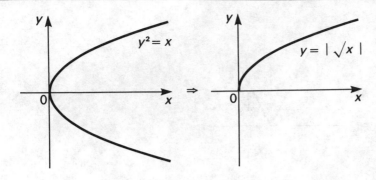

6.

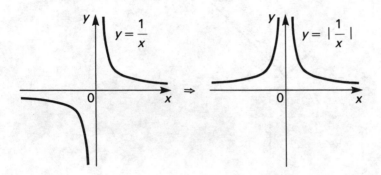

7.   From exercise 9.3 there would be no
     change in questions 1, 2 and 3.
     The graph for question 4
     would change to:

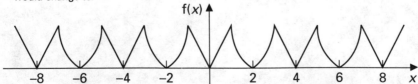

     The graph for question 5
     would change to:

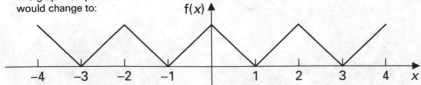

ANSWERS TO EXERCISE 9.6

1. The graph of $y = x^2 - 4$ is like this.

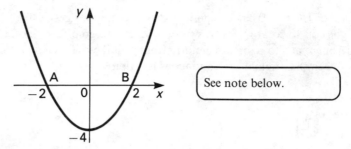

See note below.

Near A and B, i.e. as $x \to -2$ and 2, $x^2 - 4 \to 0$.

$$\therefore \frac{1}{x^2 - 4} \to \frac{1}{0} \to \infty$$

So there are asymptotes at A and B, $x = -2$, $x = 2$.
  Draw them first (dotted lines).

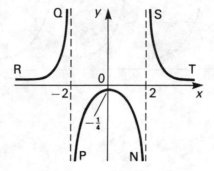

The section of the curve between A and B is negative $\therefore$ its reciprocal is negative.

On the original when $x = 0$, $f(x) = -4$
$\therefore$ on the reciprocal when $x = 0$ $f(x) = -\frac{1}{4}$

Draw the section of the curve between the asymptotes, (P to N). Now, the reciprocal having gone towards ∞ at P reappears at Q and hence we have the section of the curve QR.
  Similarly for ST.

In a similar way the function $\dfrac{1}{|x^2 - 4|}$ is like this.

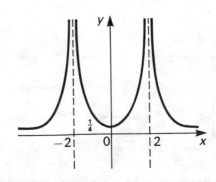

Note:

The graph of $1/(x^2 - 4)$ can be considered as a continuous graph. From ∞ at R it goes off to ∞ at Q, returns from $-\infty$ at P to go off to $-\infty$ at N, returns from ∞ at S to go off at T, returns from ∞ at R etc. This is invariably the case when the original is a continuous function.

2.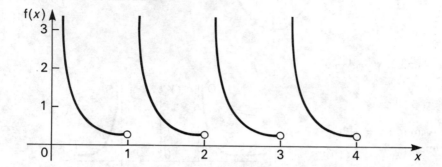

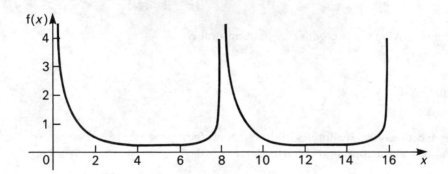

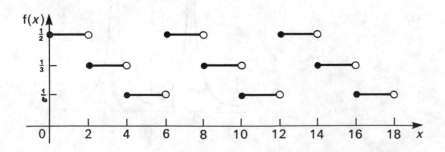

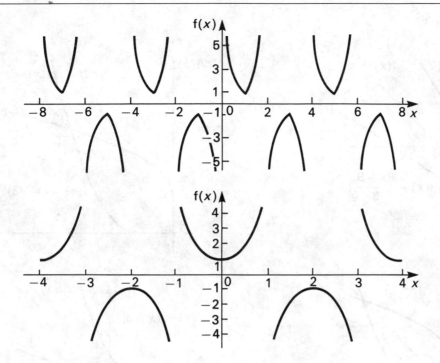

ANSWERS TO EXERCISE 9.7

1.

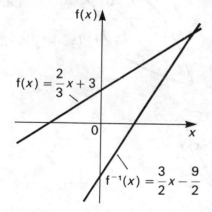

$f(x) = \dfrac{2}{3}x + 3$

$f^{-1}(x) = \dfrac{3}{2}x - \dfrac{9}{2}$

2.

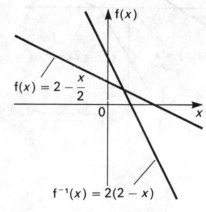

$f(x) = 2 - \dfrac{x}{2}$

$f^{-1}(x) = 2(2 - x)$

3.

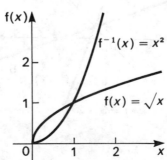

$f^{-1}(x) = x^2$

$f(x) = \sqrt{x}$

ANSWERS TO EXERCISE 9.8

1.

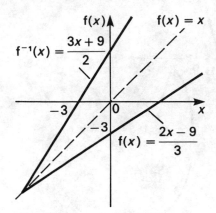

2.

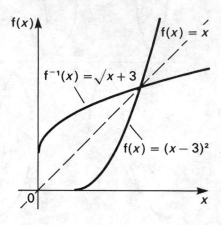

3.

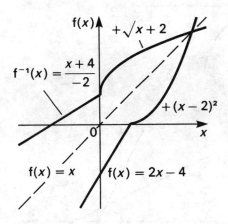

4.

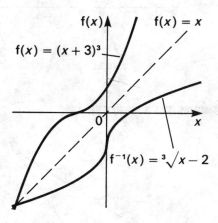

5.

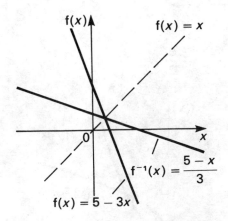

Now try worksheets 5, 6 and 7.

Chapter 10

CALCULUS: DIFFERENTIATION

Having completed this chapter you will be aware of the introduction of a more aesthetic side to your work. This continues throughout the rest of the book. Calculus, and its applications, form an immense subject area and this chapter introduces you to one of these areas, namely differentiation.

Aims and objectives

Having worked through this chapter, you will understand:
the slope of a graph

you will be able to:
differentiate from first principles   use of δy, δx

find turning points on curves   maximum, minimum

and **points of inflexion**

differentiate a function of a function
  products

$$y=(x^2 + 2)^3(3x - 1)^2 \;\Rightarrow\; \frac{dy}{dx} = 6(x^2 + 2)^2(3x - 1)(4x^2 - x + 2)$$

  quotients
$$y = \frac{x^2 + 2}{3x - 1} \;\Rightarrow\; \frac{dy}{dx} = \frac{3x^2 - 2x - 6}{(3x - 1)^2}$$

solve problems connected with rates of change. $A = \pi r^2 \;\Rightarrow\; \dfrac{dA}{dt} = 2\pi r \times \dfrac{dr}{dt}$

At the end of the chapter there is a summary.

Introduction

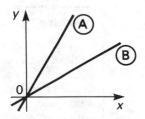

Here are two graphs with many features the same:

1. both are straight lines
2. both pass through the origin
3. both are increasing (as x gets bigger so does y).

There is only one difference.

> **Remember**
>
> x always $\rightarrow$
> y always $\uparrow$.

Five different ways of saying the same thing.

- (A) is **steeper** than (B).
- (A) has a **greater gradient** than (B).
- (A) **goes up faster** than (B) e.g. at $x = 10$ y value of (A) $> y$ value of (B).
- the **rate of increase** is **greater** for (A) than (B).
- the **rate of change** is **greater** for (A) than (B).

This is the standard wording used in mathematics.

Examples of rates of change for straight lines

Graph	Rate of change
	$\dfrac{PQ}{QO} = \dfrac{5}{7}$
	$\dfrac{PQ}{QR} = \dfrac{46 - 30}{11 - 3} = \dfrac{16}{8} = 2$
	$\dfrac{PQ}{QR} = \dfrac{7 - 1}{2 - 6} = \dfrac{6}{-4} = -\dfrac{3}{2}$ or $\dfrac{1 - 7}{6 - 2} = \dfrac{-6}{4} = -\dfrac{3}{2}$
	$\dfrac{PQ}{QR} = \dfrac{30 - 5}{15 - 0} = \dfrac{25}{15} = \dfrac{5}{3}$
	$\dfrac{PQ}{QR} = \dfrac{5 - -11}{-9 - 3} = \dfrac{5 + 11}{-12} = \dfrac{16}{-12} = -\dfrac{4}{3}$

Study carefully the order of the numbers at this stage.

Definition

This sign means a **decreasing** function: y going down as x goes up.

Definition

s stands for distance, t for time. In this case slope is the rate of change of distance and is the speed, metres per second $= \mathrm{m\,s}^{-1}$.

Differentiating by rule

We can see that rates of change are easy to measure on straight line graphs. With curved graphs it is a different matter. We first of all have to find the formula. Each graph has its own formula. Here are some functions with their slope formulae.

Function	Slope
x^2	$2x$
x^3	$3x^2$
x^4	$4x^3$
x^5	$5x^4$
x^6	$6x^5$

Have you seen the way of working out the formula now?

If not, try:

x^{19}	$19x^{18}$
x^{57}	$57x^{56}$

In fact the rule is simple. Two things happen to the power of x.

$$\begin{array}{c} \textit{goes} \\ \textit{in front} \end{array} \qquad \text{---} \textit{minus 1} \text{---}$$

$$x^{11} \qquad x^{11} \qquad 11x^{10}$$

We have just learnt the basic rule of differentiation. We shall now practice using it. What it is used for follows immediately and the proof of the rule is on page 132.

> Differentiation is the process of finding the gradient formula.

EXERCISE 10.1

(*Answers on page 150*)

Differentiate the following functions with respect to (w.r.t.) x.

Group A

1. $3x^2$
2. $7x^5$
3. $4x$
4. $\dfrac{3}{x^2}$
5. 7
6. $2x^{3/2}$
7. $7x^5 + 3x^2$
8. $x^2 + 3$

Group B

1. $x^2 + z^2$
2. $\dfrac{2}{x} + \dfrac{3}{x^2}$
3. $5x + 2$
4. a^2x^2
5. q
6. $5x^{5/2} + x^{1/2} + \dfrac{5}{x^{3/2}}$
7. $8ax + 4cx$

9. $x^3 + \dfrac{1}{x^3}$

10. $x^2 + 2ax + a^2$

8. $\sqrt{x} + \dfrac{1}{\sqrt{x}}$

9. ax^n

10. $\dfrac{c}{x^n}$

The slope formula

The graph shows the distance travelled in the first three seconds by a hundred metre sprinter.

> This shows what the slope formula is used for.

| the first second, goes 4 m | the second second, goes 9 m | the third second, goes 15 m |

His speed is increasing. We can see this on the graph by looking at the slope. As time passes it gets steeper.

The speed at any instant is given by the slope at that instant.

i.e. the speed after 2 seconds is the slope of the curve at the point where $t = 2$.

e.g.

Equation of curve $s = t^2$

Slope formula $2t$

$\therefore$ when $t = 2$ speed $= 2 \times 2 = 4\,\mathrm{m\,s}^{-1}$

We have now survived the introduction to calculus. Calculus is the mathematics of change and was first formulated by Isaac Newton (England) 1642–1727 although some would argue that Gottfried von Leibnitz (Germany) was the first. Both worked independently of each other and used the earlier work of Descartes (see section on graphs). Since we live in an ever-changing world – your height and weight, the seasons, the moving parts of the school bus, the national economy, the universe – this branch of mathematics is particularly important and useful. Examples of its use occur in physics, chemistry, biology, economics, geography and in many other situations.

> **Investigation**
>
> Read further about the life and work of Isaac Newton.

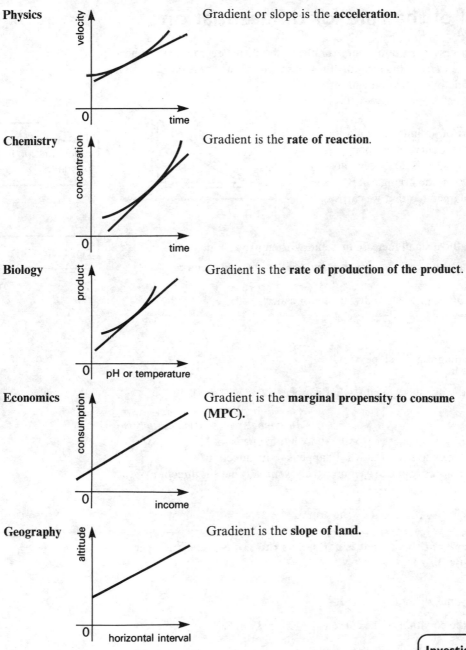

Physics

Gradient or slope is the **acceleration**.

Chemistry

Gradient is the **rate of reaction**.

Biology

Gradient is the **rate of production of the product**.

Economics

Gradient is the **marginal propensity to consume (MPC).**

Geography

Gradient is the **slope of land.**

It does not matter at all whether we understand these sketch graphs – the bold terms are used in the subjects shown and they are all determined from the slope, $\dfrac{\mathrm{d}y}{\mathrm{d}x}$, of the graphs.

> **Investigation**
>
> Find as many different subjects as possible in which calculus (differentiation) appears – you will be surprised.

Proof of the rule for differentiation

This is a necessary section because firstly we should have some idea of where the rule comes from and secondly the ideas used in it will be needed later on in work on approximation and error.

Here goes!

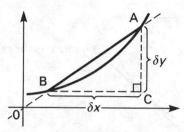

AB is part of an infinitely long line which cuts the curve in two points, A and B. A and B are very close together and the triangle ABC is drawn enlarged (so that we can see it).

> This is called differentiation from first principles.

BC is small – a small increase in x and written δx, said 'delta x'

AC is small – a small increase in y and written δy, said 'delta y'

> New notation δy, δx.

δx does *not* mean $\delta \times x$ and you cannot cancel, $\dfrac{\delta y}{\delta x}$ to get $\dfrac{y}{x}$.

From the diagram the slope of $AB = \dfrac{AC}{BC} = \dfrac{\delta y}{\delta x}$

Now for the imaginative bit – what happens as δx gets smaller?

In symbols : $\delta x \rightarrow 0$ (*tends to zero*)

Answer: δy gets smaller ($\delta y \rightarrow 0$). And what happens to AB?

Answer: It gets smaller. But what happens to its direction?

Answer: It moves round to its limit which eventually has the direction of the tangent at B.

The slope of this tangent is defined as the slope of the curve at the point B.

Now for some algebra.

Suppose the equation of the curve is $y = x^2 + 3x + 5$.

B is the point with coordinates (x, y).

$\therefore$ at B: $y = x^2 + 3x + 5$ **1**

A is a bit further along and has coordinates $(x + \delta x, y + \delta y)$.

$\therefore$ at A: $y + \delta y = (x + \delta x)^2 + 3(x + \delta x) + 5$ **2**

We are now going to solve equations **1** and **2** simultaneously to find δy.

2 can be written as:

$$y + \delta y = x^2 + 2x\delta x + (\delta x)^2 + 3x + 3\delta x + 5 \qquad \textbf{3}$$

$$\textbf{3} - \textbf{1} \Rightarrow \delta y = 2x\delta x + (\delta x)^2 + 3\delta x$$

If we now divide through by δx we will get $\dfrac{\delta y}{\delta x}$ i.e. the slope of AB.

$$\therefore \frac{\delta y}{\delta x} = 2x + \delta x + 3 \qquad \textbf{4}$$

δy and δx here are important but δx here can be ignored. Why?

The answer is that δx is insignificant when added to $2x + 3$.

e.g. £0.000 02 is negligible compared with £2 000 000 and adding a tear drop to the Atlantic Ocean would make negligible difference.

But $\delta y \div \delta x$ is *not* negligible.

$0.000\,02 \div 0.000\,03$ has the same value as $200\,000 \div 300\,000$ and the teardrop compared with a raindrop is of as much value as the Atlantic compared with the Pacific.

Back to the proof!

> The *limiting* (final) value that $\dfrac{\delta y}{\delta x}$ reaches is indicated by $\dfrac{dy}{dx}$.

New notation:

$$\frac{dy}{dx}$$

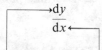

Read this as differentiate y with respect to x.

Relating this to **4** above, we finally get

$$\frac{dy}{dx} = 2x + 3$$

which is the answer we could have got in one line by using the differentiation rule. From now on we shall stick to the rule, unless specified otherwise.

EXERCISE 10.2

(*Answers on page 151*)

1. Differentiate $y = 2x^2 - 3x + 1$ from first principles.

2. Differentiate $y = \dfrac{4}{x}$ from first principles.

3. The area of a circle is given by $A = \pi r^2$. The radius of a circle is measured as 10 cm but this is to an accuracy of $\pm 0 \cdot 1$ cm. Find the range of possible values of A, giving your answer as a multiple of π. (Ponder on this question a while, it is not as bad as it reads. You will need to use your 'first principles' work in reverse.)

4. Using calculus methods find the change in the volume of a cube of edge 8 cm when the edge decreases by 1 mm. Check your answer using a calculator.

5. From first principles find $\dfrac{\mathrm{d}y}{\mathrm{d}x}$ from $y^2 + xy + 2x^2 = 0$.

A note on notation! In calculus three different letters d are used and they have different meanings. Make sure you always write the one you mean.

$$\frac{\delta y}{\delta x} \qquad\qquad \frac{\mathrm{d}y}{\mathrm{d}x} \qquad\qquad \frac{\partial y}{\partial x}$$

| δ – Greek letter delta means (in mathematics) a small increase | d – Arabic letter meaning differentiate with respect to | ∂ – meaning partial differentiation (forget this until you are at university). |

Now we shall have a look at some applications of differentiation.

Turning points

Early in chapter 9 on functions, page 104, we referred to turning points in the list of salient features of a curve.

> **Turning points are where a function stops increasing and starts to decrease or vice versa.**

The former is a maximum and the latter a minimum turning point. This diagram illustrates these.

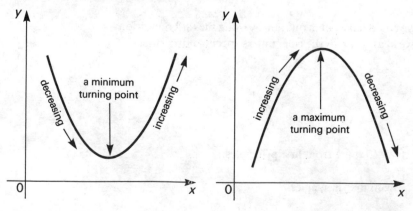

An obvious feature of a graph at a turning point is that the gradient is zero. The direction of the curve is parallel to the x-axis, and this is the feature we make use of when setting out to find where the turning points are.

An example will illustrate this well.

e.g. Find where the turning points are on the curve $y = 2x^3 - 3x^2 - 12x + 5$. Find also the type of each turning point and sketch the curve.

Firstly find where the points are with zero gradients. This means finding the coordinates.

$$y = 2x^3 - 3x^2 - 12x + 5$$

$$\frac{dy}{dx} = 6x^2 - 6x - 12$$

Making $\frac{dy}{dx}$ (i.e. the gradient) = 0:

> This not only gives the gradient at any point but we shall use it conversely to find the points which have a given gradient.

$\Rightarrow 6x^2 - 6x - 12 = 0$

$\therefore x^2 - x - 2 = 0$

$(x - 2)(x + 1) = 0$

$\therefore x = 2$ and $x = -1$

Hence the gradient is zero at two places:

When $x = -1$, $y = 2(-1)^3 - 3(-1)^2 - 12(-1) + 5 = 12$ and

when $x = 2$, $y = 2(2)^3 - 3(2)^2 - 12(2) + 5 = -15$.

The turning points are at $(-1, 12)$ and $(2, -15)$.

Now to find the type of turning point. This is done by investigating the gradient of the curve to the left and to the right of the turning point. (There is another method which we shall look at later.)

If we consider the point at $(-1, 12)$, x-values to the left and right are -2 and 0 respectively.

Now when $x = -2$ $\quad \frac{dy}{dx} = 24$ $\quad$ the important thing here is that the gradient is $+$.

and when $x = 0$ $\quad \frac{dy}{dx} = -12$ $\quad$ the important thing here is that the gradient is $-$.

$\therefore$ the gradient sequence from left to right is:

x-values	left $x = -2$	point $x = -1$	right $x = 0$
gradient	+	0	−
i.e.	/		\

and the only way these can fit together is if the turning point is like this:

a maximum.

Now for the other turning point.

	left	point	right
x-values	1	2	3
gradient	$-(12)$	0	$+(24)$
i.e.	\	—	/

This gives: _/ a minimum.

At this stage our sketch looks like this, showing that we know there is a maximum turning point at $(-1, 12)$ and a minimum at $(2, -15)$.

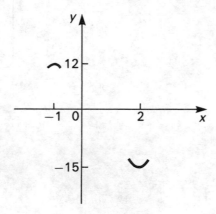

Now consider where the curve crosses the axes.

x-axis: These points are found by putting $y = 0$.

$$2x^3 - 3x^2 - 12x + 5 = 0$$

Since this has no readily found solution we forget the idea. Finding these points is not meant to be a major problem and we bother *only* if they are easily found.

y-axis: These are found by putting $x = 0$.

$$y = 5$$

∴ the curve passes through $(0, 5)$.

Finally consider what happens as $|x| \to \infty$.

In the function $2x^3 - 3x^2 - 12x + 5$, $2x^3$ is the **dominant** term when x takes large values.

When $x \to \infty \quad 2x^3 \to \infty$

$\qquad x \to -\infty \quad 2x^3 \to -\infty$.

> Verify this by putting $x = 1000$.

At this point we can complete the sketch to get this.

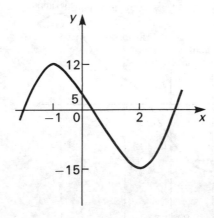

Now consider another one.

$y = x^3 - 6x^2 + 12x - 12$

$\dfrac{dy}{dx} = 3x^2 - 12x + 12$

Putting $\dfrac{dy}{dx} = 0 \Rightarrow 3x^2 - 12x + 12 = 0 \Rightarrow x^2 - 4x + 4 = 0$

$\therefore (x - 2)^2 = 0 \Rightarrow x = 2$ (twice)

Substituting for $x \Rightarrow y = 2^3 - 6.2^2 + 12.2 - 12 = -4$

Now to consider gradients to left and right of $x = 2$.

Note:

6.2^2 here means 6×2^2 and 12.2 means 12×2.

	left	**point**	**right**
x-values	$x = 1$	$x = 2$	$x = 3$
gradient	$+$	$\underline{0}$	$+$
i.e.	$/$		$/$

This is neither maximum nor minimum but $\diagup\!\!\diagup$.

Such a point is called a *point of inflexion*.

A point of inflexion may also take the shape $\diagdown\!\!\diagdown$.

A further complication is that points of inflexion may also occur, in fact they more often do, when the gradient is *not* zero.

Study these diagrams.

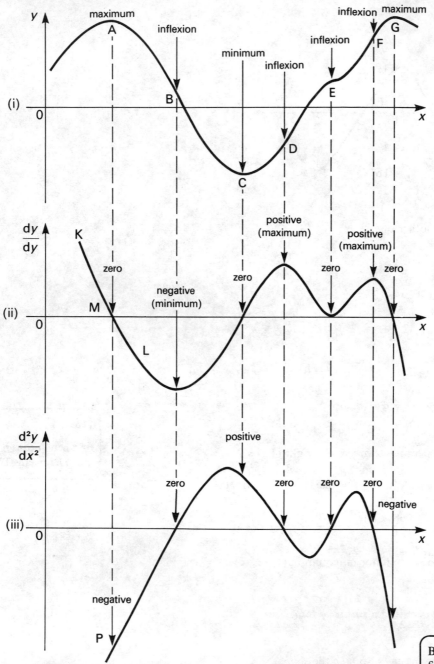

The figure consists of three graphs (i), (ii) and (iii). (i) is a graph showing a function with minimum, maximum and inflexion points. (ii) is a graph of the gradient of (i) with corresponding points in line. (iii) is a graph of the

Be warned! You will find this confusing the first time through (and the second . . .).

gradient of (ii) again with corresponding abscissae in line. They are not accurate graphs and we are concerned only with whether they are positive, negative or zero. The aim is find the link between the three graphs.

Consider the point A, a maximum on (i). We know that the gradient sequence for a maximum is $(+\ 0\ -)$ and this is shown by the section KL on (ii) where values go from positive at K to negative at L. Looking at graph (iii) it is seen that it takes a negative value at the point P corresponding with M on (ii) and A on (i).

A further note on the graphs:

(i) is the graph of the function $y = f(x)$

(ii) is the graph of the function $\dfrac{dy}{dx} = f'(x)$

Differential notation

(iii) is the graph of the function $\dfrac{d^2y}{dx^2} = f''(x)$

$\dfrac{dy}{dx}$ is the differential of y with respect to x.

$\dfrac{d^2y}{dx^2}$ is the differential of $\dfrac{dy}{dx}$ with respect to x.

It could be written $\dfrac{d(\frac{dy}{dx})}{dx}$

but $\dfrac{d^2y}{dx^2}$ is more convenient and it is read as

'd two y by d x squared'.

Rather than being known as the differential of $\dfrac{dy}{dx}\ldots$

it is usually called the **second differential** of y with respect to x.

It follows, then, that:

$\dfrac{d^3y}{dx^3}$ is the third differential of y with respect to x

$\dfrac{d^ny}{dx^n}$ is the nth differential of y with respect to x.

Spend some time now studying the diagrams, following through each point as indicated by the dotted lines. The following chart summarises the main points.

On the diagram	y	$\dfrac{dy}{dx}$	$\dfrac{d^2y}{dx^2}$
A, G	any	0	$-\;\Rightarrow$ maximum turning point
E	any	0	$\left.\begin{array}{l}0\\0\end{array}\right\}\Rightarrow$ point of inflexion
B, D, F	any	any except 0	
C	any	0	$+\;\Rightarrow$ minimum turning point

> **Any point on a curve where $\dfrac{dy}{dy} = 0$ is called a *stationary point* because the function is neither increasing nor decreasing.**

We often use f(x) instead of y and then the first derivative is written f$'(x)$ and read, 'f dash x', and the second derivative f$''(x)$, read, 'f double dash x', and so on.

We now have a second method for determining types of turning points and points of inflexion – looking at the second derivative.

We now go back to the example on page 135 and break into the solution at the point where the coordinates of the zero gradient points have just been found.

e.g. The points with zero gradient are at $(-1, 12)$ and $(2, -15)$.

Find the second derivative: $\dfrac{d^2y}{dx^2} = 12x - 6$

Now when $x = -1$ $\qquad \dfrac{d^2y}{dx^2} = -12 - 6 < 0$ $\quad \therefore$ a maximum

and when $x = 2$ $\qquad \dfrac{d^2y}{dx^2} = 24 - 6 > 0$ $\quad \therefore$ a minimum

This is a much neater and shorter method than the 'left and right' system and it is the one which is usually used. Occasionally, however, because of a complicated second differential, the left and right system may be preferred.

Questions on this work come later in Exercise 10.2.

Differentiating the function of a function

We must now consider some further rules of differentiation, after which we shall be able to look at a good range of examples. We really must *learn* these rules: they are used frequently in subsequent chapters.

| e.g. |

Differentiate $(x^2 + 5)^{10}$ w.r.t. x.

Firstly look at what we are trying to differentiate.

Remember

w.r.t. = with respect to.

$(x^2 + 5)^{10}$ is really a composite function of x.

If we restate the function so that $f(x) = x^2 + 5$ and $g(x) = x^{10}$, then $gf(x) = (x^2 + 5)^{10}$. Now we can tackle the problem by recognising this fact and combining it with the following simple but important result.

Remember from page 133 that $\dfrac{dy}{dx}$ is defined as the limiting value of $\dfrac{\delta y}{\delta x}$ as

δx gets smaller and smaller, written mathematically as:

$$\frac{dy}{dx} = \lim_{\delta x \to 0} \frac{\delta y}{\delta x}$$

$\dfrac{dy}{dx}$ is the limit as δx tends to zero of $\dfrac{\delta y}{\delta x}$.

Now $\dfrac{\delta y}{\delta x} = \dfrac{\delta y}{\delta u} \times \dfrac{\delta u}{\delta x}$

by ordinary rules of fractions, where u is a function of x, and as $\delta x \to 0$ so do δu and δy and hence:

$$\frac{dy}{dx} = \lim_{\delta x \to 0} \frac{\delta y}{\delta x} = \lim_{\delta x \to 0} \frac{\delta y}{\delta u} \times \frac{\delta u}{\delta x} = \frac{dy}{du} \times \frac{du}{dx}$$

So $\dfrac{dy}{dx} = \dfrac{dy}{du} \times \dfrac{du}{dx}$

This is a simple rule and we can use it in the present problem if we change

$y = (x^2 + 5)^{10}$ into $y = u^{10}$ where $u = x^2 + 5$.

Differentiating: $\dfrac{dy}{du} = 10u^9$ and $\dfrac{du}{dx} = 2x$

$$\therefore \frac{dy}{dx} = 10u^9 \times 2x = 20x(x^2 + 5)^9$$

Try another one.

e.g. Find $\dfrac{dy}{dx}$ if $y = (3x^2 + x - 4)^7$.

Put $u = 3x^2 + x - 4$ then $y = u^7$

and $\dfrac{du}{dx} = 6x + 1$ $\qquad\qquad \dfrac{dy}{du} = 7u^6$

Combining these: $\dfrac{dy}{dx} = \dfrac{dy}{du} \times \dfrac{du}{dx}$

$$= 7u^6 \times (6x + 1)$$

$$7(3x^2 + x - 4)^6 \times (6x + 1)$$

Look at this carefully.

the differential of the bracket ×
itself regardless of its content

the differential of the content
or inside of the bracket

Is this the case in the previous example?

e.g. Differentiate $\left(x + \dfrac{1}{x}\right)^{12}$ w.r.t. x.

Firstly, we do this by trying the routine just mentioned.

Let $y = \left(x + \dfrac{1}{x}\right)^{12}$ then $\dfrac{dy}{dx} = 12\left(\quad\right)^{11} \times \left(1 - \dfrac{1}{x^2}\right)$

i.e. $\dfrac{dy}{dx} = 12\left(x + \dfrac{1}{x}\right)^{11}\left(1 - \dfrac{1}{x^2}\right)$

Secondly, using the substitution idea.

Let $u = x + \dfrac{1}{x}$ $y = u^{12}$

$$\dfrac{du}{dx} = 1 - \dfrac{1}{x^2} \qquad \dfrac{dy}{du} = 12u^{11}$$

Combining $\dfrac{dy}{dx} = \dfrac{dy}{du} \times \dfrac{du}{dx} = 12u^{11}\left(1 - \dfrac{1}{x^2}\right) = 12\left(x + \dfrac{1}{x}\right)^{11}\left(1 - \dfrac{1}{x^2}\right)$

There is no difference in these methods. The first is just the verbal variation of the formal algebriac routine of the second. Once we have mastered the first variation we are home and dry for differentiating the function of a function.

EXERCISE 10.3

(*Answers on page 152*)

Differentiate the following w.r.t. x.

Group A
1. $(2x + 1)^{10}$
2. $(5 - 3x)^6$
3. $(x^2 + x + 1)^3$
4. $\left(2 - \dfrac{1}{x}\right)^4$
5. $\left(x^3 + \dfrac{1}{x^3}\right)^{1/2}$

Group B
1. $\sqrt{(3x - 1)}$
2. $(x^2 + 4)^{3/4}$
3. $(x^5 - a^5)^{1/5}$
4. $\sqrt[3]{\left(x - \dfrac{1}{x}\right)^5}$
5. $\left(x + 1 + \dfrac{1}{x}\right)^7$

Connected rates of change

Using the idea of $\dfrac{dy}{dx} = \dfrac{dy}{du} \times \dfrac{du}{dx}$ introduced on page 141 we can tackle other problems.

 A spherical balloon is being filled with air at the rate of $400\,\text{cm}^3$ per second. Find the rate at which the radius is increasing when the radius is $10\,\text{cm}$. Volume of sphere $= \frac{4}{3}\pi r^3$.

First we must interpret the words of the question.

$$400\,\text{cm}^3 \text{ per second} = \text{rate of change of volume} = \frac{dV}{dt}$$

$$\text{rate at which the radius is increasing} = \frac{dr}{dt}$$

A link between $\dfrac{dV}{dt}$ and $\dfrac{dr}{dt}$ is obtained from $\dfrac{dV}{dt} = \dfrac{dV}{dr} \times \dfrac{dr}{dt}$

$$\uparrow$$
given   *to find*

What can you do with this?

$$V = \frac{4}{3}\pi r^3 \quad \therefore \frac{dV}{dr} = 4\pi r^2$$

$\therefore$ we now have $\dfrac{dV}{dt} = 4\pi r^2 \times \dfrac{dr}{dt}$ and with this we can answer the question.

$$400 = 4\pi \cdot 10^2 \times \frac{dr}{dt}$$

$$\therefore \frac{dr}{dt} = \frac{400}{4 \cdot \pi \cdot 10^2} = \frac{1}{\pi} = 0 \cdot 3\,\text{cm s}^{-1}.$$

This type of question, in which we are dealing with the rates at which quantities are changing, can only be dealt with by calculus and it helps to demonstrate how calculus is the mathematics of movement. We meet this often, not only in pure mathematics, but in other subjects as well.

 Boyle's law states that

$$pV = c$$

where p is pressure, V is volume, c is a constant. Find the rate of change of volume when the pressure is $20 \, \text{kg cm}^{-2}$ and changing at the rate of $2 \, \text{kg cm}^{-2} \text{s}^{-1}$.

$$V = \frac{c}{p} = cp^{-1}$$

rate of change of pressure ⌐

$$\frac{dV}{dt} = -\frac{c}{p^2}\frac{dp}{dt} \qquad \qquad \therefore \frac{dV}{dt} = \frac{d(cp^{-1})}{dt} = \frac{d(cp^{-1})}{dp} \times \frac{dp}{dt}$$

rate of change of volume

$$\therefore \frac{dV}{dt} = -\frac{c}{20^2} \times 2 = -\frac{c}{200} \, \text{cm}^3 \text{s}^{-1} \quad \therefore \frac{dp}{dt} = 2 \quad \textit{given in the question}$$

The working for this question is short but it illustrates well the power of calculus. A complex problem has been solved so easily.

EXERCISE 10.4

(*Answers on page 153*)

1. The radius of a circular patch of oil floating on water is changing at the rate of $2 \, \text{cm s}^{-1}$. Find the rates at which (a) the area, (b) the circumference are changing when the radius is 20 cm.

2. A bell jar of radius 5 cm is being filled with water at the rate of $15 \, \text{cm}^3$ per second. Find the rate at which the level of the liquid is rising.

3. A ladder of length 13 ft leans against a wall. It slips and the end against the wall falls at the rate of 3 ft/s. Find the speed of the lower end of the ladder when it is 5 ft from the wall.

4. A sugar cube dissolves in such a way that the rate of change of the surface area is constant and equal to $-0.5 \, \text{cm}^2 \text{s}^{-1}$. Find the rate of change of the volume at the instant when the edge of the cube is 0.75 cm.

5. A lamp is at a height of H ft and a man of height h ft walks away from the lamp at a speed of 5 ft/s. Find, in terms of H and h, the rate at which his shadow is increasing.

Products and quotients

We now cover two further basic rules used in differentiation, and these are the last two.

The remaining types of functions we have to deal with are products and quotients of functions (multiplication and division). These are things like:

$(x^2 + 2)^3(1 - 3x)^5$, product of two functions

and $\dfrac{(x^2 + 2)^3}{(1 - 3x)^5}$, quotient of two functions.

Before we tackle this we had better look at some basic theory: products first.

If u and v are both functions of x then:

$y = uv$

and considering corresponding small increases gives:

$y + \delta y = (u + \delta u)(v + \delta v)$

Subtracting: $\Rightarrow \quad \delta y = (u + \delta u)(v + \delta v) - uv$

$\therefore \delta y = v\delta u + u\delta v + \delta u\delta v$

Dividing by δx: $\Rightarrow \quad \dfrac{\delta y}{\delta x} = v\dfrac{\delta u}{\delta x} + u\dfrac{\delta v}{\delta x} + \delta u\dfrac{\delta v}{\delta x}$

$\lim_{\delta x \to 0} \quad \dfrac{dy}{dx} = v\dfrac{du}{dx} + u\dfrac{dv}{dx} + \delta u\dfrac{dv}{dx}$

If we consider the term $\delta u\dfrac{dv}{dx}$ (or it could also have been $\dfrac{du}{dx}\delta v$) we have some real quantity $\dfrac{dv}{dx}$ multiplied by δu which in the limit is zero. Therefore the term $\delta u\dfrac{dv}{dx}$ is zero. Hence we have:

$\dfrac{d(uv)}{dx} = v\dfrac{du}{dx} + u\dfrac{dv}{dx}$

which is the rule for differentiating products. It is easier to remember it in words:

> **The differential of a product is the differential of the first times the second plus the differential of the second times the first.**

We now look at the example quoted above.

e.g.

$$y = (x^2 + 2)^3(1 - 3x)^5$$

$$\frac{dy}{dx} = \underbrace{3(x^2 + 2)^2.2x} \times \underbrace{(1 - 3x)^5} + \underbrace{5(1 - 3x)^4. -3} \times \underbrace{(x^2 + 2)^3}$$

differential   the second   differential   the first
of the first   of the second
$(x^2 + 2)^3$ $(1 - 3x)^5$

$$\therefore \frac{dy}{dx} = 6x(x^2 + 2)^2(1 - 3x)^5 - 15(1 - 3x)^4(x^2 + 2)^3$$

$$= 3(x^2 + 2)^2(1 - 3x)^4\{2x(1 - 3x) - 5(x^2 + 2)\}$$

$$= 3(x^2 + 2)^2(1 - 3x)^4(2x - 11x^2 - 10)$$

> **Investigation**
>
> What happens if $y = uvw$, the product of three functions?

And now for quotients. $\qquad y = \dfrac{u}{v}$

Small increments: $\Rightarrow \qquad y + \delta y = \dfrac{u + \delta y}{v + \delta v}$

Subtracting: $\Rightarrow \qquad \delta y = \dfrac{u + \delta u}{v + \delta v} - \dfrac{u}{v}$

$$= \frac{v(u + \delta u) - u(v + \delta v)}{v(v + \delta v)}$$

$$= \frac{v\delta u - u\delta v}{v^2 + v\delta v}$$

Dividing by δx: $\Rightarrow \qquad \dfrac{\delta y}{\delta x} = \dfrac{v\dfrac{\delta u}{\delta x} - u\dfrac{\delta v}{\delta x}}{v^2 + v\delta v}$

$\lim \delta x \to 0 \qquad\qquad \dfrac{dy}{dv} = \dfrac{v\dfrac{du}{dx} - u\dfrac{dv}{dx}}{v^2 + v\delta v}$

> And what happens to the term $v\delta v$ in the denominator?
> Yes, it disappears, but why?
> We need the same reasoning as that used for $\delta u\dfrac{dv}{dx}$ on page 145.

Hence we have:

$$\frac{d}{dx}\left(\frac{u}{v}\right) = \frac{v\dfrac{du}{dx} - u\dfrac{dv}{dx}}{v^2}$$

This also is easier remembered in words:

> **The differential of a quotient is the differential of the top times the bottom minus the differential of the bottom times the top all over the bottom squared.**

Look at the example above.

e.g. $y = \dfrac{(x^2 + 2)^3}{(1 - 3x)^5}$

$$\underbrace{\text{differential}}_{\text{of top}} \qquad \underbrace{\text{bottom}} \qquad \underbrace{\text{differential}}_{\text{of bottom}} \qquad \underbrace{\text{top}}$$

$$\frac{dy}{dx} = \frac{\overbrace{3(x^2 + 2)^2.2x} \times \overbrace{(1 - 3x)^5} - \overbrace{5(1 - 3x)^4.-3} \times \overbrace{(x^2 + 2)^3}}{(1 - 3x)^{10}}$$

$$\underbrace{\text{bottom squared}}$$

$$= \frac{3(x^2 + 2)^2(1 - 3x)^4\{2x(1 - 3x) + 5(x^2 + 2)\}}{(1 - 3x)^{10}}$$

$$= \frac{3(x^2 + 2)^2(10 + 2x - x^2)}{(1 - 3x)^6}$$

This has been a long chapter with not many exercises but now we are in a position to try a whole variety of examples. We have done things this way to reinforce the fact that, at this stage in the study of mathematics, calculus is a useful tool to help solve many varied problems.

Summary

Before we start the next exercise here is a summary of the results developed in this chapter.

Differentation by rule: if $y = ax^n$ $\dfrac{dy}{dx} = nax^{n-1}$

Differentiation from first principles: $y = f(x)$ then $y + \delta y = f(x + \delta x)$

Subtract the first from the second to get $\delta y = f(x + \delta x) - f(x)$

Divide by δx $\Rightarrow$ $\dfrac{\delta y}{\delta x} = \dfrac{f(x + \delta x) - f(x)}{\delta x}$ let $\delta x \to 0$

Stationary points:

$\dfrac{dy}{dx} = 0,$ $\dfrac{d^2y}{dx^2} < 0 \Rightarrow$ maximum

$\dfrac{dy}{dx} = 0,$ $\dfrac{d^2y}{dx^2} = 0 \Rightarrow$ point of inflexion

$\dfrac{dy}{dx} = 0,$ $\dfrac{d^2y}{dx^2} > 0 \Rightarrow$ minimum

$\dfrac{dy}{dx} \neq 0,$ $\dfrac{d^2y}{dx^2} = 0 \Rightarrow$ point of inflexion

Beware! there are exceptions e.g. consider $y = x^4$.

Differentiation of a function of a function:

differential of main function × differential of inner function

Rates of change: $\dfrac{dy}{dx} = \dfrac{dy}{dt} \times \dfrac{dt}{dx} = \dfrac{dy}{dt} \bigg/ \dfrac{dx}{dt}$

Products: (differential of first) × second + (differential of second) × first

Quotients: $\dfrac{\text{(differential of top)} \times \text{bottom} - \text{(differential of bottom)} \times \text{top}}{\text{(bottom)}^2}$

EXERCISE 10.5

(*Answers on page 154*)

Group A

1. Differentiate $\left(x^2 + \dfrac{1}{x^2}\right)^9$ w.r.t. x.

2. Locate the turning points of $y = x^3 - 6x^2 + 9$ and state the type of each one.

3. If $V = 5x^2$ find $\dfrac{dx}{dt}$ if $\dfrac{dV}{dt} = 30$ when $x = 1$.

4. Differentiate $\dfrac{(x+1)^4}{(x^2+1)}$ w.r.t. x.

5. What is the name given to:
   (a) rate of change of distance w.r.t. time
   (b) rate of change of velocity w.r.t. time?

6. Differentiate $(x^2 + 5x + 7)^3(2-x)^4$ w.r.t. x.

7. A cube has edge x cm. Its volume increases at $24\,\text{cm}^3$ per minute. Find the rate of increase of the surface area of the cube when $x = 2$ cm.

> This is a harder question – more initiative required.

8. Using two different methods sketch the curve $y = 2x^2 - 12x + 14$. One of your methods should not involve calculus – see chapter 9.

9. Find $\dfrac{dy}{dx}$ if $y = 4$. Prove your result and illustrate it geometrically.

10. Given that $y = (x - 1)^3(x + 3)^4(2x - 1)^2$ find $\dfrac{dy}{dx}$.

> A bit naughty this question but have a go by making one intelligent guess or deduction from the rule for the product of *two* factors. It should not be too much of a problem if you did the investigation of $y = uvw$ on page 146.

Group B

1. Find the differential coefficient of $\left(2x - \dfrac{2}{x^3}\right)^{-4}$.

2. Find the position and type of the turning points on $y = 50 + 24x + 6x^2 - 4x^3$.

3. Given that $M = xyz$ and $\dfrac{dx}{dt} = 5$, $\dfrac{dy}{dt} = 3$, $\dfrac{dz}{dt} = -6$ find $\dfrac{dM}{dt}$ when $x = y = z = 1$.

4. Differentiate $\dfrac{(x^2 + 3x + 1)^3}{(2x^2 + 1)}$ w.r.t. x.

5. Differentiate $y = 3 - 2x + x^2$ from first principles.

6. Find the x-coordinate of the point(s) of inflexion on the curve in question B2.

7. Find the rate at which the surface area of a soap bubble, assumed to be a sphere, is increasing if the volume is increasing at 8 cm^3 per second when the radius is 2 cm.

8. Of the two graphs, $y = x^3 + 4x^2 + 4x - 5$ and $y = x^5 + 3x^3 - 16x$ which has (a) the greater rate of change, (b) the greater rate of increase when $x = -1$?

9. Differentiate $\dfrac{(2x + 1)^3}{(1 - 2x)^2(x^2 + 1)^3}$ w.r.t. x.

10. The distance a particle travels in time t is given, in metres, by the equation $d = t^3 + 2t^2 - 3t + 1$. Find (a) the velocity, (b) the acceleration when $t = 2$ seconds.

> You may need to refer to question A5 to help you with this one.

Answers to exercises

ANSWERS TO EXERCISE 10.1

Group A

1. $2 \times 3x^{2-1} = 6x$
2. $5 \times 7x^{5-1} = 35x^4$
3. $1 \times 4x^{1-1} = 4x^0 = 4$
4. $\dfrac{3}{x^2} = 3x^{-2} : -2 \times 3x^{-2-1} = -6x^{-3} = \dfrac{-6}{x^3}$
5. $7 = 7x^0 : 0 \times 7x^{0-1} = 0.x^{-1} = 0$

> ⇒ any constant differentiates to zero. Illustrate this by diagram.

6. $\dfrac{3}{2} \times 2x^{3/2-1} = 3x^{1/2}$
7. $5 \times 7x^{5-1} + 2 \times 3x^{2-1} = 35x^4 + 6x$
8. $2x^{2-1} + 0 = 2x$
9. $x^3 + \dfrac{1}{x^3} = x^3 + x^{-3} : 3x^{3-2} + -3x^{-3-1} = 3x^2 - \dfrac{3}{x^4}$
10. $2x^{2-1} + 1 \times 2ax^{1-1} + 0 \times a^2.x^{0-1} = 2x + 2a$

> ⇒ a^2 is not a function of x and is treated as a constant, which it is.

Group B

1. $2x$
2. $-\dfrac{2}{x^2} - \dfrac{6}{x^3}$
3. 5
4. $2a^2x$
5. 0
6. $\dfrac{25}{2}x^{3/2} + \dfrac{1}{2}x^{-1/2} - \dfrac{15}{2}x^{-5/2} = \dfrac{25}{2}x^{3/2} + \dfrac{1}{2x^{1/2}} - \dfrac{15}{2x^{5/2}}$
7. $8a + 4c$
8. $\dfrac{1}{2\sqrt{x}} - \dfrac{1}{2x^{3/2}}$
9. nax^{n-1}
10. $-\dfrac{nc}{x^{n+1}}$

ANSWERS TO EXERCISE 10.2

1. $y = 2x^2 - 3x + 1$

$\Rightarrow (y + \delta y) = 2(x + \delta x)^2 - 3(x + \delta x) + 1$ *increasing x and y by δx and δy*

$\therefore \delta y = 4x\delta x + 2(\delta x)^2 - 3\delta x$ *subtracting*

$\Rightarrow \dfrac{\delta y}{\delta x} = 4x + 2\delta x - 3$

$\delta x \to 0 \quad \dfrac{\delta y}{\delta x} \to \dfrac{dy}{dx} = 4x - 3$ *2δx is negligible*

2. $y = \dfrac{4}{x}$

$y + \delta y = \dfrac{4}{x + \delta x}$

$\Rightarrow \delta y = \dfrac{4}{(x + \delta x)} - \dfrac{4}{x} = \dfrac{4x - 4(x + \delta x)}{x(x + \delta x)} = \dfrac{-4\delta x}{x(x + \delta x)}$

$\therefore \dfrac{\delta y}{\delta x} = -\dfrac{4}{x(x + \delta x)}$

$\delta x \to 0 \Rightarrow \dfrac{dy}{dx} = -\dfrac{4}{x^2}$ *δx negligible compared with x*

3. $A = \pi r^2 \Rightarrow A = 100\pi\,\text{cm}^2$ when $r = 10\,\text{cm}$

Now $\dfrac{dA}{dr} = 2\pi r$

$\Rightarrow \dfrac{\delta A}{\delta r} = 2\pi r$

i.e. $\delta A = 2\pi r \delta r$ *this tells us that a small change in A is 2πr times a small change in r*

When $\delta r = -0.1 \quad \delta A = 2\pi.10.(-0.1) = -2\pi$ *in this case r = 9·9 cm*

and when $\delta r = 0.1 \quad \delta A = 2\pi.10.0.1 = 2\pi$ *in this case r = 10·1 cm*

and then minimum A is $100\pi - 2\pi = 98\pi\,\text{cm}^2$

and maximum A is $100\pi + 2\pi = 102\pi\,\text{cm}^2$.

4. $v = x^3$

$\dfrac{dv}{dx} = 3x^2$

$\Rightarrow \delta v = 3x^2 \delta x$

$\Rightarrow \delta v = 3 \times 8^2 \times (-0.1)\,\text{cm}^3 \quad \because x = 8 \quad \text{and} \quad \delta x = -1\text{mm} = -0.1\,\text{cm}$

$= -19.2\,\text{cm}^3$

Calculator answer is $-18.96\,\text{cm}^3$. Why the difference?

Answer: In the third line of the solution, we should really have written $\delta v \approx 3x^2 \delta x$. This is important and should be remembered throughout this type of work. The approximation arises through assumptions made. You can clarify this if you find δv from $(x + \delta x)^3 - x^3$, which is accurate. You get $\delta v = 3x^2 \delta x + 3x(\delta x)^2 + (\delta x)^3$.

Ignoring the latter two terms accounts for the discrepancy.

In practice the initial method of solution is correct, just remember

$$\delta v \approx 3x^2 \delta x$$

$$\Rightarrow \delta v \approx -19 \cdot 2 \, \text{cm}^3 \qquad \textit{It is this approximate change which you will be asked to find.}$$

Now apply this to modify question 3.

5. $(y + \delta y)^2 + (x + \delta x)(y + \delta y) + 2(x + \delta x)^2 = 0$ and $y^2 + xy + 2x^2 = 0$

$\Rightarrow y^2 + 2y\delta y + (\delta y)^2 + xy + y\delta x + x\delta y + \delta x\delta y + 2x^2 + 4x\delta x + 2(\delta x)^2 = 0$

Subtracting and dividing by $\delta x \Rightarrow 2y\dfrac{\delta y}{\delta x} + \dfrac{(\delta y)^2}{\delta x} + y + x\dfrac{\delta y}{\delta x} + \delta y + 4x + 2\delta x = 0$

$\Rightarrow (2y + x)\dfrac{dy}{dx} + y + 4x = 0$

$\Rightarrow \dfrac{dy}{dx} = -\dfrac{(y + 4x)}{(2y + x)}$

ANSWERS TO EXERCISE 10.3

Group A

1. $10(2x + 1)^9 \times 2 = 20(2x + 1)^9$

2. $6(5 - 3x)^5 \times -3 = -18(5 - 3x)^5$

3. $3(x^2 + x + 1)^2(2x + 1)$

4. $4\left(2 - \dfrac{1}{x}\right)^3 \times \dfrac{1}{x^2} = \dfrac{4}{x^2}\left(2 - \dfrac{1}{x}\right)^3$

5. $\dfrac{1}{2}\left(x^3 + \dfrac{1}{x^3}\right)^{-1/2} \times \left(3x^2 - \dfrac{3}{x^4}\right) = \dfrac{3}{2}\left(x^3 + \dfrac{1}{x^3}\right)^{-1/2}\left(x^2 - \dfrac{1}{x^4}\right)$

Group B

1. $\frac{1}{2}(3x - 1)^{-1/2} \times 3 = \dfrac{3}{2\sqrt{(3x - 1)}}$

2. $\frac{3}{4}(x^2 + 4)^{-1/4} \times 2x = \dfrac{3x}{2(x^2 + 4)^{1/4}}$

3. $\frac{1}{5}(x^5 - a^5)^{-4/5} \times 5x^4 = \dfrac{x^4}{(x^5 - a^5)^{4/5}}$

4. $\dfrac{5}{3}\left(x-\dfrac{1}{x}\right)^{2/3}\left(1+\dfrac{1}{x^2}\right) = \dfrac{5}{3}\left(x-\dfrac{1}{x}\right)^{2/3}\left(1+\dfrac{1}{x^2}\right)$

5. $7\left(x+1+\dfrac{1}{x}\right)^{6}\left(1-\dfrac{1}{x^2}\right)$

ANSWERS TO EXERCISE 10.4

1. (a) $A = \pi r^2$ $\qquad \dfrac{dA}{dt} = 2\pi r\dfrac{dr}{dt} \quad \Rightarrow \quad \dfrac{dA}{dt} = 2\pi + 20 \times 2 = 80\pi\,\text{cm}^2\,\text{s}^{-1}$

   (b) $C = 2\pi r$ $\qquad \dfrac{dC}{dt} = 2\pi\dfrac{dr}{dt} \quad \Rightarrow \quad \dfrac{dC}{dt} = 2\pi + 2 = 4\pi\,\text{cm s}^{-1}$

2. $V = \pi r^2 h \quad \therefore \dfrac{dV}{dt} = \pi r^2\dfrac{dh}{dt} \quad \Rightarrow \quad 15 = \pi + 5^2 \times \dfrac{dh}{dt} \quad \therefore \dfrac{dh}{dt} = \dfrac{3}{5\pi}\,\text{cm s}^{-1}$

3. $L^2 = y^2 + x^2 \quad \therefore 13^2 = y^2 + x^2$

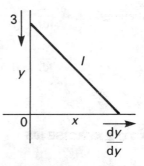

   differentiating w.r.t. t: $\quad \dfrac{d(13^2)}{dt} = \dfrac{d(y^2)}{dy}\dfrac{dy}{dt} + \dfrac{d(x^2)}{dx}\dfrac{dx}{dt}$

   $\Rightarrow 0 = 2y\dfrac{dy}{dt} + 2x\dfrac{dx}{dt}$

   When $x = 5$, $y = 12$ and $\dfrac{dy}{dx} = -3$ ($\because$ in direction of y decreasing)

   $\therefore 0 = 12 \times -3 + 5 \times \dfrac{dx}{dt} \quad \Rightarrow \quad \dfrac{dx}{dt} = \dfrac{36}{5}\,\text{ft/s}.$

> ### Investigation
>
> Now consider the following deduction from this solution and explain. Assume the ladder starts from the vertical.
>
> The upper ends falls 13 feet at 3 ft/s, taking $\frac{13}{3}$ s.
>
> The lower end we have found moves at $\frac{36}{5}$ ft/s.
>
> $\therefore$ in $\frac{13}{3}$ s the lower end moves $\frac{36}{5} \times \frac{13}{3} = 31\frac{1}{5}$ ft.
>
> Then the top of the ladder will be at the foot of the wall and the lower end will be $31\frac{1}{5}$ ft away; but the ladder is only 13 ft long!

4. $V = x^3 \quad \therefore \dfrac{dV}{dt} = 3x^2 \cdot \dfrac{dx}{dt}$

   A value for $\dfrac{dx}{dt}$ is found from: $\quad A = 6x^2 \Rightarrow \dfrac{dA}{dt} = 12x\dfrac{dx}{dt}$

   $\Rightarrow -0 \cdot 5 = 12 \cdot 0 \cdot 75 \cdot \dfrac{dx}{dt}$

$$\Rightarrow \frac{dV}{dt} = 3.0 \cdot 75^2 \cdot \frac{-0 \cdot 5}{12.0 \cdot 75} = -0 \cdot 09 \, \text{cm}^3 \, \text{s}^{-1}$$

5. x is the distance from lamp to man

       L is the length of the shadow.

       Required to find: $\dfrac{dl}{dt}$

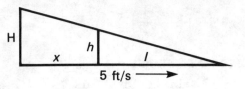

By similar triangles: $\quad \dfrac{l}{h} = \dfrac{l+x}{H}$

$$lH = lh + xh$$

$$l(H - h) = xh \Rightarrow l = \frac{h}{(H-h)} x$$

Differentiating w.r.t. t: $\quad \dfrac{dl}{dt} = \dfrac{h}{(H-h)} \dfrac{dx}{dt}$

$$\therefore \frac{dl}{dt} = \frac{5h}{H-h} \, \text{ft/s} \qquad \because \frac{dx}{dt} = 5 \, \text{ft/s}$$

ANSWERS TO EXERCISE 10.5

Group A

1. $9\left(x^2 + \dfrac{1}{x^2}\right)^8 \left(2x - \dfrac{2}{x^3}\right) = 18\left(x - \dfrac{1}{x^3}\right)\left(x^2 + \dfrac{1}{x^2}\right)^8$

2. $\dfrac{dy}{dx} = 3x^2 - 12x$. TP where $3x^2 - 12x = 0 \Rightarrow x = 0, x = 4$

    $\therefore$ TP at $(0, 9)$ and $(4, -23)$.

    $\dfrac{d^2y}{dx^2} = 6x - 12$.

    When $x = 0 \quad \dfrac{d^2y}{dx^2} < 0 \therefore$ TP at $(0, 9)$ is maximum

    When $x = 4 \quad \dfrac{d^2y}{dx^2} > 0 \therefore$ TP at $(4, -23)$ is minimum

3. $\dfrac{dV}{dx} = \dfrac{dV}{dt} \cdot \dfrac{dt}{dx} \Rightarrow 10x = 30 \bigg/ \dfrac{dx}{dt} \Rightarrow \dfrac{dx}{dt} = \dfrac{30}{10x} = 3$ when $x = 1$

4. $\dfrac{4(x+1)^3(x^2+1) - 2x(x+1)^4}{(x^2+1)^2} = \dfrac{2(x+1)^3\{2(x^2+1) - x(x+1)\}}{(x^2+1)^2} = \dfrac{2(x+1)^3(x^2 - x + 2)}{(x^2+1)^2}$

5. (a) velocity (or speed)   (b) acceleration

6. $3(x^2 + 5x + 7)^2(2x + 5)(2 - x)^4 + 4(2 - x)^3 \cdot -1 \cdot (x^2 + 5x + 7)^3 = (2 - x)^3(x^2 + 5x + 7)^2(2 - 23x - 10x^2)$

7. $V = x^3$ $\dfrac{dV}{dt} = \dfrac{dV}{dx} \cdot \dfrac{dx}{dt} \Rightarrow 24 = 3x^2 \cdot \dfrac{dx}{dt}$ $\therefore \dfrac{dx}{dt} = 2\,\text{cm min}^{-1}$ when $x = 2$.

$A = 6x^2$ $\dfrac{dA}{dt} = \dfrac{dA}{dx} \cdot \dfrac{dx}{dt} \Rightarrow \dfrac{dA}{dt} = 12x \cdot \dfrac{dx}{dt} = 12 \times 2 \times 2 = 48\,\text{cm}^2\,\text{min}^{-1}$.

8. Method 1, using calculus:

   When $x = 0$, $y = 14$.

   $\dfrac{dy}{dx} = 4x - 12 \Rightarrow \dfrac{dy}{dx} = 0$ when $x = 3$

   $\therefore$ TP at $(3, -4)$

   $\dfrac{d^2y}{dx^2} = 4 > 0$

   $\therefore$ TP is minimum

   Method 2, without calculus:

   $y = 2(x^2 - 6x + 7)$
   $= 2\{(x - 3)^2 - 2\}$
   $= 2\{(x - 3)^2 - 2\}$
   $= 2(x - 3)^2 - 4$

   $\therefore$ minimum value is -4 when $x = 3$

   transformation of $y = x^2$

   by 3 units $\rightarrow$,
   2 units $\downarrow$
   and finally scaled by 2

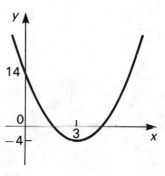

9. $y = 4 = 4x^0 \Rightarrow \dfrac{dy}{dx} = 0 \times 4x^{-1} = 0$

10. $y = (x - 1)^3(x + 3)^4(2x - 1)^2$

    Extending $\dfrac{d(uv)}{dx} = u\dfrac{dv}{dx} + v\dfrac{du}{dx}$ we have

    $\dfrac{d(uvw)}{dx} = vw\dfrac{du}{dx} + uw\dfrac{dv}{dx} + uv\dfrac{dw}{dx}$

    $\therefore \dfrac{dy}{dx} = 3(x - 1)^2(x + 3)^4(2x - 1)^2 + 4(x + 3)^3(x - 1)^3(2x - 1)^2 + 2 \cdot 2(2x - 1)(x - 1)^3(x + 3)^4$

    $= (x - 1)^2(x + 3)^3(2x - 1)\{3(x + 3)(2x - 1) + 4(x - 1)(2x - 1) + 4(x - 1)(x + 3)\}$

    $= (x - 1)^2(x + 3)^3(2x - 1)(18x^2 + 11x - 17)$

Group B

1. $-8\left(2x - \dfrac{2}{x^3}\right)^{-5}\left(1 + \dfrac{3}{x^4}\right) = -8 \cdot 2^{-5}\left(x - \dfrac{1}{x^3}\right)^{-5}\left(1 + \dfrac{3}{x^4}\right) = -\tfrac{1}{4}\left(x - \dfrac{1}{x^3}\right)^{-5}\left(1 + \dfrac{3}{x^4}\right)$

2. maximum at $(2, 90)$, minimum at $(-1, 36)$

3. 2

4. $\dfrac{(x^2 + 3x + 1)^2}{(2x^2 + 1)^2}(8x^3 + 6x^2 + 2x + 9)$

5. $2x - 2$

6. $x = \frac{1}{2}$

7. $8\,\text{cm}^2\,\text{s}^{-1}$

8. (a) $y = x^5 + 3x^3 - 16x$ (b) $y = x^3 + 4x^2 + 4x - 5$

9. $\dfrac{10(2x + 1)^2(2x^3 + x^2 - x + 1)}{(1 - 2x)^3(x^2 + 1)^4}$

10. (a) $17\,\text{m}\,\text{s}^{-}1$ (b) $16\,\text{m}\,\text{s}^{-2}$

Now try worksheets 8 and 9.

Chapter 11

CALCULUS: INTEGRATION

Aims and objectives

Having worked through this chapter, you will:

know the basic rule of integration

$$y = x^3 \Rightarrow \int y\,dx = \frac{x^4}{4} + A$$

be able to integrate functions of the type $af'(x)[f(x)]^n$

$$y = 6x(x^2 + 1)^4 \Rightarrow \int y\,dx = \frac{3}{5}(x^2 + 1)^5 + A$$

know the meaning of integration   summation, area

including definite and indefinite integrals

$$\int_1^3 3x^2\,dx = 26 \quad \text{and} \quad \int 3x^2\,dx = x^3 + A$$

know the meaning of negative areas

be able to find mean values by integration.

mean value of x^2 between $x = 1$ and $x = 3$ is $8\frac{2}{3}$.

Introduction

After a long and detailed look at differentiation in chapter 10, we now have a look at the inverse of differentiation, **integration**. Some A level students may say that integration is a harder topic than differentiation, but it needn't be.

The study of integration does require a different approach from that for differentiation. Differentiation follows certain rules e.g. the rule for differentiating a quotient was given on page 146 and once that rule is known and understood it can be applied to all quotients. In integration we find that there is no equivalent rule for quotients. Different types of quotient have to be recognised and dealt with accordingly. Integration becomes very much a matter of recognising types of functions and remembering how to deal with them. This accumulation of knowledge of types of function takes a long time to build up, but we shall find that it builds up steadily as we work through this book.

This chapter serves only as an introduction to integration and to give it some meaning.

The basic rule

The basic rule for integration can be treated as the inverse of differentiation.

Rule for differentiation   **Example**

x^3

Step 1   multiply by index $3x^3$
Step 2   subtract 1 from the index $3x^2$

The rule for integration is to be formed by carrying out the inverse of Step 2 above and then the inverse of Step 1.

Rule for integration   **Example**

$3x^2$

Inverse Step 2   add 1 to the index $3x^3$

Inverse Step 1   divide by the new index $\dfrac{3x^3}{3} = x^3$

> Similarity here with other inverse work e.g. changing the subject, inverse of function.

e.g. Integrate $2x^4$.

index + 1 $\Rightarrow 2x^5$

$\div$ index $\Rightarrow \dfrac{2x^5}{5}$

> Check by differentiating
> $\dfrac{2x^5}{5}$.

e.g. Integrate $\dfrac{3}{x^2}$.

$\dfrac{3}{x^2} = 3x^{-2}$

index + 1 $\Rightarrow 3x^{-1}$

$\div$ index $\Rightarrow \dfrac{3x^{-1}}{-1} = -3x^{-1} = -\dfrac{3}{x}$

And now an awkward one...

e.g. Integrate $\dfrac{3}{x}$.

$\dfrac{3}{x} = 3x^{-1}$

index + 1 $\Rightarrow 3x^0$

$\div$ index $\Rightarrow \dfrac{3x^0}{0} = \dfrac{3}{0} = \infty$ or something indeterminate.

> **Investigation**
> Using your knowledge of indices show that the integration of 7 is $7x$.

In other words we cannot integrate *at this stage* terms like $\dfrac{a}{x}$. The technique for these will come later.

Using our knowledge of the differential of a constant such as 5, what can we deduce to be the integral of 0 (zero)?

We cannot be precise at this stage but we *can* say it will be a constant, which may include the value 0, because all constants are differentiated to give 0.

> For this reason, we usually include a constant term in our answer.

EXERCISE 11.1

(*Answers on page 169*)

Integrate the following functions and check by differentiating your answers.

Group A

1. $x^5 + 3x$

2. $x^2 + 1 + \dfrac{1}{x^2}$

3. $3x^{1/2} + 4x^{2/3}$

4. $3 - \dfrac{2}{x^2} - \dfrac{1}{x^4}$

5. $(x^2 + 1)^2$

Group B

1. $x^7 + x^3$

2. $\left(x + \dfrac{1}{x}\right)^2$

3. $\sqrt{x} + \sqrt[3]{x}$

4. $\sqrt[4]{x^3} - \dfrac{1}{\sqrt[3]{x^2}}$

5. $\left(x^2 - \dfrac{1}{x^2}\right)^2$

Harder integration: inverse of function of function

Investigation

You should give considerable thought to this next problem. Here are two functions to be integrated.

1. $3x(x^3 + 1)^5$
2. $3x^2(x^3 + 1)^5$

(a) Expansion of the bracket is not allowed
(b) You can only do *one* of these.

Which can you do?

In each case look at the structure of the function and think along the lines of 'what could have been differentiated to give this'? Give yourself 15 minutes on this before you read the next bit.

Another hint: the function of a function rule in differentiation is where you should concentrate your thoughts.

Both functions are products:

1. of the function x and the function $(x^3 + 1)^5$
2. of the function x^2 and the function $(x^3 + 1)^5$.

Is there a link between the two functions in each case?

In function **1** in the investigation above there is not an obvious link but in **2** there is the fact that x^2 is the differential, in principle, of $x^3 + 1$. By *in principal* we mean that differentiating a function of the type $x^3 + 1$ will give a function of the type x^2, putting to the back of our minds for a moment the fact that it is $3x^2$.

Now remember that the function of a function rule in differentiation always produces a product from a single function. Look again at pages 141–2.

All this suggests that $3x^2(x^3 + 1)^5$ may be the result of differentiating something like $(x^3 + 1)^6$.

Well, let's try it!

$$\frac{d}{dx}(x^3 + 1)^6 = 6(x^3 + 1)^5 . 3x^2 = 18x^2(x^3 + 1)^5$$

This result is of the right order but it is six times too big.

$\therefore$ the integration of $3x^2(x^3 + 1)^5$ is $\dfrac{1}{6}(x^3 + 1)^6$.

Go over this last bit again and make sure you have got the idea. This is the first type of integration and it is a very important one.

EXERCISE 11.2

(Answers on page 170)

Look at these differential coefficients: decide which are of the type where the function of a function rule may have been applied to get them.

1. $5x(x^2 + 3)^4$

2. $2(x^3 + 1)^6$

3. $(x + 1)(x^2 + 2x)^7$

4. $(x + 1)(x^2 + 2)^7$

5. $x^3(x^4 + x^2)^8$

6. $\left(1 - \dfrac{1}{x^2}\right)\left(x + \dfrac{1}{x}\right)^{10}$

7. $(x^2 + 3x + 5)^5(4x + 6)$

8. $\left(x^3 + 1 + \dfrac{1}{x^3}\right)\left(3x^2 - \dfrac{3}{x^4}\right)$

This work is slow and it takes time but it is well worth mastering. The ability to look at the structure of a function and realise whether or not one part is the differential of the other is important. (This is called 'integration by inspection'.)

EXERCISE 11.3

(Answers on page 170)

This is the same type as Exercise 11.2. Look at the products and decide which may have been obtained by using the function of a function rule.

1. $x^2(x^3 + 1)^2$

2. $(x^3 + x)^5(x^2 + 1)$

3. $(2x^3 + 3x^2)(x^2 + x)$

4. $(x^4 + 2x^2 + 1)^3(x^3 + x)$

5. $\dfrac{1}{\sqrt{x}}(\sqrt{x} + 2)^4$

6. $5x(x^2 + a^2)^4$

7. $5(x + a)(x^2 + a^2)^4$

8. $(x + a)(x^2 + 2ax)^{-4}$

9. $(2 - x)(4x - x^2)^{-3}$

10. $(x^3 + a^3)^{-2}.x^2$

Before you check through the answers make sure you are quite clear on what you are looking for. In these questions when we talk about one part being the differential of another we mean it is of the *right order*, but not necessarily exactly correct as it stands. Look again at the example on page 160 and notice how the answer being 'out' by a multiple was compensated for: it was necessary to divide by 6. Also look at answers 1, 3 and 7 in Exercise 11.2. In these cases it is necessary to adjust by a factor. In answers 6 and 8 in that exercise one part is exactly the differential of the other.

EXERCISE 11.4

(*Answers on page 170*)

Go through Exercises 11.2 and 11.3 integrating wherever possible.

The meaning of integration – area

It is all very well carrying out these integrations but what meaning does integration have? What have we got when we have done it? Now is the time to find out.

Consider this diagram, where A, P, R and B are on the curve.

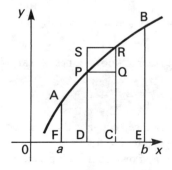

P is any point (x, y) and R is $(x + \delta x, y + \delta y)$ where δx and δy have their usual meanings.

PRCD is a small element of the area ABEF and it is represented by δA.

Now   area PQCD   <   area PRCD   <   area SRCD

$\therefore$ $y.\delta x$ $<$ δA $<$ $(y + \delta y)\delta x$

$\therefore$ y $<$ $\dfrac{\delta A}{\delta x}$ $<$ $y + \delta y$

As $\delta x \to 0$ y $<$ $\dfrac{\mathrm{d}A}{\mathrm{d}x}$ $<$ y

i.e. $\dfrac{\mathrm{d}A}{\mathrm{d}x} = y$

If we integrate both sides $A = $ integral of y w.r.t. x and this is written mathematically as

$$A = \int y\,\mathrm{d}x$$

> $\int$ is the sign for integrate and it is a distortion of the letter s. It means the sum, hence s, of an infinite number of elements.

The integral of a function gives us a value of the *area under the function*.

In this case, which is a general one because the diagram represents a function which has not been defined, we are interested in the area ABEF. We have found a formula in a general sense as

$$A = \int y\,\mathrm{d}x$$

Let us now make our function something specific say $y = 8x - x^2$.

Using the newfound formula: $A = \displaystyle\int y\,\mathrm{d}x$

$$= \int (8x - x^2)\,\mathrm{d}x$$

$$= \frac{8x^2}{2} - \frac{x^3}{3} + c = 4x^2 - \frac{x^3}{3} + c$$

So far so good, but to evaluate the area we need to know values of a and b.

Let them be 2 and 6.

If we substitute 2 in the formula we get $A = \frac{40}{3} + c$

and if we substitute 6 in the formula we get $A = 72 + c$.

What do these two answers mean? They give, respectively, the area under the curve from $x = 0$ to $x = 2$ and from $x = 0$ to $x = 6$.

A more accurate sketch for this example is shown in this diagram.

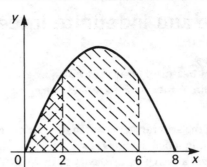

The area from $x = 0$ to $x = 2$ is shaded ///

The area from $x = 0$ to $x = 6$ is shaded \\\\\\

The area we require is that shaded \\\\\\ only and it can be seen that it will be obtained by subtraction:

$$\underset{\underset{0 \text{ to } 6}{\uparrow}}{(72 + c)} \; - \; \underset{\underset{0 \text{ to } 2}{\uparrow}}{(\frac{40}{3} + c)} \; = \; \underset{\underset{2 \text{ to } 6}{\uparrow}}{\frac{176}{3}}$$

Looking carefully at this we can see why the arbitrary constant, c, always disappears in this sort of question.

> Remember this.

Limits

In the last example the values for x of 2 and 6 are known as the **lower** and **upper limits**, a rather obvious name because they define the boundaries or limits of the area in question. We will now rewrite this example in the usual way.

Find the area bounded by the curve $y = 8x - x^2$, the x − axis and the ordinates at $x = 2$ and $x = 6$.

e.g.

$$A = \int_2^6 (8x - x^2)\mathrm{d}x$$

the upper limit here

the lower limit here

> The lower limit is always the lesser value of x and the upper the greater.

$$= \left[\frac{8x^2}{2} - \frac{x^3}{3} \right]_2^6$$

$$= \left[4x^2 - \frac{x^3}{3} \right]_2^6$$

> Notice the absence of the arbitrary constant here. It is not written because it will always cancel out, as explained above.

$$= \underset{\underset{\substack{upper\ limit \\ substituted\ here}}{\uparrow}}{\left(4 \times 6^2 - \frac{6^3}{3} \right)} - \underset{\underset{\substack{lower\ limit \\ substituted\ here}}{\uparrow}}{\left(4 \times 2^2 - \frac{2^3}{3} \right)}$$

$$= 72 - \frac{40}{3}$$

$$= \frac{176}{3}$$

Definite and indefinite integrals

An integral between limits is known as a *definite integral*.
One without limits is an *indefinite integral*.

We can forget the arbitrary constant in the case of definite integrals, but we must include it in indefinite integrals.

This has been a heavy bit of theory at the first reading and it probably seems a bit vague or confused. Don't worry about it. We shall do some examples and an exercise and then it will be time to re-read the theory.

e.g. Evaluate $\int_0^3 (x + 3)\mathrm{d}x$ and explain what you have found.

$$\int_0^3 (x + 3)\mathrm{d}x = \left[\frac{x^2}{2} + 3x \right]_0^3 = \left(\frac{3^2}{2} + 3 \times 3 \right) - (0) = \frac{27}{2}$$

The area between the line $y = x + 3$, the x-axis and ordinates $x = 0$ and $x = 3$ is $\frac{27}{2}$ units.

e.g. Find the area between the curve $y = (x + 4)^3$, the x-axis and the y-axis.

Before we start automatically using the formula it is worth considering the function for a minute. From the work on functions and transformation of them (chapter 9) we can see that $(x + 4)^3$ is x^3 displaced 4 units to the left.

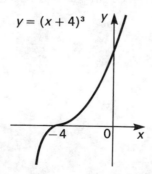

$$y = (x + 4)^3$$

From the diagram it is clear which area is being asked for.

$$A = \int_{-4}^0 (x + 4)^3 \mathrm{d}x = \left[\frac{1}{4}(x + 4)^4 \right]_{-4}^0$$

$$= \left(\frac{1}{4} \times 4^4 \right) - \left(\frac{1}{4} \times 0^4 \right)$$

$$= 64$$

NB $(x + 4)^3$
$= 1 \times (x + 4)^3$

The introduction to this answer is typical of good mathematical technique.

We should always take our time, think carefully about problems and try to find as much as we can, within reason, about the problem in hand.

e.g. The velocity of a particle is given by $v = t^2 + 2$.

Find: (a) the acceleration when $t = 2$ seconds

(b) the distance travelled after 3 seconds

(c) the distance travelled in the third second.

Illustrate all your answers graphically, on the same graph.

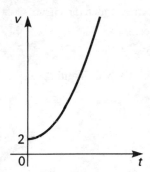

The diagram illustrates the original information i.e. $v = t^2 + 2$.

(a) acceleration $a = \dfrac{dv}{dt}$

$$\therefore a = 2t$$

and when $t = 2$ $a = 2 \times 2 = 4\,\mathrm{m\,s^{-2}}$.

(b) distance $s = \int v\,dt$

$$\therefore s = \int_0^3 (t^2 + 2)\,dt = \left[\frac{t^3}{3} + 2t\right]_0^3$$

$$\therefore s = 15\,\mathrm{m}$$

> Note the limits: from 0 s to 3 s.

(c) $s = \int_2^3 v\,dt$

$$= \left[\frac{t^3}{3} + 2t\right]_2^3$$

$$= 15 - 6\tfrac{2}{3}$$

$$= 8\tfrac{1}{3}\,\mathrm{m}$$

> Again note the limits: the 3rd second is from the end of 2 seconds up to the end of 3 seconds.

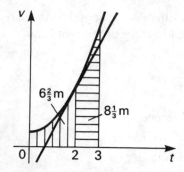

The velocity-time graph illustrates well how all parts of a graph have meaning and are useful:

- distance travelled is represented by the area under the curve
- velocity is represented by the graph itself
- acceleration is represented by the slope.

e.g. Find the area enclosed by the graph $y = x^3$, the x-axis and the ordinates at $x = -3$ and $x = 3$.

The diagram shows the area required.

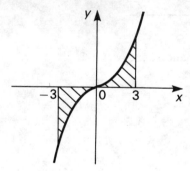

$$A = \int_{-3}^{3} y\,dx = \int_{-3}^{3} x^3\,dx = \left[\frac{x^4}{4}\right]_{-3}^{3}$$

$$\therefore A = \left(\frac{3^4}{4}\right) - \left(\frac{-3^3}{4}\right) = \frac{3^4}{4} - \frac{3^4}{4} = 0$$

$\therefore$ the area is zero!

But we can see that it isn't! The explanation lies in the fact that the area below the x-axis is negative. In this case the area below is the same size as that above and consequently when added they cancel each other out.

This problem highlights one of the pitfalls of finding area by integration and it is something we have to be prepared for. The answer lies in knowing where a given function is zero and hence evaluating separately the areas above and below these points.

The area enclosed is

$$2 \times \frac{3^4}{4} = \frac{81}{2}$$

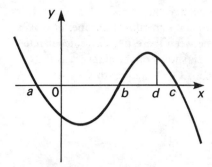

To find the area enclosed in this diagram by the curve and the x-axis we would work out

$\int_b^c y\,dx$ which would be positive, and

$\int_a^b y\,dx$ which would be negative.

The answer would be the numerical values added together.

If we were asked to find the area enclosed by the curve, the axes and the ordinate at $x = d$ we should evaluate

$\int_b^d y\,dx$ and $\int_0^b y\,dx$

and again add, ignoring signs.

We may well ask, 'How can an area be negative?' The answer is simple and we need to refer to the first diagram, on page 161, which is where all this started. If the curve had been drawn below the x-axis then the ordinates would have been negative and the area of the element would have been a negative quantity multiplied by δx, hence a negative area. So, as stated earlier, a negative area means only that it is below the x-axis but we must be careful when combining areas above and below the x-axis.

Mean value

Another, and for now final, application of integration is in using it to find a mean value.

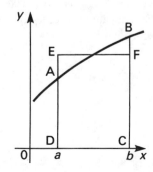

Consider the function shown, particularly the section AB. Over this domain as x goes from a to b the function takes an infinite number of values ranging from AD to BC. Somewhere between these two extremes it must have an **average** or **mean** value. This value is shown on the diagram as ED (or FC) and it is the value such that the area EFCD is equal to area ABCD.

$$ED \times (b - a) = \int_a^b y \, dx$$

$$\text{mean value} = \frac{1}{(b - a)} \int_a^b y \, dx$$

e.g.

Find the mean value of the function $(x + 4)^3$ for the domain $-4 \leqslant x \leqslant 0$.

$$\text{Mean value} = \frac{1}{0 - - 4} \int_{-4}^{0} (x + 4)^3 \, dx$$

$$= \frac{1}{4} \left[\frac{[x + 4]^4}{4} \right]_{-4}^{0} = \frac{1}{4} \times 64 = 16$$

EXERCISE 11.5

(*Answers on page 171*)

1. Evaluate $\int_2^5 (x - 1)^3 \, dx$.

2. Find the mean value of $(x - 1)^3$ as x varies from 2 to 5.

3. Integrate $x(x^2 + 1)^3$ w.r.t. x.

4. If $f(x)$ is an odd function, what is the area it encloses with the x-axis and the ordinates $x = \pm a$?

5. With reference to the curve $y = x^3$, the area enclosed between $x = -3$ and $x = +3$ is $\frac{81}{2}$. What is the value of $\int_{-3}^{3} x^3 dx$?

6. The gradient, m, of a curve is given by $m = 2x + 3$. Find the equation of the curve given that it passes through the origin.

7. The acceleration due to gravity is g ($= 9\cdot8 \, \text{m s}^{-2}$). Find formulae for (a) the velocity (b) the distance of a particle, measured vertically upwards from the ground, given that the initial velocity is u.

Now try worksheets 10 and 11.

This is the second time we have mentioned 'particle', a wonderful creation of mechanics and physics students. A particle may have acceleration, velocity, mass, weight, and it may exert or absorb force! A marvellous invention and very convenient because it has no size!!

Answers to exercises

ANSWERS TO EXERCISE 11.1

Group A

1. Integrating $x^5 + 3x \Rightarrow \dfrac{x^6}{6} + \dfrac{3x^2}{2} + A$

   where A is a constant representing the integration of 0.

   > A is usually called the **arbitrary constant**.

2. $x^2 + 1 + \dfrac{1}{x^2} = x^2 + 1.x^0 + 1.x^{-2}$

   Integrating: $\Rightarrow \dfrac{x^3}{3} + \dfrac{x^1}{1} + \dfrac{x^{-1}}{-1} + A = \dfrac{x^3}{3} + x - \dfrac{1}{x} + A$

   > The middle term of this question explains the investigation you were asked to do on page 158.

3. $3x^{1/2} + 4x^{2/3}$

   Integrating: $\Rightarrow \dfrac{3x^{3/2}}{3/2} + \dfrac{4x^{5/3}}{5/3} + A = 2x^{3/2} + \dfrac{12}{5}x^{5/3} + A$

4. $3 - \dfrac{2}{x^2} - \dfrac{1}{x^4} = 3 - 2x^{-2} - 1x^{-4}$

   Integrating: $\Rightarrow 3x - \dfrac{2x^{-1}}{-1} - \dfrac{x^{-3}}{-3} + A = 3x + \dfrac{2}{x} + \dfrac{1}{3x^3} + A$

5. $(x^2 + 1)^2 = x^4 + 2x^2 + 1$

   Integrating: $\Rightarrow \dfrac{x^5}{5} + \dfrac{2x^3}{3} + x + A$

Group B

1. $\dfrac{x^8}{8} + \dfrac{x^4}{4} + A$

2. $\dfrac{x^3}{3} + 2x - \dfrac{1}{x} + A$

3. $\dfrac{2}{3}x^{3/2} + \dfrac{3}{4}x^{4/3} + A$

4. $\dfrac{4}{7}x^{7/4} - 3x^{1/3} + A$

5. $\dfrac{x^5}{5} - 2x - \dfrac{1}{3x^3} + A$

ANSWERS TO EXERCISE 11.2

1. Yes $\because$ differential of $x^2 + 3$ is $(2)x$

2. No $\because$ differential of $x^3 + 1$ is $(3)x^2$ and x^2 is not in the product

3. Yes $\because$ differential of $x^2 + 2x$ is $2x + 2 = 2(x + 1)$

4. No $\because$ differential of $x^2 + 2$ is $2x$ which won't do (c.f. question 3.)

5. No $\because$ differential of $x^4 + x^2$ is $4x^3 + 2x$ but we only have x^3

6. Yes $\because$ differential of $x + \dfrac{1}{x}$ is $1 - \dfrac{1}{x^2}$

7. Yes $\because$ differential of $x^2 + 3x + 5$ is $2x + 3$ and we have $2(2x + 3)$

8. Yes $\because$ differential of $x^3 + 1 + \dfrac{1}{x^3}$ is $3x^2 - \dfrac{3}{x^4}$

ANSWERS TO EXERCISE 11.3

1. Yes $\because$ x^2 is the differential of $x^3 + 1$

2. No $\because$ the derivative of $x^3 + x$ is $3x^2 + 1$ which is not a multiple of $x^2 + 1$

3. Yes $\because$ the derivative of $2x^3 + 3x^2$ is $6x^2 + 6x = 6(x^2 + 1)$ i.e. a multiple of $x^2 + 1$

4. Yes $\because$ the derivative of $x^4 + 2x^2 + 1$ is $4x^3 + 4x = 4(x^3 + x)$ i.e. a multiple of $x^3 + x$

5. Yes $\because$ the derivative of $\sqrt{x} + 2$ is $\dfrac{1}{2\sqrt{x}}$

6. Yes $\because$ the derivative of $x^2 + a^2$ is $2x$

7. No $\because$ the derivative of $x^2 + a^2$ is not $x + a$ or a multiple of $x + a$

8. Yes $\because$ the derivative of $x^2 + 2ax$ is $2x + 2a = 2(x + a)$

9. Yes $\because$ the derivative of $4x - x^2$ is $4 - 2x = 2(2 - x)$

10. Yes $\because$ the derivative of $x^3 + a^3$ is $3x^2$

ANSWERS TO EXERCISE 11.4

Try (the first stab at an answer)	**Differentiate** (to check if first try is correct)	**Answer** (after adjusting your first try by $\times$ or $\div$).
Ex Exercise 11.2		
1. $(x^2 + 3)^5$	$5.2x(x^2 + 3)^4$	$\frac{1}{2}(x^2 + 3)^5 + A$
3. $(x^2 + 2x)^8$	$8(x^2 + 2x)^7(2x + 2)$	$\frac{1}{16}(x^2 + 2x)^8 + A$
6. $\left(x + \dfrac{1}{x}\right)^{11}$	$11\left(x + \dfrac{1}{x}\right)^{10}\left(1 - \dfrac{1}{x^2}\right)$	$\dfrac{1}{11}\left(x + \dfrac{1}{x}\right)^{11} + A$
7. $(x^2 + 3x + 5)^6$	$6(x^2 + 3x + 5)^5(2x + 3)$	$\frac{1}{3}(x^2 + 3x + 5)^5 + A$

8. $\left(x^3 + 1 + \dfrac{1}{x^3}\right)^2$ $\qquad$ $2\left(x^3 + 1 + \dfrac{1}{x^3}\right)\left(3x^2 - \dfrac{3}{x^4}\right)$ $\qquad$ $\dfrac{1}{2}\left(x^3 + 1 + \dfrac{1}{x^3}\right)^2 + A$

Exercise 11.3

1. $(x^3 + 1)^3$ $\qquad$ $3(x^3 + 1)^2 \cdot 3x^2$ $\qquad$ $\frac{1}{9}(x^3 + 1)^3 + A$
3. $(2x^3 + 3x^2)^2$ $\qquad$ $2(2x^3 + 3x^2)(6x^2 + 6x)$ $\qquad$ $\frac{1}{12}(2x^3 + 3x^2)^2 + A$
4. $(x^4 + 2x^2 + 1)^4$ $\qquad$ $4(x^4 + 2x^2 + 1)^3(4x^3 + 4x)$ $\qquad$ $\frac{1}{16}(x^4 + 2x^2 + 1)^4 + A$

5. $(\sqrt{x} + 2)^5$ $\qquad$ $5(\sqrt{x} + 2)^4 \cdot \dfrac{1}{2\sqrt{x}}$ $\qquad$ $\frac{2}{5}(\sqrt{x} + 2)^5 + A$

6. $(x^2 + a^2)^5$ $\qquad$ $5(x^2 + a^2)^4 \cdot 2x$ $\qquad$ $\frac{1}{2}(x^2 + a^2)^5 + A$
8. $(x^2 + 2ax)^{-3}$ $\qquad$ $-3(x^2 + 2ax)^{-4}(2x + 2a)$ $\qquad$ $-\frac{1}{6}(x^2 + 2ax)^{-3} + A$
9. $(4x - x^2)^{-2}$ $\qquad$ $-2(4x - x^2)^{-3}(4 - 2x)$ $\qquad$ $-\frac{1}{4}(4x - x^2)^{-2} + A$
10. $(x^3 + a^3)^{-1}$ $\qquad$ $-(x^3 + a^3) \cdot 3x^2$ $\qquad$ $-\frac{1}{3}(x^3 + a^3)^{-1} + A$

ANSWERS TO EXERCISE 11.5

1. $\displaystyle\int_2^5 1 \times (x - 1)^3 \, dx = \left[\dfrac{(x - 1)^4}{4}\right]_2^5 = \left(\dfrac{4^4}{4}\right) - \left(\dfrac{1^4}{4}\right) = \dfrac{255}{4}$

2. Mean value $= \dfrac{1}{3}\displaystyle\int_2^5 (x - 1)^3 \, dx = \dfrac{1}{3} \times \dfrac{225}{4}\text{(from question 1)} = \dfrac{85}{4}$

3. $\displaystyle\int x(x^2 + 1)^3 \, dx = \dfrac{1}{8}(x^2 + 1)^4 + c$

4. $A = 2\displaystyle\int_0^a f(x)dx.$ Odd function $\therefore$ rotational symmetry order 2 about O.

$\Rightarrow$ + and − areas of equal magnitude between $-a$ and $+a$.

$\therefore \displaystyle\int_{-a}^a f(x) \, dx = 0$

5. $\displaystyle\int_{-3}^3 x^3 \, dx = 0$

The example question 4 above illustrated the significance of + and − areas but don't think that this answer is impossible. For example, if the function had represented some sort of rate of flow of money against time and the area beneath it the sum of money then the total sum of money between these limits would be zero.

6. $\dfrac{dy}{dx} = 2x + 3 \Rightarrow y = \displaystyle\int(2x + 3)dx = x^2 + 3x + c$

Passes through origin $\therefore$ (0, 0) satisfies $\Rightarrow 0 = 0 + 0 + c \Rightarrow c = 0$

$\therefore$ equation is $y = x^2 + 3x$

7. (a) $\dfrac{\mathrm{d}v}{\mathrm{d}t} = -g \quad -g \; \because$ acceleration acts downwards and we are measuring upwards.

$\therefore v = -gt + c \quad$ When $t = 0,\, v = u$ (given) $\quad \therefore u = 0 + c \quad \therefore c = u$

so $v = u - gt$

(b) $\dfrac{\mathrm{d}s}{\mathrm{d}t} = u - gt$

$\therefore s = ut - \dfrac{gt^2}{2} + B \quad$ When $t = 0,\, s = 0 \quad \therefore 0 = 0 - 0 + B \quad \therefore B = 0$

so $s = ut - \dfrac{gt^2}{2}.$

Chapter 12

TRIGONOMETRY

Aims and objectives

Having worked through this chapter you will:

know what radians are $\qquad\qquad\qquad\qquad$ π rads $= 180°$

be able to work with angles of any size $\pm$ hundreds of degrees, and beyond

know the definitions of sine, cosine and tangent

know the special angles $\qquad\qquad\qquad\qquad$ $0°, 30°, 45°, 60°, 90°$

be able to work with compound angles

$$\sin(A + B) = \sin A \cos B + \cos A \sin B$$

including **double angles** and $\qquad\qquad\qquad$ $\sin 2A = 2 \sin A \cos A$

$\qquad$ **half angles** $\qquad\qquad\qquad\qquad$ $\sin A = 2 \sin\dfrac{A}{2} \cos \dfrac{A}{2}$

be able to factorise the sum or difference of two sines or cosines

$$\sin C + \sin D = 2 \sin \frac{C + D}{2} \cos \frac{C - D}{2}$$

know the small angle approximations $\qquad$ $\sin \theta \approx \theta,\ \cos \theta \approx 1 - \dfrac{\theta^2}{2}$

know three methods for solving trigonometric equations

using $\dfrac{\text{S}\ |\ \text{A}}{\text{T}\ |\ \text{C}}$ $\qquad\qquad\qquad\qquad\qquad$ $\sin \theta = \dfrac{1}{2}$, using $\dfrac{\text{S}\ |\ \text{A}}{\text{T}\ |\ \text{C}}$

$\qquad$ using **graphs** $\qquad\qquad\qquad\qquad\qquad$ $\sin \theta = \dfrac{1}{2}$, using a graph

$\qquad$ using **general solutions** $\qquad\qquad$ $\sin \theta = \dfrac{1}{2}$, using the general solution

be able to solve trigonometric equations of the type $\quad 3 \sin \theta + 4 \cos \theta = 5$

be able to differentiate and integrate trigonometric functions

$$\frac{\text{d}(\sin \theta)}{\text{d}\theta} = \cos \theta, \int \sin \theta \text{d}\theta = -\cos \theta$$

$\qquad$ **and their inverse** $\qquad\qquad\qquad\qquad$ arc $\sin \theta$, $\sin^{-1} \theta$

> The summary tells us that for angles in the second quadrant the sin is $+ve$, the cos and tan are $-ve$.

Radians

You will need a scientific calculator for this and following chapters.

So far we have been used to measuring angles in degrees but now is the time to introduce another measure of angle, the **radian**.

Radians are used more than degrees and as your work progresses you will think of radians more naturally than degrees. Gradians are hardly ever used but they will be explained shortly.

You will have seen radians on your calculator, together with gradians, and wondered, or better still found out, what they are.

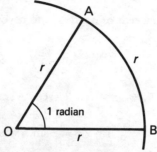

In the diagram, AB is an arc of a circle centre O. In particular, arc AB is of the same length as the radius of the circle, as shown.

The angle AOB is **1 radian**.

The number of radians in one revolution is the number of times _r_ will divide into the circumference.

Investigation

Satisfy yourself that the same size of angle is obtained no matter what the size of _r_.

$$\Rightarrow \frac{2\pi r}{r} = 2\pi$$

$$\therefore 2\pi \text{ radians} = 360°$$

$$\pi \text{ radians} = 180°$$

$$1 \text{ radian} = \frac{180°}{\pi} \approx 57 \cdot 3°.$$

The idea of the radian is not a difficult one to grasp. We need to understand it because we shall not be able to go much further without it.

Gradians

The gradian was an attempt to introduce metric measure into angles. One revolution is divided into 400 equal parts so that $90° = 100$ grads. We do not need to know this measure for A level work.

Investigation

Find out who uses gradians, then let me know!

Angles of any size

Angles may be of any size and they may be negative as well as positive. Just as there are conventions for setting down things such as x and y axes, so there are for angles.

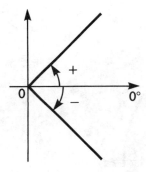

This diagram shows the positive and negative directions for measuring angles from the $0°$ angle.

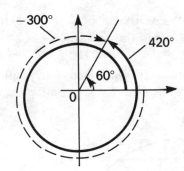

This diagram illustrates angles of any size. The angle shown is basically $60°$ but it also could be $420°$ ($360° + 60°$) or $-300°$, and it could have many other values described as $(360n + 60°)$ where n can take values $0, 1, 2, \ldots$.

This idea of angles of any magnitude may seem a bit odd but it is important, particularly to students of physics and engineering.

It will be useful to complete the following table and learn it or use it for reference.

degrees	°	0	30	45	60	90	120	135	150	180
radians	rad	0	$\dfrac{\pi}{6}$			$\dfrac{\pi}{2}$		$\dfrac{3\pi}{4}$		π

The trigonometry we have done so far can be summed up in the words 'right-angled triangles' or 'sohcahtoa' or 'sailors on holiday can always have tons of ale' or some such. We are now going to look at the subject much more deeply.

Trigonometry is basically the study and application of two functions.

Projections

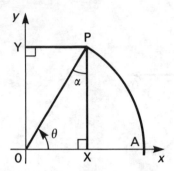

Consider this diagram. OP is a line, of fixed length, rotating about the point O and starting from the position OA. $\hat{PYO} = \hat{PXO} = 90°$. Imagine what happens to OX and OY as OP rotates. Originally OX = OA and OY = 0; then OX decreases as OY increases, and vice-versa.

> **OY is called the *projection* of OP onto the axis O*y***
> **OX is called the *projection* of OP onto the axis O*x*.**

We now turn our attention to the full diagram which shows four positions of OP, suffixed 1, 2, 3, 4 and the corresponding projections on the *x* and *y* axes.

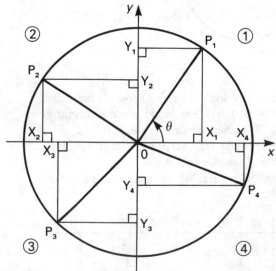

OP is always a positive length but notice what happens to the signs of the projections. They change from positive to negative depending on which quadrant OP is in.

The quadrants are numbered ① to ④ in the direction of the positive angle as shown on the diagram.

Sine, cosine and tangent

Now look at the trigonometric functions.

1. The function **sine** of angle XOP is defined as the ratio

$$\frac{\text{protection on } Oy}{\text{OP}}$$

$$\sin\theta = \frac{\text{OY}}{\text{OP}}$$

2. The function **tangent** of angle XOP is defined as the ratio

$$\frac{\text{projection on } Oy}{\text{projection on } Ox}$$

$$\tan\theta = \frac{\text{OY}}{\text{OX}}$$

So what has happened to the cosine? The cosine function is really the same as the sine. In the diagram the angles θ and α are **complementary** (which means they add up to 90°) and the cosine of angle XOP is defined as

$$\frac{\text{projection on } Ox}{\text{OP}}$$

$$\cos\theta = \frac{\text{OX}}{\text{OP}}$$

But we can see that $\sin\alpha = \dfrac{\text{OX}}{\text{OP}}$

and hence the cosine of an angle is the sine of the complementary angle and the word cosine is an abbreviation of **complementary sine**.

The trigometric functions, sin, cos and tan, are **varying** functions in that they each have a range and a domain like most functions. They are not static formulae, which repeated use of 'sohcahtoa' etc. tends to make us think.

Sine, cosine, tangent of angles of any size

Investigation

Use your calculator to help you draw the graphs of the sine, cosine and tangent functions for values of x from $0°$ to $360°$. (In the case of the tangent your calculator will show E for $90°$ and $270°$ but it will give readings for $89·999999°$ and $90·000001°$.) Having drawn the graphs satisfy yourself that they are >0 or <0 in agreement with the signs of the projections on page 176.

You should conclude that:

(a) the sine >0 for $0° < x < 180°$ and the sine < 0 for $180° < x < 360°$
(b) the cosine >0 for $0° < x < 90°$ and $270° < x < 360°$ and
    the cosine <0 for $90° < x < 270°$
(c) the tangent >0 for $0° < x < 90°$ and $180° < x < 270°$ and
    the tangent <0 for $90° < x < 180°$ and $270° < x < 360°$

This is summarised on a wellknown chart:

② sine is positive	① all functions positive
tangent is positive ③	cosine is positive ④

Which can be further summarised like thus.

S	A
T	C

A scientific calculator will readily give the trigonometric function value of any angle but it is essential to understand where these values come from and how to manipulate them.

Let us consider an angle of $510°$.

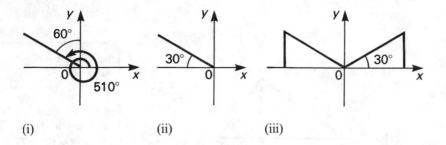

(i) (ii) (iii)

Figure (i) shows an angle of 510° drawn.

Figure (ii) is (i) simplified, introducing the angle of 30° as marked.

Figure (iii) shows the two projections to be the same as for an angle of 30°.

Combining this with the summary above we can now write:

$\sin 510° = \sin 30°$

$\cos 510° = -\cos 30°$

$\tan 510° = -\tan 30°$

> The summary tells us that for angles in the second quadrant the sin is $+ve$, the cos and tan are $-ve$.

EXERCISE 12.1

(*Answers on page 201*)

Express the trigonometric functions of each angle as functions of acute angles.

Group A	Group B
1. 210°	1. 400°
2. 350°	2. −600°
3. −200°	3. 175°
4. 678°	4. −500°
5. 960°	5. 290°

In A level work the main value of trigonometry is in its application to other problems. It is a very useful medium for solving problems in other areas of pure mathematics, in mechanics, in physics and technology. That is why so far we have concentrated on building up the reservoir of basic knowledge and that is why we continue to do so now as we look at two simple rules concerning the application of trigonometry to triangles.

Sine rule

In $\triangle$ ADC: $\sin C = \dfrac{h}{b}$

$\Rightarrow b\sin C = h$

In $\triangle$ ADB: $\sin B = \dfrac{h}{c}$

$\Rightarrow c\sin B = h$

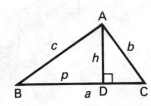

From these two results $b\sin C = c\sin B \Rightarrow \dfrac{b}{\sin B} = \dfrac{c}{\sin C}$

In a similar way it can be shown that $\dfrac{a}{\sin A} = \dfrac{b}{\sin B}$

Hence

$$\frac{a}{\sin A} = \frac{b}{\sin B} = \frac{c}{\sin C}$$

   This is the **sine rule** which is a rule connecting the sides and angles of any triangle. It is a collection of three equations in one rule, and we can only use one at a time in practice.

They are: $\dfrac{a}{\sin A} = \dfrac{b}{\sin B}$ $\dfrac{b}{\sin B} = \dfrac{c}{\sin C}$ $\dfrac{c}{\sin C} = \dfrac{a}{\sin A}$

This diagram shows the **circumcircle** of $\triangle$ ABC and from the diagram we have $\sin F = \dfrac{c}{2R}$

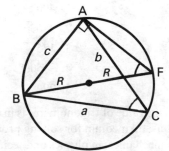

but $\hat{F} = \hat{C}$ (angles in same segment)

$\Rightarrow \sin C = \dfrac{c}{2R}$

$\therefore 2R = \dfrac{c}{\sin C}$

which gives us a fourth but seldom used part to the sine rule.

$$\frac{a}{\sin A} = \frac{b}{\sin B} = \frac{c}{\sin C} = 2R$$

Cosine rule

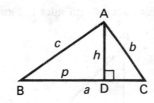

And now for the second rule.

In $\triangle$ ABD: $c^2 = p^2 + h^2$ (*Pythagoras' theorem*)

and in $\triangle$ ACD: $b^2 = (a-p)^2 + h^2$ (*Pythagoras' theorem*)
$$(CD = CB - DB = a - p)$$

Subtracting: $b^2 - c^2 = a^2 - 2ap$

$\therefore$ $b^2 = a^2 + c^2 - 2ap$ **1**

Now in $\triangle$ ADB: $\cos B = \dfrac{p}{c}$

$\therefore$ $p = c\cos B$

> This result is the extension to Pythagoras' theorem in which p is the projection of c onto a. Used to be in O level long ago. Not now.

Substituting for p in **1** we get

$$b^2 = a^2 + c^2 - 2ac\cos B \quad \text{which is the \textbf{cosine rule},}$$

and again this is a rule using only the sides and angles of the triangle. We shall use these two rules shortly, but before we do a note on some commonly used ratios and ones which you must know.

Angles of 0°, 30°, 45°, 60°, 90°

$\triangle$ ABC is equilateral, with side 2 units.

$AM \perp BC \therefore MC = 1$ and $AM = \sqrt{3}$

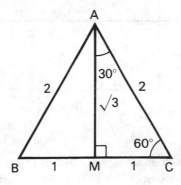

from the diagram, $\sin 30° = \dfrac{1}{2}$ $\cos 30° = \dfrac{\sqrt{3}}{2}$ $\tan 30° = \dfrac{1}{\sqrt{3}}$

$\quad\quad\quad\quad\quad\quad\quad\sin 60° = \dfrac{\sqrt{3}}{2}$ $\cos 60° = \dfrac{1}{2}$ $\tan 60° = \sqrt{3}$

Δ PQR is right-angled isosceles with sides 1, 1 and $\sqrt{2}$.

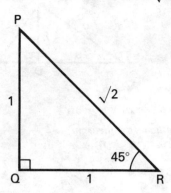

From the diagram, $\sin45° = \dfrac{1}{\sqrt{2}}$ $\cos45° = \dfrac{1}{\sqrt{2}}$ $\tan45° = 1$

The following table summarises these results. Learn it.

Angle / Trig ratio	0 / 0	30° / $\dfrac{\pi}{6}$	45° / $\dfrac{\pi}{4}$	60° / $\dfrac{\pi}{3}$	90° / $\dfrac{\pi}{2}$
sin	0	$\dfrac{1}{2}$	$\dfrac{1}{\sqrt{2}}$	$\dfrac{\sqrt{3}}{2}$	1
cos	1	$\dfrac{\sqrt{3}}{2}$	$\dfrac{1}{\sqrt{2}}$	$\dfrac{1}{2}$	0
tan	0	$\dfrac{1}{\sqrt{3}}$	1	$\sqrt{3}$	∞

EXERCISE 12.2

(*Answers on page 202*)

1. A ship P leaves harbour on a bearing of 040° at 15 knots. Ship Q leaves at the same time on a bearing of 150° at 10 knots. Find their distance apart after 1 hour and the bearing of Q from P at the same time.
2. In a triangle ABC $a = 7$, $c = 5$, $C = 33°$. Solve the triangle (find the other sides and angles).
3. A pyramid stands on a rectangular base ABCD where AB = 6 ft and BC = 8 ft. The vertex of the pyramid is 12 ft above the centre of the base.

Find:

(a) the length of a sloping edge

(b) the angle an edge makes with the base

(c) the angle each sloping face makes with the base

(d) the angle between opposite pairs of sloping faces.

Compound angles

An expression which occurs frequently throughout science is one such as $\sin(A + B)$ and we shall now look at what we can do with this.

One thing we *cannot* do is to say $\sin(A + B) = \sin A + \sin B$.

This is yet another popular mistake.

With reference to the diagram:

$$\sin(A + B) = \frac{PS}{PO} = \frac{PQ + QS}{PO}$$

$$= \frac{PR\cos A + OR\sin A}{PO}$$

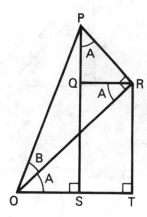

$$\because \cos A = \frac{PQ}{PR}$$

$$\text{and } \sin A = \frac{RT}{OR} = \frac{QS}{OR}$$

$$= \frac{PO\sin B\cos A + PO\cos B\sin A}{PO}$$

$$= \sin B\cos A + \cos B\sin A$$

Hence $\sin(A + B) = \sin A\cos B + \cos A\sin B$

$$\because \sin B = \frac{PR}{PO}$$

$$\text{and } \cos B = \frac{RO}{PO}$$

This is the first of many such statements which you need to know. In fact this list of trigonometric statements constitutes the biggest block of learning within the course. They often appear on reference leaflets which are issued at examinations but you would be making a big mistake if you did not bother to learn them because they are on the leaflets: you will not be able to use them efficiently if you do not know them. They are all listed on page 185. You must read through the notes preceding them before you attempt to learn them.

Formulae

Notes:
These refer to the list of formulae which follows.

(a) These are all identities which means they are true for any values of A, B, C and D.

(b) Rule **1** has been derived in the text: you will not be expected to know the derivation. That one has been done only as an example.

(c) There is a definite pattern about these identities. Look at it and let it help you to remember them.

(d) Proofs of rules **14** and **15**: you should know these.

(i) $\quad \dfrac{\sin A}{\cos A} = \dfrac{a/b}{c/b} = \dfrac{a}{c} = \tan A \qquad \therefore \tan A = \dfrac{\sin A}{\cos A}$

(ii) $\quad \sin^2 A + \cos^2 A = \left(\dfrac{a}{b}\right)^2 + \left(\dfrac{c}{b}\right)^2 = \dfrac{a^2 + c^2}{b^2} = \dfrac{b^2}{b^2} = 1$

$\therefore \sin^2 A + \cos^2 A = 1$

> **Note:**
>
> $(\sin A)^2$ is written $\sin^2 A$, $(\tan\theta)^n$ is written $\tan^n\theta$.

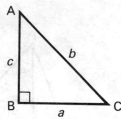

Using $\sin^2 A + \cos^2 A = 1$ you should be able to account for the three versions of $\cos 2A$ (rule **8**).

(e) Derivation of rule **10**.

Adding **1** + **2** $\Rightarrow \sin(A + B) + \sin(A - B) = 2\sin A\cos B$

Now let $\left. \begin{array}{l} A + B = C \\ \\ \text{and} \quad A - B = D \end{array} \right\} \Rightarrow$

$2A = C + D \quad$ i.e. $\quad A = \dfrac{C + D}{2}$

$2B = C - D \qquad B = \dfrac{C - D}{2}$

Substituting for A and B:

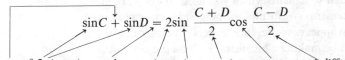

$$\sin C + \sin D = 2\sin\dfrac{C + D}{2}\cos\dfrac{C - D}{2}$$

sum of 2 sines is equal to twice sine semi-sum cos semi-difference.

(f) The reciprocals of sin, cos and tan are cosec, sec and cot respectively. Although not as frequently used as the original functions they must be known.

Compound angle formulae

1. $\sin(A + B) = \sin A \cos B + \cos A \sin B$
2. $\sin(A - B) = \sin A \cos B - \cos A \sin B$
3. $\cos(A + B) = \cos A \cos B - \sin A \sin B$
4. $\cos(A - B) = \cos A \cos B + \sin A \sin B$
5. $\tan(A + B) = \dfrac{\tan A + \tan B}{1 - \tan A \tan B}$
6. $\tan(A - B) = \dfrac{\tan A - \tan B}{1 + \tan A \tan B}$

Double angle formulae

7. $\sin 2A = 2\sin A \cos A$ *obtained by putting A = B in 1*
8. $\cos 2A = \cos^2 A - \sin^2 A$ *obtained by putting A = B in 3*
   $= 2\cos^2 A - 1$
   $= 1 - 2\sin^2 A$
9. $\tan 2A = \dfrac{2\tan A}{1 - \tan^2 A}$ *obtained by putting A = B in 5*

Factorisation formulae

10. $\sin C + \sin D = 2\sin \dfrac{C + D}{2} \cos \dfrac{C - D}{2}$

11. $\sin C - \sin D = 2\sin \dfrac{C - D}{2} \cos \dfrac{C + D}{2}$

12. $\cos C + \cos D = 2\cos \dfrac{C + D}{2} \cos \dfrac{C - D}{2}$

13. $\cos C - \cos D = 2\sin \dfrac{C + D}{2} \sin \dfrac{C - D}{2}$

14. $\tan A = \dfrac{\sin A}{\cos A}$

15. $\sin^2 A + \cos^2 A = 1$

> In rules **10–13** the $+/-$ of two terms has been expressed as a product, hence factorisation.

Three further trigonometric functions

16. $\text{cosecant } x = \dfrac{1}{\sin x}$ $\operatorname{cosec} x = \dfrac{1}{\sin x}$

17. $\text{secant } x = \dfrac{1}{\cos x}$ $\sec x = \dfrac{1}{\cos x}$

18. $\text{cotangent } x = \dfrac{1}{\tan x}$ $\cot x = \dfrac{1}{\tan x}$

> **Investigation**
>
> Rules **16-18** are three further trigonometric functions.
> Investigate their graphs.

General solutions

19. General solution of $\sin x = c$ is $x = n\pi + (-1)^n \alpha$, where n is any integer

$\boxed{\alpha = \sin^{-1}c \text{ or arc } \sin c}$

20. General solution of $\cos x = c$ is $x = 2n\pi \pm \alpha$, where n is any integer

$\boxed{\alpha = \cos^{-1}c \text{ or arc } \cos \cos c}$

21. General solution of $\tan x = c$ is $x = n\pi + \alpha$, where n is any integer

$\boxed{\alpha = \tan^{-1}c \text{ or arc } \tan c}$

Small angle approximations

Investigation

Complete the following table.

x in degrees	0	0·5	1	1·5	2	2·5	3	3·5	4
x in radians	0	0·009							0·07
$\sin x$	0	0·009							0·07
x rads $-\sin x$	0	-1×10^{-7}							$5{\cdot}6 \times 10^{-5}$

Calculator sequence:

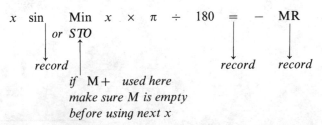

x sin   Min x $\times$ π $\div$ 180 $=$ $-$ MR
      or *STO*

record   *record*   *record*

if M+ *used here*
make sure M is empty
before using next x

Comment on the values in the last row of the table.

You should have found that $\sin x \approx x$ with the important condition that x is in radians. As you will see shortly this is an important result.

Carry out a similar investigation for $\tan x$ and $\cos x$.

Trigonometric equations

Trigonometric equations occur quite often and now is the time to look at them.

e.g. Solve $2\sin x = 1$ for $0° \leqslant x < 360°$. *tells you answers wanted in degrees*

$\sin x = \frac{1}{2}$

$\Rightarrow x = 30°$ *but we must look for other solutions where* $\sin x = +\frac{1}{2}$

$\Rightarrow$ also gives $x = 150°$

$\therefore$ solutions are $30°$ and $150°$.

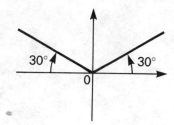

e.g. Solve $\tan x - 1 = 0$ for $0 \leqslant x < 4\pi$. *tells you answers wanted in radians*

$\tan x = +1$

$\Rightarrow x = \dfrac{\pi}{4}, \dfrac{5\pi}{4}, \dfrac{9\pi}{4}, \dfrac{13\pi}{4}$

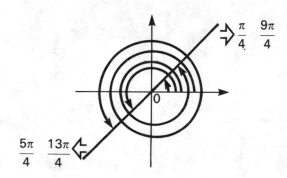

e.g. Solve $2\cos x + 1 = 0$ for $0° \leqslant x \leqslant 360°$.

Instead of using the $\dfrac{S \mid A}{T \mid C}$ method it is possible to use the graphs drawn in the investigations on pages 178 and 185.

The graphs should look like those below.

$2\cos x + 1 = 0$

$\Rightarrow \cos x = -\frac{1}{2}$

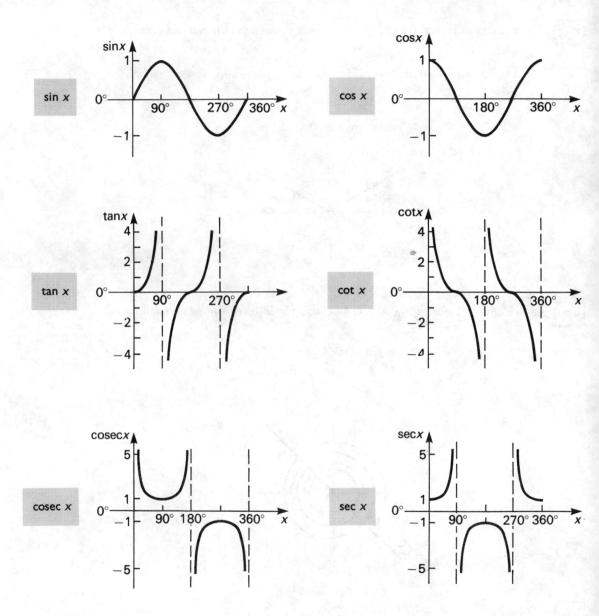

The cos graph tells us the angles are between 90° and 270°.

The value $\frac{1}{2}$ $\Rightarrow$ an angle of 60°.

In this case the angle is 60° either side of 180° $\Rightarrow$ 120° and 240°.

Trigonometric graphs

It is a good idea to become familiar with the sin, cos and tan graphs particularly.

Note:

> **sin x – odd function – periodic, period 360° or 2π rad**
>
> **cos x – even function – periodic, period 360° or 2π rad and**
>
> $$\cos x = \sin\left(x+\frac{\pi}{2}\right) \text{ i.e. } \sin x \text{ translated } \frac{\pi}{2} \text{ to the left}$$
>
> **tan x – odd function – periodic, period 180° or π rad**

We can see that there are two parts to solving a trigonometric equation:
(a) the sign of the ratio
(b) the modulus of the ratio leading to an acute angle.
In determining the solutions this angle is added or subtracted to 0° or 180° according to the sign in part (a).

e.g. Solve the equation $3\cos 2x - \cos x + 2 = 0$ for $0° \leqslant x \leqslant 360°$.

$3\cos 2x - \cos x + 2 = 0$

$\cos 2x$ in this equation presents a complication and we must deal with that first.

From the identities $\cos 2x = 2\cos^2 x - 1$

∴ the equation becomes $3(2\cos^2 x - 1) - \cos x + 2 = 0$

$$6\cos^2 x - 3 - \cos x + 2 = 0$$
$$6\cos^2 x - \cos x - 1 = 0 \quad \textit{a quadratic in } \cos x$$
$$(3\cos x + 1)(2\cos x - 1) = 0$$
$$\Rightarrow \cos x = -\tfrac{1}{3} \quad \text{or} \quad \cos x = \tfrac{1}{2}$$

$\cos x = -\tfrac{1}{3} \Rightarrow$ angles between 90° and 270° using 70·5°

i.e. $180° - 70·5° = 109·5°$
and $180° + 70·5° = 250·5°$

$\cos x = \tfrac{1}{2} \Rightarrow$ angles between 0 and 90° and between 270° and 360° using 60°

i.e. $0 + 60° = 60°$
and $360° - 60° = 300°$

∴ the solutions are 60°, 109·5°, 250·5° and 300°.

Investigation

Draw the graphs of $2\sin x$, $\sin^2 x$, $\sin 2x$, $\sin x$ on one diagram and compare them. This can be very well done using a microcomputer.

e.g. Solve the equation $5\sin x = 4$ for $-2\pi \leqslant x \leqslant 2\pi$.

$\sin x = \frac{4}{5} \Rightarrow$ angles between 0 and π *from graph*

and angles between -2π and $-\pi$ using 0·9 rad.   *using period of 2π*

$\therefore$ the solutions are $x = 0 + 0{\cdot}9, \pi - 0{\cdot}9, -2\pi + 0{\cdot}9, -\pi - 0{\cdot}9$

or $x = 0{\cdot}9, 2{\cdot}2, -5{\cdot}4, -4$ rad.

EXERCISE 12.3

(*Answers on page 206*)

Solve the following equations giving solutions as specified.

1. $3\cos x = 2 \quad 0° \leqslant x \leqslant 360°$

2. $3\tan x + 1 = 0 \quad -\pi < x \leqslant \pi$

3. $4\sin^2 x = 1 \quad 0 \leqslant x \leqslant 4\pi$

4. $5\tan 2x + 2 = 0 \quad -\pi < x < \pi$ (solve first for $2x$)

5. $5\cos 3x = 3 \quad -180° < x \leqslant 180°$

6. $4\sin 2x = 1 \quad 0 \leqslant x < 360°$

7. $6\tan^2 x - \tan x - 1 = 0 \quad 0 \leqslant x < 2\pi$

8. $3\sin(x + 30°) = 2 \quad 0° \leqslant x \leqslant 300°$

9. $2\cos\dfrac{x}{2} + 1 = 0 \quad 0 \leqslant x \leqslant 2\pi$

10. $\operatorname{cosec}\dfrac{x}{3} = 5 \quad 0° \leqslant x < 360°$

General solutions

We have found the pattern and repetition in solutions to trigonometric equations and we can make use of that pattern to summarise solutions.

e.g. Solve the equation $\sin x = c$.

We obviously cannot obtain a numerical value for x but let us suppose the value $x = \alpha$ satisfies the equation. Some of the solutions are illustrated here.

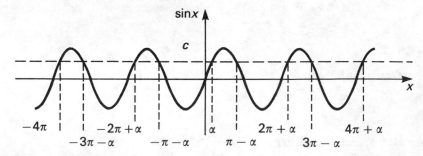

These solutions, and all the others not shown, can be summarised in the statement:

$x = n\pi + (-1)^n\alpha$, where n is any integer.

Check by substituting $n = 0, 1, 2, -1, -2$ etc.

Notice particularly the device for making the 'α' term positive or negative.

When n is odd $(-1)^n = -1$ and when n is even $(-1)^n = 1$.

Remember this technique. It occurs frequently in this subject. The solution $x = n\pi + (-1)^n\alpha$, where n is any integer is called the **general solution** to $\sin x = c$. Check that we would get the same result if we had chosen
$c < 0$.

Now find the general solutions for $\cos x = c$ and $\tan x = c$ by a similar method. Results for all three are in the list on page 186.

EXERCISE 12.4

(*Answers on page 206*)

Write down the general solutions to the questions in Exercise 12.3.
This does lead to a third approach to solving these equations.

e.g. Solve the equation $\sin x = 0.7$ for $-2\pi \leqslant x \leqslant 2\pi$.

$\sin x = 0.7 \Rightarrow x = 0.8$ rad

The general solution is $x = n\pi + (-1)^n 0.8$

Substitute values of n:

$n = 0 \quad \Rightarrow x = 0.8$
$n = 1 \quad \Rightarrow x = \pi - 0.8 = 2.3$
$n = 2 \quad \Rightarrow x = 2\pi + 0.8 \quad$ *outside required range*
$n = -1 \Rightarrow x = -\pi - 0.8 = -3.9$
$n = -2 \Rightarrow x = -2\pi + 0.8 = -5.5$
$n = -3 \Rightarrow x = -3\pi - 0.8 \quad$ *outside range*

$\therefore$ the solutions are $x = -5.5, -3.9, 0.8, 2.3$ rad

We now have three approaches to solving a trigonometric equation.

1. Use the $\dfrac{S \mid A}{T \mid C}$ system.

2. Use the graphs as a guide to the solutions.

3. Use the general solution.

You should know them all but you will certainly develop a favourite method.

Equations of form $a\sin\theta + b\cos\theta = c$

There is another type of trigonometric equation which is not difficult to solve and it involves an interesting method.

| e.g. |

Solve the equation $3\sin\theta + 5\cos\theta = 4$.

In the final stage this equation can be solved in the ways we already know but only after the form of the LHS has been changed.

Let $3\sin\theta + 5\cos\theta \equiv R\sin(\theta + \alpha)$, where R and α are constants. We are now going to convert it to a single sine function.

$\therefore 3\sin\theta + 5\cos\theta \equiv R\sin\theta\,\cos\alpha + R\cos\theta\,\sin\alpha$ *using rule 1 on p. 185.*

Then $3 = R\cos\alpha$ and $5 = R\sin\alpha$ *using the properties of an identity*

Squaring and adding:

$\Rightarrow 9 + 25 = R^2\cos^2\alpha + R^2\sin^2\alpha = R^2(\cos^2\alpha + \sin^2\alpha) = R^2$

$\therefore R^2 = 34$ $R = 5\cdot8$ *taking positive root*

Dividing: $\Rightarrow \dfrac{5}{3} = \dfrac{R\sin\alpha}{R\cos\alpha} = \tan\alpha$ $\therefore \alpha = \text{arc tan}\dfrac{5}{3} = 59°$

Now we can write the original equation as:

$5\cdot8\sin(\theta + 59°) = 4$ $\Rightarrow \sin(\theta + 59°) = \dfrac{4}{5\cdot8}$

$\Rightarrow \theta + 59° = 43\cdot6°$ *taking the primary solution*

General solution: $\theta + 59° = 180n + (-1)^n 43\cdot6°$

i.e. $\theta = 180n + (-1)^n 43\cdot6° - 59°$

When forming your identity in the first place if you have

$a\underline{\sin x} + b\underline{\cos x}$ use $R\sin(x + \alpha)$

$\qquad\qquad\qquad\qquad \because R\sin(x + \alpha) = R\underline{\sin x}\cos\alpha \underline{+} R\underline{\cos x}\sin\alpha$

$a\underline{\sin x} - b\underline{\cos x}$ use $R\sin(x - \alpha)$

$\qquad\qquad\qquad\qquad \because R\sin(x - \alpha) = R\underline{\sin x}\cos x \underline{-} R\underline{\cos x}\sin\alpha$

$a\underline{\cos x} - b\underline{\sin x}$ use $R\cos(x + \alpha)$

$\qquad\qquad\qquad\qquad \because R\cos(x + \alpha) = R\underline{\cos x}\cos\alpha \underline{-} R\underline{\sin x}\sin\alpha$

The underlined factors and signs must balance in each case.

EXERCISE 12.5

(*Answers on page 207*)

Group A

1. Solve the equation $2\sin\frac{1}{2}x + 1 = 0$ for $0 \leqslant x < 2\pi$.

2. Find the maximum and minimum value of $3\sin x + 4\cos x$.

3. Find the general solution of the equation $\sec^2 x - 2\tan x = 0$.

4. Solve the equation $3\sin x - 2\cos x = 1$ for $0° \leqslant x < 360°$.

5. Find the range of values of c for the equation
   $2\cos x - 5\sin x = c$ to have real solutions.

Group B

1. Find the general solution of the equation $4\tan x - 2\sec x = 3$.

2. Solve the equation $5\cos^2(\theta + \dfrac{\pi}{3}) = 4$ for $-\pi < \theta < \pi$.

3. In the equation $cp^2 + 2p - c = 0$ you are given that $p = \tan\theta$.
   Show that $c = \tan 2\theta$.

4. Find the range of values of a for $a\cos x - 5\sin x = 7$ to have real solutions.

5. ADE is a rigid wire bent to form a right angle at D, with AD $= 7$ cm and DE $= 9$ cm. AB is a fixed line.

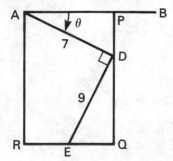

The wire is pivoted at A and rotated, as shown, through a varying angle θ. In each case the rectangle ARQP is completed. Find the maximum perimeter of the rectangle.

Differentiation of sin x from first principles

We now turn our attention to differentiation and integration associated with trigonometry. We begin by differentiating $\sin x$ from first principles.

$$y = \sin x$$
$$y + \delta y = \sin(x + \delta x)$$
$$\therefore \delta y = \sin(x + \delta x) - \sin x$$

$$\therefore \delta y = 2\cos\left(\frac{2x + \delta x}{2}\right)\sin\frac{\delta x}{2} \quad \textit{using rule 11 page 185}$$

Now $\sin\dfrac{\delta x}{2} \approx \dfrac{\delta x}{2}$ with the important condition that x is in radians

(*Investigation, page 186*)

$$\therefore \delta y = 2\frac{\delta x}{2}\cos\frac{(2x + \delta x)}{2}$$

$$\Rightarrow \frac{\delta y}{\delta x} = \cos\frac{(2x + \delta x)}{2}$$

$\delta x + 0$ we have $\dfrac{dy}{dx} = \cos x$

$$\frac{d(\sin x)}{dx} = \cos x$$

By a similar method it is easy to show that:

$$\frac{d(\cos x)}{dx} = -\sin x$$

If $y = \tan x$

then $y = \dfrac{\sin x}{\cos x}$ *a quotient and we use the quotient rule*

and $\dfrac{dy}{dx} = \dfrac{\cos^2 x + \sin^2 x}{\cos^2 x} = \dfrac{1}{\cos^2 x} = \sec^2 x$

$$\frac{d(\tan x)}{dx} = \sec^2 x$$

and similarly:

$$\frac{d(\cot x)}{dx} = -\mathrm{cosec}^2 x$$

If $y = \sec x$

$y \quad = \dfrac{1}{\cos x}$ *again a quotient*

$\dfrac{dy}{dx} \quad = \dfrac{\sin x}{\cos^2 x} = \dfrac{1}{\cos x}.\dfrac{\sin x}{\cos x} = \sec x \,.\, \tan x$

$$\frac{d(\sec x)}{dx} = \sec x \,.\, \tan x$$

and similarly:

$$\frac{d(\operatorname{cosec} x)}{dx} = -\operatorname{cosec} x . \cot x$$

We have now covered the basic six trigonometric functions and we move on to the inverses of some of them.

$$y = \sin^{-1} x$$
$$\Rightarrow \sin y = x$$
$$\cos y \frac{dy}{dx} = 1$$
$$\frac{dy}{dx} = \frac{1}{\cos y} = \frac{1}{\sqrt{\cos^2 y}} = \frac{1}{\sqrt{1 - \sin^2 y}} = \frac{1}{\sqrt{1 - x^2}}$$

$$\frac{d(\sin^{-1} x)}{dx} = \frac{1}{\sqrt{1 - x^2}}$$

Similarly:

$$\frac{d(\cos^{-1} x)}{dx} = -\frac{1}{\sqrt{1 - x^2}} \qquad \frac{d(\tan^{-1} x)}{dx} = \frac{1}{1 + x^2}$$

To establish a full understanding of this work you should now go back and wherever a result has been written following the word *similarly* you should prove it for yourself. The results have been listed below.

This list can be read two ways:
- from left to right for differentiation
- from right to left for integration.

$$\xrightarrow{\textit{differentiate}}$$
$$\xleftarrow{\textit{integrate}}$$

1. $\sin x$ $\cos x$
2. $\cos x$ $-\sin x$
3. $\tan x$ $\sec^2 x$
4. $\sec x$ $\sec x \tan x$
5. $\operatorname{cosec} x$ $-\operatorname{cosec} x \cot x$
6. $\cot x$ $-\operatorname{cosec}^2 x$

7. $\sin^{-1}x$ $\qquad \dfrac{1}{\sqrt{1-x^2}}$

8. $\cos^{-1}x$ $\qquad -\dfrac{1}{\sqrt{(1-x^2)}}$

9. $\tan^{-1}x$ $\qquad \dfrac{1}{1+x^2}$

EXERCISE 12.6

(*Answers on page 208*)

Group A

1. Differentiate $2\tan x$ w.r.t. x.
2. Differeniate $\tan^2 x$ w.r.t. x.
3. Integrate $\dfrac{2}{1+x^2}$ w.r.t. x.
4. Differentiate $x\sin x$ w.r.t. x.
5. Differentiate $\sin x \tan x$ w.r.t. x.

Group B

1. Integrate $\dfrac{5}{\sqrt{(1-x^2)}}$ w.r.t. x.
2. Differentiate $\operatorname{cosec}^2 x$ w.r.t. x.
3. Differentiate $\sin^{-1}2x$ w.r.t. x.
4. Integrate $\operatorname{cosec}^2 x$ w.r.t. x.
5. Integrate $\dfrac{3}{1+9x^2}$ w.r.t. x.

Integration using inverse functions

The differentiation of the inverse trigonometric functions, **7**, **8** and **9** at the top of this page, opens up the way to the integration of some quite complex algebraic functions.

Let us reconsider questions like B3 and B5 from Exercise 12.6 in more general terms.

If $y = \sin^{-1}px$ then $\dfrac{dy}{dx} = \dfrac{p}{\sqrt{1-p^2x^2}}$

If we are asked to integrate

$$\frac{k}{\sqrt{1 - k^2 x^2}} \quad \text{we would say, correctly,} \quad \sin^{-1} kx + A.$$

But what if the question was to find $\int \dfrac{k}{\sqrt{1 - p^2 x^2}} \, \mathrm{d}x$?

A little manipulation gives us:

$$\int \frac{k}{p} \cdot \frac{p}{\sqrt{1 - p^2 x^2}} \, \mathrm{d}x = \frac{k}{p} \cdot \sin^{-1} px + A$$

e.g. Integrate $\dfrac{2}{\sqrt{1 - 9x^2}}$ w.r.t. x.

$$\int \frac{2}{\sqrt{1 - 9x^2}} \, \mathrm{d}x = \int \frac{2}{3} \cdot \frac{3}{\sqrt{1 - 9x^2}} \, \mathrm{d}x = \frac{2}{3} \sin^{-1} 3x$$

Now what if the question was to find $\int \dfrac{k}{\sqrt{a - x^2}} \, \mathrm{d}x$?
A little manipulation gives us

$$\int \frac{k}{a \sqrt{1 - \dfrac{x^2}{a}}} \, \mathrm{d}x$$

> **Remember**
>
> We said in the early days that our algebraic manipulation had to be good!

$$\because \sqrt{a - x^2} = (a - x^2)^{1/2} = \left[a \left(1 - \frac{x^2}{a} \right) \right]^{1/2} = a^{1/2} \left(1 - \frac{x^2}{a} \right)^{1/2}$$

$$= \sqrt{a} \sqrt{\left(1 - \frac{x^2}{a} \right)}$$

and the integration is $k \sin^{-1} \dfrac{x}{\sqrt{a}}$.

e.g. Find $\int \dfrac{5}{\sqrt{9 - x^2}} \, \mathrm{d}x$.

$$\int \frac{5}{\sqrt{9 - x^2}} \, \mathrm{d}x = \int \frac{5}{3 \sqrt{1 - x^2/9}} \, \mathrm{d}x = \int \frac{5}{3 \sqrt{1 - (x/3)^2}} \, \mathrm{d}x = 5 \sin^{-1} \frac{x}{3} + A$$

The important part of all this is that we are talking about integrating functions of the form $\dfrac{a}{\sqrt{b - cx^2}}$, where a, b and c are constants. The particular features that we have to recognise are:

1. the constant on top
2. the square root below
3. the minus sign within the root

4. the variable appearing as x^2 after the minus sign.

The principles behind the whole of pages 196 and 197 can be repeated in the case of integrals of such functions as $\dfrac{p}{q + rx^2}$ which lead to a $\tan^{-1}$ solution.

In this case the features we notice are:

1. the constant on top
2. the plus sign below
3. the variable appearing as second degree (x^2).

 Find $\displaystyle\int \dfrac{9}{16 + x^2}\,\mathrm{d}x$.

Inspection of the function gives us:

● constant over constant plus x^2

∴ integral is of the form $\tan^{-1}$.

We now manipulate as necessary.

$$\int \frac{9}{16 + x^2}\,\mathrm{d}x = \int \frac{9}{16(1 + (x/4)^2)}\,\mathrm{d}x = \frac{9}{16}\int \frac{1}{1 + (x/4)^2}\,\mathrm{d}x$$

$$= \frac{9}{16}.4\tan^{-1}\frac{x}{4} + A$$

It would be reasonable to think $\displaystyle\int \frac{1}{1 + (x/4)^2}\,\mathrm{d}x = \tan^{-1}\frac{x}{4}$

But differentiating $\tan^{-1}\dfrac{x}{4}$ gives $\dfrac{1}{4}.\dfrac{1}{1 + (x/4)^2}$

and it is because of this that the integral is $\quad 4\tan^{-1}\dfrac{x}{4}$.

$$\therefore \int \frac{9}{16 + x^2}\,\mathrm{d}x = -\frac{9}{4}\tan^{-1}\frac{x}{4} + A$$

The ideas behind this approach to integration are those which we have used before, particularly in Exercise 11.4. It is only the functions which are different.

Now let's try a harder example.

 Find $\displaystyle\int \dfrac{1}{x^2 + 4x + 5}\,\mathrm{d}x$.

We have not met this type of denominator before, or have we?

What is it?

Quadratic!

And what have we previously shown quadratics to be transformations of?

Can this be manipulated?

$$\int \frac{1}{x^2 + 4x + 5} dx = \int \frac{1}{(x+2)^2 + 1} dx = \int \frac{1}{1 + (x+2)^2} dx$$

$$= \tan^{-1}(x+2) + A$$

> x^2

> You may need to revise 'completing the square' at this point.

e.g. Find $\int \frac{1}{\sqrt{(6x - x^2 - 5)}} dx$.

> First thoughts: $-$ sign before x^2, completing the square, $\sqrt{} \ \therefore \ \sin^{-1}$.

Work first on $6x - x^2 - 5$.

$$6x - x^2 - 5 = -(x^2 - 6x + 5) = -((x-3)^2 - 4) = 4 - (x-3)^2$$

$$= 4\left\{1 - \left(\frac{x-3}{2}\right)^2\right\}$$

$$\therefore \int \frac{1}{\sqrt{(6x - x^2 - 5)}} dx = \int \frac{1}{\sqrt{4\left\{1 - \left(\frac{x-3}{2}\right)^2\right\}}} dx \qquad \text{which is the form we want}$$

$$- \int \frac{1}{2\sqrt{1 - \left(\frac{x-3}{2}\right)^2}} dx$$

Then $\int \frac{1}{2\sqrt{\left(1 - \left(\frac{x-3}{2}\right)^2\right)}} dx = \sin^{-1}\left(\frac{x-3}{2}\right) + A$

EXERCISE 12.7

(*Answers on page 209*)

Group A

1. Differentiate $\sin^2\theta \cos 2\theta$ w.r.t. θ.

2. Find $\int (\sec^2 x \tan x) dx$.

3. Integrate $\frac{x}{\sqrt{1 - x^2}}$ w.r.t. x.   (*Be careful!*)

4. Find the value of $\int_0^1 \frac{1}{\sqrt{16 - 9x^2}} dx$.

5. Find $\int \frac{1}{x^2 + 4x + 13} dx$.

Group B

1. Integrate $\sin^3 x \cos x$ w.r.t. x.

2. Find $\displaystyle\int \frac{1}{\sqrt{2x - x^2}}\,dx$.

3. Differentiate $\sin^{-1}\cos x$ w.r.t. x.

4. Evaluate $\displaystyle\int_0^5 \frac{1}{25 + x^2}\,dx$.

5. Find $\displaystyle\int \frac{k}{\sqrt{k^2 - x^2}}\,dx$.

Group C

Integrate the following.

1. $\displaystyle\int_0^3 \frac{1}{9 + x^2}\,dx$

2. $\displaystyle\int_0^1 \frac{2}{\sqrt{4 - x^2}}\,dx$

3. $\displaystyle\int \frac{1}{\sqrt{5 + 4x - x^2}}\,dx$

4. $\displaystyle\int \frac{2x}{\sqrt{1 - 4x^2}}\,dx$

5. $\displaystyle\int \frac{1}{x^2 - 6x + 10}\,dx$

Group D

Integrate the following.

1. $\displaystyle\int -\frac{3}{\sqrt{1 - x^2}}\,dx$

2. $\displaystyle\int \frac{a}{1 + a^2 x^2}\,dx$

3. $\displaystyle\int \frac{1}{9x^2 - 12x + 5}\,dx$

4. $\displaystyle\int \frac{\sec^2 x}{\sqrt{1 - \tan x}}\,dx$

5. $\displaystyle\int (7 - 30x - 25x^2)^{-1/2}\,dx$

Answers to exercises

ANSWERS TO EXERCISE 12.1

Group A

1.

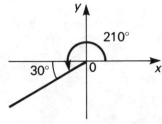

$$\sin 210° = -\sin 30°$$
$$\Rightarrow \cos 210° = -\cos 30°$$
$$\tan 210° = +\tan 30°$$

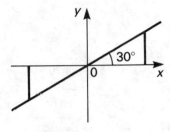

2.

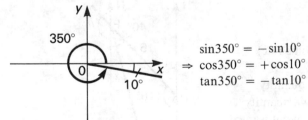

$$\sin 350° = -\sin 10°$$
$$\Rightarrow \cos 350° = +\cos 10°$$
$$\tan 350° = -\tan 10°$$

3.

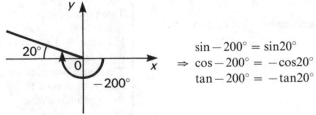

$$\sin -200° = \sin 20°$$
$$\Rightarrow \cos -200° = -\cos 20°$$
$$\tan -200° = -\tan 20°$$

4.

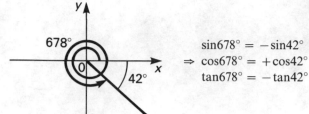

$$\sin 678° = -\sin 42°$$
$$\Rightarrow \cos 678° = +\cos 42°$$
$$\tan 678° = -\tan 42°$$

5.

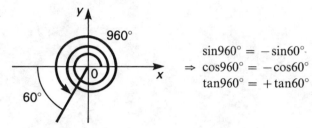

$$\sin 960° = -\sin 60°$$
$$\Rightarrow \cos 960° = -\cos 60°$$
$$\tan 960° = +\tan 60°$$

Group B

1. $+\sin 40°$	2. $+\sin 60°$	3. $+\sin 5°$	4. $-\sin 40°$	5. $-\sin 70°$
$+\cos 40°$	$-\cos 60°$	$-\cos 5°$	$-\cos 40°$	$+\cos 70°$
$+\tan 40°$	$-\tan 60°$	$-\tan 5°$	$+\tan 40°$	$-\tan 70°$.

ANSWERS TO EXERCISE 12.2

1. ΔPHQ is not right-angled.

∴ sohcahtoa is out.

Next try the sine rule (it is easier to use than the cosine rule).

Ⓐ $\quad \dfrac{p^{\checkmark}}{\sin P}^{\times} = \dfrac{h^{?}}{\sin H}^{\checkmark} = \dfrac{q^{\checkmark}}{\sin Q}^{\times}$

$\checkmark$ means known quantity

$\times$ means unknown quantity

? means unknown but wanted

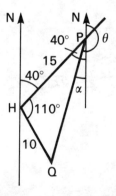

From this no equation can be formed with only one unknown, so it does not help us.

We can here deduce the test to decide if the sine rule can be used.

Looking at Ⓐ it is clear that if we are to form a useful equation we must know at least one angle and the side opposite to it.

> Two points to remember:
> 1. 1 knot = 1 sea mile per hour.
> 2. 3 figure bearings are always measured from the north clockwise.

Try using the cosine rule.

$$h^2 = p^2 + q^2 - 2pq\cos H$$
$$h^2 = 10^2 + 15^2 - 2 \times 10 \times 15 \times \cos 110°$$
$$= 100 + 225 - 300 \times \cos 110°$$
$$= 325 - 300 \times \cos 110°$$
$$= 325 + 300 \times \cos 70°$$
$$\therefore h = 20{\cdot}7\,\text{m}$$

> Normal practice would be to put this line in the calculator but the following highlights a popular mistake:
>
> $325 - 300\cos 110°$
> $= 25\cos 110°$.
>
> You won't make it, will you?

The bearing of Q from P is the angle marked θ and $\theta = 180° + \alpha$, $\alpha = 40° - H\hat{P}Q$.

$\therefore$ find $H\hat{P}Q$ which is P in Ⓐ .

Hence $\dfrac{p}{\sin P} = \dfrac{h}{\sin H}$

$\dfrac{10}{\sin P} = \dfrac{20{\cdot}7}{\sin 110°}$

$\therefore \quad \sin P = \dfrac{10\sin 110°}{20{\cdot}7}$

$\therefore \quad P = 27°$

$\therefore$ bearing of Q from P is 193°.

2. There is more to this question than meets the eye, as we shall see!

Angle and side opposite known, so we use sine rule.

$\dfrac{a}{\sin A} = \dfrac{c}{\sin C} \Rightarrow \dfrac{7}{\sin A} = \dfrac{5}{\sin 33°}$

$\therefore \sin A = \dfrac{7 \times \sin 33°}{5}$

$\therefore \sin A = 0{\cdot}762$

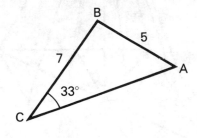

> This is called the ambiguous case.

$\Rightarrow A = 49{\cdot}7°$ or $A = 130{\cdot}3°$ $\therefore \sin 130{\cdot}3° = \sin 49{\cdot}7° = 0{\cdot}762$

the obvious answer which the calculator gives

the easily lost answer which you have to be aware of and which the calculator does not give

This means that there are two answers. It is possible to make two triangles using the initial information. We now have

$$\frac{b}{\sin 97 \cdot 3°} = \frac{5}{\sin 33°}$$

$$\therefore \quad b = 9 \cdot 1$$

$$\frac{b}{\sin 16 \cdot 7°} = \frac{5}{\sin 33°}$$

$$b = 2 \cdot 6$$

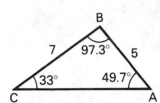

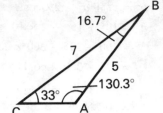

3. There is always a problem in trying to represent a three-dimensional situation in two dimensions. You need to form a mental picture in your mind of what the three-dimensional diagram would look like.

This diagram represents a view from above, looking down with AD in the foreground and BC to the rear. The technique with problems like these is to identify on your main diagram the things you want to find and then to extract the appropriate triangles, usually right-angled.

(a) We wish to find VD: it is the hypotenuse in ΔVOD. VO is known but not OD. From the main diagram OD is the hypotenuse in ΔPOD.

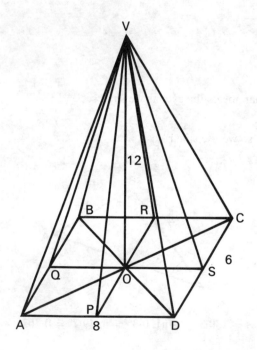

OD = 5   (3, 4, 5Δ – Pythagoras)

Transferring this value to ΔVOD we have

VD = 13   (5, 12, 13Δ – Pythagoras)

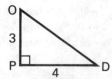

(b) Angle required is VD̂O and from △VDO we have
   $\tan V\hat{D}O = \frac{12}{5} = 2{\cdot}4$
   $\therefore V\hat{D}O = \tan^{-1} 2{\cdot}4$
   or $V\hat{D}O = \arctan 2{\cdot}4$
   $\therefore V\hat{D}O = 67{\cdot}4°$.

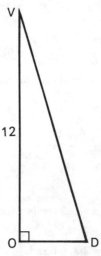

Both these are read as: VD̂O is the angle whose tangent is 2·4. Both notations are used, and both appear on calculators, and the first is probably the more popular. However it does cause much confusion and there is a move to using the 'arc tan' notation rather than the 'tan⁻¹' notation.

Popular mistake:

$$\tan^{-1} 2{\cdot}4 = \frac{1}{\tan 2{\cdot}4}$$

(c) The angle the face VCD makes with the base is VŜO. Angles between planes are not always easy to see. The angle between two planes is the angle between two lines, which meet in the line of intersection of the planes and they must both be at right angles to the line of intersection. In this case VS and OS are in the two planes, they meet at S in the line of intersection, CD, and they are both perpendicular to CD. Hence
   $V\hat{S}O = \arctan\frac{12}{4} = 71{\cdot}6°$
   ∴ face VCD makes 71·6° with the base and similarly VBA makes 71.6° with the base.

For the face VBC the angle required is VR̂O.

$V\hat{R}O = \arctan\frac{12}{3} = 76°$

∴ faces VBC and VAD both make 76° with the base.

(d) The angle between faces VBA and VCD is QV̂S.

$Q\hat{V}S = 2 \times O\hat{V}S = 2 \times (90° - 71{\cdot}6°) = 2 \times 18{\cdot}4° = 36{\cdot}8°$

The angle between faces VBC and VAD is RV̂P.

$R\hat{V}P = 2 \times R\hat{V}O = 2 \times (90° - 76°) = 2 \times 14° = 28°$

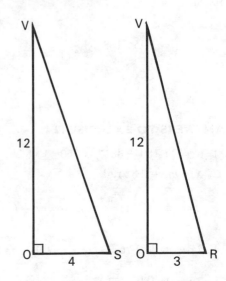

ANSWERS TO EXERCISE 12.3

1. $48 \cdot 2°$, $311 \cdot 8°$

2. $2 \cdot 82$ rad, $5 \cdot 96$ rad

3. $\dfrac{\pi}{6}$ $(0 \cdot 52)$, $\dfrac{5\pi}{6}$ $(2 \cdot 6)$, $\dfrac{7\pi}{6}$ $(3 \cdot 7)$, $\dfrac{11\pi}{6}$ $(5 \cdot 7)$, $\dfrac{13\pi}{6}$ $(6 \cdot 8)$, $\dfrac{17\pi}{6}$ $(8 \cdot 9)$, $\dfrac{19\pi}{6}$ $(9 \cdot 9)$, $\dfrac{23\pi}{6}$ (12)

> Answers are often easily given in multiples of π.

4. $2x = -3 \cdot 52°, -0 \cdot 38°, 2 \cdot 76°, 5 \cdot 9°$,   *these angles are outside the range but*

   $\Rightarrow$ $x = -1 \cdot 76°, -0 \cdot 19°, 1 \cdot 38°, 2 \cdot 95°$

5. $3x = -413 \cdot 1°, -306 \cdot 9°, -53 \cdot 1°, 53 \cdot 1°, 306 \cdot 9°, 413 \cdot 1°$
   $\Rightarrow$ $x = -137 \cdot 7°, -102 \cdot 3°, -17 \cdot 7°, 17 \cdot 7°, 102 \cdot 3°, 137 \cdot 7°$.

6. $2x = 14 \cdot 5°, 165 \cdot 5°, 374 \cdot 5°, 525 \cdot 5°$

   $\Rightarrow$ $x = 7 \cdot 25°, 82 \cdot 75°, 187 \cdot 25°, 262 \cdot 75°$

7. $6\tan^2 x - \tan x - 1 = 0$ *this is a quadratic in* $\tan x$.

   $\Rightarrow (3\tan x + 1)(2\tan x - 1) = 0$

   $\Rightarrow \tan x = -\frac{1}{3} \Rightarrow x = \pi - 0 \cdot 3, 2\pi - 0 \cdot 3 \Rightarrow x = 2 \cdot 8, 6 \cdot 0$ rad.

   or $\tan x = \frac{1}{2} \Rightarrow x = 0 \cdot 5, \pi + 0 \cdot 5 \Rightarrow x = 0 \cdot 5, 3 \cdot 6$ rad.

8. $x + 30° = 41 \cdot 8°, 138 \cdot 2°$

   $\Rightarrow x \quad = 11 \cdot 8°, 108 \cdot 2°$

9. $\dfrac{x}{2} = \dfrac{2\pi}{3}$ $(2 \cdot 1)$, $\dfrac{4\pi}{3}$ $(4 \cdot 2)$

   $\Rightarrow x = \dfrac{4\pi}{3}$ $(4 \cdot 2)$, $\dfrac{8\pi}{3}$ $(8 \cdot 4)$ i.e. $x = \dfrac{4\pi}{3}$ *is the only solution in the required range.*

10. $\sin \dfrac{x}{3} = \dfrac{1}{5}$

   $\Rightarrow \dfrac{x}{3} = 11 \cdot 5°, 168 \cdot 5°$

   $x = 34 \cdot 5°$ *only solution*

ANSWERS TO EXERCISE 12.4

1. $x = 2n . 180 \pm 48 \cdot 2° = 360n \pm 48 \cdot 2°$

2. $x = n\pi + 2 \cdot 82$ rad

> $n\pi - 0 \cdot 32$ rad would do but it is more usual to use the positive angle wherever possible.

3. $x = n\pi + (-1)^n \dfrac{\pi}{6}$ and $x = n\pi + (-1)^n \dfrac{7\pi}{6}$ rad

4. $2x = n\pi + 2 \cdot 76 \Rightarrow x = \dfrac{n\pi}{2} + 1 \cdot 38$ rad

5. $3x = 2n . 180 \pm 53 \cdot 1° \Rightarrow x = 120n \pm 17.7°$

6. $2x = 180n + (-1)^n 14 \cdot 5° \Rightarrow x = 90n + (-1)^n 7 \cdot 25°$

7. $x = n\pi - 0 \cdot 3$ and $x = n\pi + 0 \cdot 5$

8. $x + 30° = 180n + (-1)^n 41 \cdot 8° \Rightarrow x = 180n + (-1)^n 41 \cdot 8° - 30°$

9. $\dfrac{x}{2} = 2n\pi \pm \dfrac{2\pi}{3} \Rightarrow x = 4n\pi \pm \dfrac{4\pi}{3}$

10. $\dfrac{x}{3} = n\pi + (-1)^n 11 \cdot 5° \Rightarrow x = 540° + (-1)^n 34 \cdot 5°$

ANSWERS TO EXERCISE 12.5

Group A

solving for $\frac{1}{2}x$ firstly

1. $\sin\dfrac{1}{2}x = \dfrac{1}{2} \quad \therefore \dfrac{1}{2}x = \dfrac{7\pi}{6}, \dfrac{11\pi}{6} \Rightarrow x - \dfrac{7\pi}{3}, \dfrac{11\pi}{3}$ $\therefore$ no solutions

2. $3\sin x + 4\cos x \equiv R\sin(x + \alpha) \Rightarrow 3 = R\cos\alpha, 4 = R\sin\alpha \Rightarrow 5 = R$

   $\therefore 3\sin x + 4\cos x \equiv 5\sin(x + \alpha) \Rightarrow$ maximum value $= 5$ $\because$ maximum sine is 1

   minimum value $= -5$ $\because$ minimum sine is -1

3. $\sec^2 x - 2\tan x = 0$

   From $\sin^2 x + \cos^2 x = 1$ we have $\dfrac{\sin^2 x}{\cos^2 x} + \dfrac{\cos^2 x}{\cos^2 x} = \dfrac{1}{\cos^2 x}$

   i.e. $\tan^2 x + 1 = \sec^2 x$

   $\therefore$ equation becomes $\tan^2 x + 1 - 2\tan x = 0$

   $(\tan x - 1)^2 = 0$

   $\Rightarrow \tan x = 1 \Rightarrow x = \dfrac{\pi}{4}$

   The general solution is $x = n\pi + \dfrac{\pi}{4}$

4. $3\sin x - 2\cos x = 1$ $\quad 3\sin x - 2\cos x \equiv R\sin(x - \alpha)$

   $\Rightarrow 3 = R\cos\alpha, 2 = R\sin\alpha$

   $\Rightarrow R = \sqrt{13}$ and $\alpha = \tan^{-1}\frac{2}{3} = 33 \cdot 7°$

   $\therefore \sqrt{13}\sin(x - 33 \cdot 7°) = 1$

   $\sin(x - 33 \cdot 7°) = \dfrac{1}{\sqrt{13}}$

   $\therefore x - 33 \cdot 7° = 16 \cdot 1°, 163 \cdot 9°$

   $\therefore x = 49 \cdot 8°, 197 \cdot 6°$

5. $2\cos x - 5\sin x \equiv R\cos(x + \alpha)$
   $\Rightarrow 2 = R\cos x, \ 5 = R\sin\alpha \quad \Rightarrow R = \sqrt{29}$

   $\therefore \sqrt{29}\cos(x + \alpha) = c \quad \Rightarrow \cos(x + \alpha) = \dfrac{c}{\sqrt{29}}$

   for real solutions $-1 \leqslant \dfrac{c}{\sqrt{29}} \leqslant 1 \quad \therefore -\sqrt{29} \leqslant c \leqslant \sqrt{29}$

Group B

1. $x = n\pi + (-1)^n 0\cdot 64$ rad
2. $\theta = -1\cdot 51, \ -0\cdot 59, \ 1\cdot 63$ rad
4. $a > 4\cdot 9$
5. $34\cdot 9$ cm

ANSWERS TO EXERCISE 12.6

Group A

1. $\dfrac{d(2\tan x)}{dx} = 2\sec^2 x$

2. $\dfrac{d(\tan^2 x)}{dx} = 2\tan x \sec^2 x \quad$ *function of a function rule*

3. $\displaystyle\int \dfrac{2}{1 + x^2}\,dx = 2\tan^{-1}x + A$

4. $\dfrac{d(x\sin x)}{dx} = \sin x + x\cos x \quad$ *product rule*

5. $\dfrac{d(\sin x \tan x)}{dx} = \cos x \tan x + \sin x \sec^2 x = \sin x + \sin x \sec^2 x = \sin x (1 + \sec^2 x)$

Group B

1. $5\sin^{-1}x + A$
2. $-2\csc^2 x \cot x$

3. $\dfrac{2}{\sqrt{1 - 4x^2}}$

4. $-\cot x + A$
5. $\tan^{-1} 3x + A$

ANSWERS TO EXERCISE 12.7

Group A

1. $\dfrac{d}{d\theta}(\sin^2\theta\cos2\theta) = 2\sin\theta\cos\theta\cos2\theta - 2\sin2\theta\sin^2\theta = \sin2\theta\cos2\theta - 2\sin2\theta\sin^2\theta$

$\qquad = \sin2\theta(\cos2\theta - 2\cos^2\theta) = \sin2\theta(2\cos^2\theta - 1 - 2\cos^2\theta) = -\sin2\theta$

2. $\displaystyle\int \sec^2 x\tan x\,dx = \tfrac{1}{2}\tan^2 x + A$

> Remember: $\sec^2 x$ is the differential of $\tan x$.

3. $\displaystyle\int \dfrac{x}{\sqrt{1-x^2}}\,dx = -\sqrt{1-x^2} + A$

> The differential of $f(x)]^{1/2}$ always leads to $\dfrac{f'(x)}{f(x)]^{1/2}}$ and that is what we have in this case. Be aware of this and don't confuse it with the $\sin^{-1}$ type.

4. $\displaystyle\int_0^1 \dfrac{1}{\sqrt{16-9x^2}}\,dx = \int_0^1 \dfrac{1}{4\sqrt{1-\left(\dfrac{3x}{4}\right)^2}}\,dx = \left[\dfrac{1}{3}\sin^{-1}\left(\dfrac{3x}{4}\right)\right]_0^1 = \left(\dfrac{1}{3}\sin^{-1}\dfrac{3}{4}\right) - (0) = 0\cdot28$

5. $\displaystyle\int \dfrac{1}{x^2+4x+13}\,dx = \int \dfrac{1}{(x+2)^2+9}\,dx = \int \dfrac{1}{9\left(1+\left(\dfrac{x+2}{3}\right)^2\right)}\,dx = \dfrac{1}{3}\tan^{-1}\left(\dfrac{x+2}{3}\right) + A$

Group B

1. $\tfrac{1}{4}\sin^4 x + A$

2. $-\sin^{-1}(1-x) + A$

3. $\dfrac{-\sin x}{\sqrt{1-\cos^2 x}} + A = -1 + A$

> *Alternatively*: $y = \sin^{-1}\cos x \Rightarrow \sin y = \cos x = \sin\left(\dfrac{\pi}{2} - x\right)$
>
> $\therefore y = \dfrac{\pi}{2} - x$ and $\dfrac{dy}{dx} = -1$.
>
> This also illustrates that the integral can take different forms
>
> e.g. $\displaystyle\int -1\,dx = -x + A$
>
> you would never think of saying $\sin^{-1}\cos x + A$.

4. $\dfrac{\pi}{20}$

5. $k\sin^{-1}\left(\dfrac{x}{k}\right) + A$

Group C

1. $\displaystyle\int_0^3 \dfrac{1}{9+x^2}\,dx = \int_0^3 \dfrac{1}{9\left(1+\left(\dfrac{x}{3}\right)^2\right)}\,dx = \left[\dfrac{1}{3}\tan^{-1}\dfrac{x}{3}\right]_0^3 = \dfrac{\pi}{12}$

2. $\displaystyle\int_0^1 \frac{2}{\sqrt{4-x^2}}\,dx = \int_0^1 \frac{2}{2\sqrt{1-\left(\frac{x}{2}\right)^2}} = \left[2\sin^{-1}\frac{x}{2}\right]_0^1 = \frac{\pi}{3}$

3. $\displaystyle\int \frac{1}{\sqrt{5+4x-x^2}}\,dx = \int \frac{1}{\sqrt{9-(x-2)^2}}\,dx = \int \frac{1}{3\sqrt{1-\left(\frac{x-2}{3}\right)^2}}\,dx = \sin^{-1}\left(\frac{x-2}{3}\right) + A$

4. $\displaystyle\int \frac{2x}{\sqrt{1-4x^2}}\,dx = -\tfrac{1}{2}\sqrt{1-4x^2} + A$

5. $\displaystyle\int \frac{1}{x^2-6x+10}\,dx = \int \frac{1}{1+(x-3)^2}\,dx = \tan^{-1}(x-3) + A$

Group D

1. $\displaystyle\int -\frac{3}{\sqrt{1-x^2}}\,dx = -3\sin^{-1}x + A$

2. $\displaystyle\int \frac{a}{1+a^2x^2}\,dx = \tan^{-1}(ax) + A$

3. $\displaystyle\int_{2/3}^1 \frac{1}{9x^2-12x+5}\,dx = \int_{2/3}^1 \frac{1}{(3x-2)^2+1}\,dx = \left[\frac{1}{3}\tan^{-1}(3x-2)\right]_{2/3}^1 = \frac{\pi}{12}$

4. $\displaystyle\int \frac{\sec^2 x}{\sqrt{1-\tan x}}\,dx = \sqrt{1-\tan x} + A$

5. $\displaystyle\int (7-30x-25x^2)^{-1/2}\,dx = \int \frac{1}{(16-(3+5x)^2)^{1/2}}\,dx = \int \frac{1}{4\left(1-\left(\frac{3+5x}{4}\right)^2\right)^{1/2}}\,dx = \frac{1}{5}\sin^{-1}\left(\frac{3+5x}{4}\right) + A$

Now try worksheets 12, 13 and 14.

Chapter 13

SERIES

Aims and objectives

Having worked through this chapter you will:

know and be able to apply Maclaurin's expansion

$$f(x) = f(0) + f'(0).x + f''\frac{(0)}{2}.x^2 + \ldots$$

know the series for sin x

$$\sin x = x - \frac{x^3}{3!} + \frac{x^5}{5!} - \ldots$$

and cos x

$$\cos x = 1 - \frac{x^2}{2!} + \frac{x^4}{4!} - \ldots$$

know and be able to use binomial theorem

$$(1 + ax)^x = 1 + nax + n\frac{(n-1)}{2}(ax)^2 + \ldots$$

understand permutations and combinations
$$_nP_r \text{ and } _nC_r \text{ or } \binom{n}{r}$$

understand finite and infinite series

know Pascal's triangle

know when the binomial theorem is valid

    know and be able to work with arithmetic progressions
$$1 + 4 + 7 + 10 + \ldots$$

and **geometric progressions**.
$$1 + 3 + 9 + 27 + \ldots$$

Introduction

When we expand $(x + y)^2$ we get $x^2 + 2xy + y^2$, a **series of terms**. This is a very simple example of a series, and it is a **finite series** because it has a finite number of terms, three.

    If we consider the problem of the bug, wishing to cross the road, which always manages to jump half the distance it is trying to jump, when does it get to the other side? The answer theoretically is never, but it does get nearer. If we wrote down all the distances jumped and added an infinite number of them together you would get a distance equal to the width of the road. Such a series (the jumps) is **infinite** in number but the **total is finite**.

    On the other hand if all the paving stones in London were numbered and one grain of sand was put on the first one, two on the second, four on the third, and so on we should have something approaching an infinite series because of the large number of stones. The total number of grains of sands would approach the infinite.

The series based on the jumping bug tends to a fixed total and because of that it is **convergent**. The one based on sand on the paving stones continues to get bigger and bigger in total and it is **divergent**.

Illustrate these two situations graphically.

To help us in this work we firstly look at a theorem attributed to Maclaurin.

Find out and write up what you can about Maclaurin.

Suppose we have a function, f(x), which has two properties:

1. it can be repeatedly differentiated

2. it can be expressed as a series.

Then let:

$$f(x) \equiv a_0 + a_1 x + a_2 x^2 + a_3 x^3 + a_4 x^4 + \ldots \Rightarrow f(0) = a_0$$
$$f'(x) \equiv a_1 + 2a_2 x + 3a_3 x^2 + 4a_4 x^3 + \ldots \quad \Rightarrow f'(0) = a_0$$

Just to clarify what's going on, remember:

(a) in an identity we can substitute any value we like for x; using 0 gives us the result on the right

(b) $\dfrac{d(f(x))}{dx}$ is written f'(x) for convenience

(c) a_0, a_1, a_2 etc. are constant.

Let us continue:

$$f''(x) = 2a_2 + 2.3a_3 x + 4.3a_4 x^2 + \ldots \Rightarrow f''(0) = 2a_2 \Rightarrow \frac{f''(0)}{2} = a_2$$

$$f'''(x) = 3.2a_3 + 4.3.2a_4 x + \ldots \qquad \Rightarrow f'''(0) = 3.2a_3 \Rightarrow \frac{f'''(0)}{3!} = a_3$$

$$3! = 3 \times 2 \times 1$$
$$8! = 8 \times 7 \times 6 \times 5 \times 4 \times 3 \times 2 \times 1$$
$$n! = n \times (n-1) \times (n-2) \times \ldots 4 \times 3 \times 2 \times 1$$

! is read 'factorial' and 3! is read as 'three factorial'.

Another note:

At this stage you might like to think that the exclamation mark, !, which has appeared represents an expletive but that is not the case. It is a bit more proper mathematical notation.

The factorial idea only applies to positive integers.

Why? Find out.

Some calculators have ! buttons. It is interesting to experiment and see which is the largest factorial it will work out. It takes a little while (approximately five seconds) to do the calculation but think how long it would take on paper!

Let us get back to what we were doing and the next line would be:

$$f^{IV}(x) = 4.3.2a_4 + \ldots \quad \Rightarrow f^{IV}(0) = 4.3.2a_4 \Rightarrow \frac{f^{IV}(0)}{4!} = a_3$$

and so on.

If we now go back to our first line of working and replace the constants we get:

$$f(x) = f(0) + f'(0).x + \frac{f''(0)}{2}.x^2 + \frac{f'''(0)}{3!}.x^3 + \frac{f^{IV}(0)}{4!}.x^4 + \ldots$$

This is a useful result to know and remember, and it is easy to remember because all the terms are of the form $\dfrac{f^n(0)}{n!}.x^n$.

The sine series

An easy function to consider is $f(x) = \sin x$.

$$f(x) = \sin x \qquad f(0) = 0$$
$$f'(x) = \cos x \qquad f'(0) = 1$$
$$f''(x) = -\sin x \quad f''(0) = 0$$
$$f'''(x) = -\cos x \quad f'''(0) = -1$$
$$f^{IV}(x) = \sin x \qquad f^{IV}(0) = 0$$

and a pattern is established which leads us to:

$$\sin x = x - \frac{x^3}{3!} + \frac{x^5}{5!} - \frac{x^7}{7!} + \ldots$$

and so $\sin x$ may be expressed as an infinite series.

Notice all the odd integers in this series and remember what type of a function $\sin x$ is (page 189).

> Maclaurin's theorem is really a special case of Taylor's theorem: research this.

> **Investigation**
>
> Now hazard a guess at the series for $\cos x$ and prove whether or not you are correct. You will find the answer on page 230.

Small angle approximations

We can reconsider the small angle approximations for the sine and cosine functions at this stage.

If x is small successive terms get smaller and smaller and become increasingly negligible so that an approximation is:

$$\sin x \approx x - \frac{x^3}{3!} + \frac{x^5}{5!} \qquad \textit{rarely used}$$

or $\sin x \approx x - \dfrac{x^3}{3!}$ *occasionally used*

or $\sin x \approx x$ *frequently used*

> **Investigation**
>
> These approximations are valid only if x is in radians.
> Why?
> **Hint:** remember that differentiation has been used in the development of them.

and in the case of $\cos x$

$$\cos x \approx 1 - \frac{x^2}{2}$$

or $\cos x \approx 1$

are the approximations.

Binomial theorem

Now we shall consider the function $f(x) = (1 + ax)^n$.

$$f(x) = (1 + ax)^n \qquad\qquad \Rightarrow \qquad f(0) = 1$$

$$f'(x) = n(1 + ax)^{n-1}.a \qquad\qquad \Rightarrow \qquad f'(0) = na$$

$$f''(x) = n(n-1)(1 + ax)^{n-2}.a^2 \qquad \Rightarrow \qquad f''(0) = n(n-1).a^2$$

$$f'''(x) = n(n-1)(n-2)(1 + ax)^{n-3}.a^3 \Rightarrow \quad f'''(0) = n(n-1)(n-2).a^2$$

A pattern emerges:

$$f^{IV}(0) = n(n-1)(n-2)(n-3).a^4$$

$$f^{V}(0) = n(n-1)(n-2)(n-3)(n-4).a^5$$

> Notice the use of the dots in products. They are put in to separate parts of the products, to avoid confusion.

Then using Maclaurin's theorem we have:

$$(1 + ax)^n = 1 + na.x + \frac{n(n-1)}{2}a^2.x^2 + \frac{n(n-1)(n-2)}{3!}a^3.x^3$$

$$+ \frac{n(n-1)(n-2)(n-3)}{4!}a^4.x^4 + \ldots$$

$$(1 + ax)^n = 1 + n(ax) + \frac{n(n-1)}{2}(ax)^2 + \frac{n(n-1)(n-2)}{3!}(ax)3$$

$$+ \frac{n(n-1)(n-2)(n-3)}{4!}(ax)^4 + \cdots.$$

> This is the binomial theorem. Binomial means 'two terms', and there are two terms in the brackets, i.e. 1 and ax.

The coefficients as written here become increasingly cumbersome and they can be simplified.

$$\frac{n(n-1)(n-2)(n-3)}{4!}$$

$$= \frac{n(n-1)(n-2)(n-3)}{4!} \cdot \frac{(n-4)(n-5)(n-6)\cdots4.3.2.1}{(n-4)(n-5)(n-6)\cdots4.3.2.1}$$

$$= \frac{n!}{4!\,(n-4)!}$$

The term in x^r in the series above would be $\dfrac{n!}{r!(n-r)!}(ax)^r$

and this used to be written: $\quad {}^nC_r(ax)^r \quad$ or $\quad {}_nC_r(ax)^r$

but nowadays is written: $\quad \dbinom{n}{r}$

Permutations and combinations – a brief look

The letter C was used because we are working out a **combination**: the number of ways we can pick r things from n.

Suppose you have 4 coloured boxes, red (R), blue (B), green (G) and yellow (Y).

The number of ways you could **pick** three boxes is 4:

1. R   B   G
2. R   B   Y
3. R   G   Y
4. B   G   Y

These are called **selections** or **combinations**, worked out from:

$$ {}^nC_r = \binom{n}{r} = \frac{n!}{r!(n-r)!} $$

in this case $\dfrac{4!}{3!1!} = 4$

The number of ways you could **arrange** three boxes is 24: each of the selections on the left can be arranged in six ways:

1. R   B   G
2. R   G   B
3. B   R   G
4. G   R   B
5. B   G   R
6. G   B   R

These are called **arrangements** or **permutations**, worked out from:

$$ {}^nP_r = \frac{n!}{(n-r)!} $$

in this case $\dfrac{4!}{(4-3)!} = 24$

Hence the expansion above may be restated as:

$$ (1+ax)^n = 1 + \binom{n}{1}(ax)^1 + \binom{n}{2}(ax)^2 + \binom{n}{3}(ax)^3 $$

$$ + \binom{n}{4}(ax)^4 + \ldots \binom{n}{r}(ax)^r \ldots $$

This statement is the **binomial theorem**, so called because in $(1+ax)^n$, $1+ax$ is a two-term or **binomial** expression. It should be remembered in both the form on page 214 and that on page 215, as we shall see from the examples.

e.g. Expand $(1 + 2x)^{11}$ as far as the term in x^4.

$$(1 + 2x)^{11} = 1 + 11(2x) + \frac{11.10}{2}(2x)^2 + \frac{11.10.9}{3!}(2x)^3$$

$$+ \frac{11.10.9.8}{4!}(2x)^4 + \dots$$

$$= 1 + 22x + 220x^2 + 1320x^3 + 5280x^4 + \dots$$

e.g. Expand $(1 + 3x)^{-3}$ as far as the term in x^4.

This question poses the question: is the theorem true for a negative index? If we look back through the theory we should find no reason why it should not be but the form using $\binom{n}{r}$ is meaningless for negative integers. (See page 212 where we defined the factorial function.)

$$\therefore (1 + 3x)^{-3} = 1 + (-3)(3x) + \frac{(-3)(-4)}{2!}(3x)^2 + \frac{(-3)(-4)(-5)}{3!}(3x)^3$$

$$+ \frac{(-3)(-4)(-5)(-6)}{4!}(3x)^4 + \dots$$

$$= 1 - 9x + 54x^2 - 270x^3 + 1215x^4 - \dots$$

e.g. Find the first four terms in ascending powers of x in the expansion of $(1 - 2x)^{1/3}$. By making a suitable substitution find an approximate value for $\sqrt[3]{0.98}$ correct to 7 decimal places (d.p.). Check your answer by finding the value directly by calculator.

$$(1 - 2x)^{1/3} = 1 + \left(\frac{1}{3}\right)(-2x) + \left(\frac{1}{3}\right)\left(-\frac{2}{3}\right)\frac{(-2x)^2}{2}$$

$$+ \left(\frac{1}{3}\right)\left(-\frac{2}{3}\right)\left(-\frac{5}{3}\right)\frac{(-2x)^3}{3!} + \dots$$

$$= 1 - \frac{2x}{3} - \frac{4}{9}x^2 - \frac{40}{81}x^3 - \dots$$

$\sqrt[3]{0.98} \quad = \sqrt[3]{(1 - 2 \times 0.01)} = (1 - 2 \times 0.01)^{1/3}$

Substituting $x = 0.01$ in the above.

$\sqrt[3]{0.98} \quad = 1 - \frac{2 \times 0.01}{3} - \frac{4 \times 0.0001}{9} - \frac{40}{81} \times 0.000\,001 \dots$

$= 0.993\,288\,4$

By calculator $\sqrt[3]{0.98} = 0.993\,288\,4$

To nine decimal places (9 d.p.) the values are 0·993 288 395 and 0·993 288 388 respectively.

e.g.

Find the first five terms in ascending powers of x of $(9 - 2x)^{1/2}$.

$$(9 - 2x)^{1/2} = \left\{ 9\left(1 - \frac{2x}{9}\right) \right\}^{1/2} = 9^{1/2}\left(1 - \frac{2x}{9}\right)^{1/2} = 3\left(1 - \frac{2x}{9}\right)^{1/2}$$

$$\therefore (9 - 2x)^{1/2} = 3\left\{ 1 + \left(\frac{1}{2}\right)\left(\frac{-2x}{9}\right) + \left(\frac{1}{2}\right)\left(-\frac{1}{2}\right)\left(-\frac{2x}{9}\right)^2 \frac{1}{2!} \right.$$

$$+ \left(\frac{1}{2}\right)\left(-\frac{1}{2}\right)\left(-\frac{3}{2}\right)\left(-\frac{2x}{9}\right)^3 \frac{1}{3!}$$

$$\left. + \left(\frac{1}{2}\right)\left(-\frac{1}{2}\right)\left(-\frac{3}{2}\right)\left(-\frac{5}{2}\right)\left(-\frac{2x}{9}\right)^4 \frac{1}{4!} + \cdots \right\}$$

$$= 3\left\{ 1 - \frac{x}{9} - \frac{x^2}{162} - \frac{x^3}{1458} - \frac{5x^4}{52\,488} \cdots \right\}$$

$$= 3 - \frac{x}{3} - \frac{x^2}{54} - \frac{x^3}{486} - \frac{5x^4}{17\,496} \cdots.$$

This is the first example covered where the first term of the binomial expression has not been 1. The technique is to change it so that it becomes 1 and then the question can be dealt with in the usual way.

e.g.

Expand $\dfrac{x^2 + x + 3}{(x - 1)(x^2 + 4)}$ as far as the term in x^3.

Let $\dfrac{x^2 + x + 3}{(x - 1)(x^2 + 4)} \equiv \dfrac{A}{x - 1} + \dfrac{Bx + C}{x^2 + 4}$ *using partial fractions*

$$\Rightarrow x^2 + x + 3 \equiv A(x^2 + 4) + (Bx + C)(x - 1)$$

$x = 1 \Rightarrow A = 1$

c.f. $x^2 \Rightarrow 1 = A + B \Rightarrow B = 0$

c.f. $x^0 \Rightarrow 3 = 4A - C \Rightarrow C = 1$

$$\therefore \frac{x^2 + x + 3}{(x - 1)(x^2 + 4)} \equiv \frac{1}{x - 1} + \frac{1}{x^2 + 4}$$

Then $\dfrac{1}{x-1} + \dfrac{1}{x^2+4} = (x-1)^{-1} + (4+x^2)^{-1}$

$$= (-1)^{-1}(1-x)^{-1} + 4^{-1}\left(1+\dfrac{x^2}{4}\right)^{-1}$$

$$\Rightarrow -(1-x)^{-1} + \dfrac{1}{4}\left(1+\dfrac{x^2}{4}\right)^{-1} = -\left\{1 + (-1)(-x) + \dfrac{(-1)(-2)}{2}(-x)^2\right.$$

$$\left. + \dfrac{(-1)(-2)(-3)(-x)^3}{3!} + \cdots\right\}$$

$$+ \dfrac{1}{4}\left\{1 + (-1)\left(\dfrac{x^2}{4}\right) + \dfrac{(-1)(-2)}{2!}\left(\dfrac{x^2}{4}\right)^2\right.$$

$$\left. + \cdots\right\}$$

$$= -\dfrac{3}{4} - x - \dfrac{17}{16}x^2 - x^3 - \cdots$$

EXERCISE 13.1

(*Answers on page 228*)

1. Expand $(1+2x)^{15}$ as far as the term in x^3.

2. Express $\sin 3x$ as a series in ascending powers of x giving the first four terms and the nth term.

3. Write down the first three terms in the expansion of $\dfrac{1}{\sqrt{9-x}}$.

4. Expand $\dfrac{(1+x)^5}{(2-x)^3}$ as far as the term in x^2.

5. Express $\dfrac{7x+2}{(x+2)^2(x-2)}$ as a series in ascending powers of x as far as the term in x^4.

6. Expand $\dfrac{1}{1+x+x^2}$ as far as the term in x^3.

7. Use the binomial theorem to calculate the value of $(16 \cdot 32)^{-1/4}$ to 6 d.p.

8. Prove that if x is so small that its cube and higher powers may be neglected,

$$\sqrt{\dfrac{(1+x)}{(1-x)}} = 1 + x + \dfrac{x^2}{2}.$$

We have seen that some examples of the binomial expansion are finite and some are infinite. We should also look into the validity of some of the expansions. These are the areas we shall consider next.

As we have shown the binomial series is an infinite series with terms of the form:

$$(1 + ax)^n = 1 + n(ax) + \frac{n(n-1)}{2}(ax)^2 + \frac{n(n-1)(n-2)}{3!}(ax)^3 + \cdots$$

If we look at these coefficients carefully we can say that:

after the 2nd term every coefficient will have the factor $n - 1$ in it

and after the 3rd term every coefficient will have the factor $n - 2$ in it

and after the 4th term every coefficient will have the factor $n - 3$ in it

and after the $(r + 1)th$ term every coefficient will have the factor $n - r$ in it.

Following from this, if $n = r$ then $n - r = 0$ and all the terms with $n - r$ in would then be zero.

Perhaps a numerical example will make this easier to follow.

e.g.

$$(1 + ax)^4 = 1 + 4(ax) + \frac{4(4-1)}{2}(ax)^2 + \frac{4(4-1)(4-2)}{3!}(ax)^3$$

$$+ \frac{4(4-1)(4-2)(4-3)}{4!}(ax)^4$$

$$+ \frac{4(4-1)(4-2)(4-3)(4-4)}{5!}(ax)^5$$

$$+ \frac{4(4-1)(4-2)(4-3)(4-4)(4-5)}{6!}(ax)^6 + \cdots$$

We can see now that the last two terms, and all subsequent terms, are zero because of the $(4 - 4)$ factor.

This situation as described here can only happen when n is a positive integer. Hence only when n is a positive integer is the binomial series finite.

Investigation

Prove this statement for yourself: see what happens when n is a fraction or negative.

Investigate the link between n and the number of terms.

Pascal's triangle

Write out the expansions of $(1 + x)^n$ for values of n from 0 to 6, integer values only.

You should have:

$(1 + x)^0 = 1$

$(1 + x)^1 = 1 + 1x$

$(1 + x)^2 = 1 + 2x + 1x^2$

Some extra coefficients like $1x^2$, $1x^3$ etc have been put in for a purpose.

$(1 + x)^3 = 1 + 3x + 3x^2 + 1x^3$

$(1 + x)^4 = 1 + 4x + 6x^2 + 4x^3 + 1x^4$

$(1 + x)^5 = 1 + 5x + 10x^2 + 10x^3 + 5x^4 + 1x^5$

$(1 + x)^6 = 1 + 6x + 15x^2 + 20x^3 + 15x^4 + 6x^5 + 1x^6$

If we now rewrite all the coefficients in a table we have this.

```
                1
             1     1
          1     2     1
       1     3     3     1
    1     4     6     4     1
 1     5    10    10     5     1
1    6    15    20    15     6     1
1  7  21   35   35   21   7   1
```

> This is known as Pascal's triangle.

Investigation

Can you see the rule for writing down a row of this table from the immediately preceding row? Addition plays a major part. Write down the next three rows.

> You may have seen this before.

If we expand $(x + y)^8$ we get:

$$(x + y)^8 = x^8\left(1 + \frac{y}{x}\right)^8$$

$$= x^8\left\{1 + 8\left(\frac{y}{x}\right) + 28\left(\frac{y}{x}\right)^2 + 56\left(\frac{y}{x}\right)^3 + 70\left(\frac{y}{x}\right)^4 + 56\left(\frac{y}{x}\right)^5\right.$$

$$\left. + 28\left(\frac{y}{x}\right)^6 + 8\left(\frac{y}{x}\right)^7 + \left(\frac{y}{x}\right)^8\right\}$$

$$= x^8 + 8x^7y + 28x^6y^2 + 56x^5y^3 + 70x^4y^4 + 56x^3y^5$$

$$+ 28x^2y^6 + 8xy^7 + y^8$$

Now if we study the order of each term (look at the combined powers of x and y) we can see that they are all of order 8, the order of the original.

We now bring together these last two developments to produce a very efficient way of writing out certain binomial expansions.

  Expand $(p + q)^6$.

We can do this in two stages:

1st stage: Write down the coefficients from row 7 of Pascal's triangle:

$$1 \qquad 6 \qquad 15 \qquad 20 \qquad 15 \qquad 6 \qquad 1$$

2nd stage: Fill in the *ps* and *qs* remembering the above rule about order:

$1p^6 + 6p^5q + 15p^4q^2 + 20p^3q^3 + 15p^2q^4 + 6pq^5 + 1q^6$

$\therefore (p + q)^6 = p^6 + 6p^5q + 15p^4q^2 + 20p^3q^3 + 15p^2q^4 + 6pq^5 + q^6$

This is a very efficient method of expanding $(x + y)^n$ for integer values of n up to about 10. Students of statistics will meet this in work on probability and find it equally useful there.

EXERCISE 13.2

(*Answers on page 230*)

1. Expand $(2x + 3y)^5$.
2. Expand $(3a - 2b)^4$.
3. Find the term in p^3 in the expansion of $(4p - 3q)^8$.
4. Find the term independent of a in $\left(a - \dfrac{1}{a^2} \right)^9$.
5. In the expansion of $(a + b)^8$ in descending powers of a the second term is equal to the third term. Find $a : b$.

Validity of the binomial theorem

We referred earlier to looking at the validity of this work we are doing. There are hints here that, after all the work we have done in this chapter, all is not well! Don't worry! All is in order but there is a further problem to consider which we will highlight by looking at an example.
The expansion of $(1 - x)^{-1}$ is:

$1 + x + x^2 + x^3 + x^4 + \cdots$

> You should verify this for yourself.

If we put $x = 5$ the expansion becomes:

$1 + 5 + 5^2 + 5^3 + 5^4 + \cdots = 1 + 5 + 25 + 125 + 625 + \cdots$

which is an infinite series. The more terms we include in the sum the bigger, and more out of control, the sum becomes. A series of this type is said to be **divergent**.
If we look at $(1 - x)^{-1}$ with $x = 5$ we get:

$(1 - 5)^{-1} = (-4)^{-1} = \dfrac{1}{-4} = -0.25$

Now this indisputably is correct and we conclude that something is amiss with the expansion.

The expansion using $x = 0.5$ should give approximately the correct value. In fact the more terms we consider the nearer we got to the correct value.

Investigation

Repeat the example we have just done but using $x = 0.5$. What do you find?

Check. Correct value: $(1 - 0.5)^{-1} = 0.5^{-1} = \dfrac{1}{0.5} = 2$

Expansion value $= 1 + 0.5 + 0.5^2 + 0.5^3 + 0.5^4 + \cdots$

$\qquad\qquad\quad = 1 + 0.5 + 0.25 + 0.125 + 0.0625 + \cdots$

$\qquad\qquad\quad = 1.9375 + \cdots$

$\qquad\qquad\quad \approx 2$

This series which, as more and more terms are added, gets nearer and nearer to a fixed value is said to be **convergent**. Now we can see the words **divergent** and **convergent** as good descriptions of their respective series.

Why is $(1 - x)^{-1}$ convergent when $x = 0.5$ and divergent when $x = 5$?

The answer obviously lies in the terms themselves. When $|x| < 1$ (or, to write it another way, $-1 < x < 1$) the higher the power then the smaller the term and the series is convergent. When $|x| < 1$ the higher the power the greater the terms become and then the series is divergent. Hence the series is only valid when convergent and the matter is summed up like this.

The expansion of $(1 + x)^n$ where n is negative or fractional or both (i.e. the series is infinite) is valid only for $|x| = <1$.

e.g. Find the first three terms in ascending powers of x of $(1 + 2x)^{1/2}$. State the range of values of x for which the expansion is valid and the range of square roots which could be evaluated using the expansion.

$(1 + 2x)^{1/2} = 1 + \dfrac{1}{2} \cdot 2x + \dfrac{1}{2} \cdot -\dfrac{1}{2} \cdot \dfrac{(2x)^2}{2} + \cdots = 1 + x - \dfrac{x^2}{2} + \cdots$

Expansion valid for $|2x| < 1 \;\Rightarrow\; -1 < 2x < 1$

$$-\dfrac{1}{2} < x < \dfrac{1}{2}$$

When $x = -\frac{1}{2}$ $1 + 2x = 0$
When $x = \;\;\frac{1}{2}$ $1 + 2x = 2$

So the expansion could be used to evaluate square roots of numbers between 0 and 2.

Progressions

Many times you will have tried, usually successfully, questions of the type where you are asked to add the next two or three terms to a series of numbers. Series such as

2 5 8 11 $\cdots$ or 2 6 18 54 $\cdots$

The first is an **arithmetic progression (AP)** and the second is a **geometric progression (GP)**.

AP and **GP** defined.

Arithmetic: The same constant amount is added to progress from term to term; this is called the **common difference**, d.

Geometric: Each term is multiplied by the same factor to progress to the next term; this is called the **common ratio**, r.

Arithmetic progressions

Starting with a as the first term an AP is:

$a \quad a+d \quad a+2d \quad a+3d \quad a+4d \quad \cdots \quad a+(n-1)d$

where n is the number of terms. The sum of these terms is:

$$S_n = a \;+\; a+d \;+\; a+2d \;+\; a+3d \;+\; \cdots \;+\; a+(n-1)d$$

where S_n means the sum of n terms. S_n can also be written:

$$S_n = a+(n-1)d \;+\; a+(n-2)d \;+\; a+(n-3)d \;+\; \cdots \;+\; a+d \;+\; a$$

If we add we get:

$$2S_n = 2a+(n-1)d \;+\; 2a+(n-1)d \;+\; 2a+(n-1)d \;+\; \cdots \; 2a+(n-1)d$$

i.e. $2S_n = n\{2a+(n-1)d\}$ *the formula for the sum of an AP*

or $S_n = \dfrac{n}{2}\{2a+(n-1)d\}$

Now $S_n = \dfrac{n}{2}\{a+a+(n-1)d\}$

But $a+(n-1)d$ is the last of n terms and it can be represented by l.

Then $S_n = \dfrac{n}{2}(a+l)$ *a variation on the formula for the sum of n terms*

The terms between the first and last terms of an AP are called the **means**. If an AP consists of seven terms, the first being 5 and the last 17 then the terms in between are the five arithmetic means of 5 and 17.

Thus   7   9   11   13   15 are the five arithmetic means of 5 and 17.

e.g. Find the sum of an AP with first term 1 and last term 81, given that there are 21 terms.

$$S_n = \frac{n}{2}(a + l) \quad \Rightarrow \quad S_{21} = \frac{21}{2}(1 + 81) = 861$$

e.g. Find the five arithmetic means of 3 and 12.

If there are five means then: $3 + 6d = 12$

$$\underset{a}{\uparrow} \quad \underset{\substack{no\ of\ means \\ plus\ one}}{\uparrow} \quad \underset{l}{\uparrow}$$

$\therefore d = 1\frac{1}{2}$

and the means are: $4\frac{1}{2}$ 6 $7\frac{1}{2}$ 9 $10\frac{1}{2}$.

e.g. An AP has first term 2 and common difference 5. How many terms will be required for the sum to be greater than 100?

$$S_n = \frac{n}{2}\{2a + (n-1)d\} \quad \Rightarrow \quad 100 = \frac{n}{2}\{4 + (n-1)5\}$$

$$\therefore \quad 200 = 4n + 5n^2 - 5n \quad \Rightarrow \quad 5n^2 - n - 200 = 0$$

$$n = \frac{-b \pm \sqrt{b^2 - 4ac}}{2a} \quad \Rightarrow \quad n = \frac{1 + \sqrt{1 + 4000}}{10} = 6\cdot4$$

This tells us that 6·4 terms would total 100 but 6·4 is an impossible number of terms and hence seven terms would be required for the total to exceed 100.

Geometric progressions

With a as the first term a GP is:

$$a \quad ar \quad ar^2 \quad ar^3 \quad ar^4 \quad ar^5 \cdots \quad ar^{n-1}$$

Where n is the number of terms and:

$$S_n = a + ar + ar^2 + ar^3 + \quad \cdots + ar^{n-2} + ar^{n-1}$$

Multiplying throughout by r gives:

$$rS_n = \quad ar + ar^2 + ar^3 + ar^4 + \cdots ar^{n-2} + ar^{n-1} + ar^n$$

Subtracting gives: $S_n - rS_n = a - ar^n$

$$\therefore \quad S_n(1-r) = a(1-r^n)$$

$$S_n = \frac{a(1-r^n)}{1-r} \qquad \textit{the formula for the sum of n terms of a GP}$$

e.g. Find the sum of 10 terms of the series: 1   2   4   8 $\cdots$.

$$S_{10} = \frac{1(1 - 2^{10})}{1 - 2} = 1023$$

e.g. Which is the first term in the series: 2   6   18   54 $\cdots$ to exceed 3000?

The general term is ar^{n-1}.

$$\therefore \text{consider}\quad 2 \times 3^{n-1} = 3000$$

$$3^{n-1} = 1500$$

$$\therefore (n - 1)\ln 3 = \ln 1500$$

$$\therefore n - 1 = \frac{\ln 1500}{\ln 3}$$

$$= 6{\cdot}7$$

$$\therefore n = 7{\cdot}7$$

> If this confuses you revise chapter 6.

So the eighth term is the first to be greater than 3000.

We could have answered this question more quickly by using the calculator and in particular its constant facility. There are variations in the routine from calculator to calculator but for a common basic scientific the routine would be:

Press	Display		
3		3	
×		3	
×	K	3	
2	K	2	1st term
=	K	6	2nd term
=	K	18	3rd term
=	K	54	4th term
=	K	162	5th term
=	K	486	6th term
=	K	1458	7th term
=	K	4374	8th term

So the 8th term is the first to be greater than 3000.

It is interesting in a case like this to carry on pressing the $=$ button and see how quickly the terms grow.

> **Investigation**
> Whilst you are at it make your initial entry 0.3 and notice how quickly the terms diminish.

> The next chapter sees a further study of this type of function.

If, in both cases, the terms were being added together we should be back with divergent and convergent series. The opening of this chapter gave us the examples: the bug jumps, convergent; the grains of sand, divergent.

In the formula:

$$S_n = \frac{a(1 - r^n)}{1 - r}$$

if $|r| < 1$ and $n \to \infty$ then $r^n \to 0$ and

$$S_\infty = \frac{a}{1 - r} \qquad \textit{the formula for the sum to infinity of a GP}$$

Earlier in this chapter we were considering the expansion:

$$1 + x + x^2 + x^3 + \cdots = (1 - x)^{-1} \qquad \textit{binomial theorem}$$

but this result is only valid for $|x| < 1$, in which case:

$$1 + x + x^2 + x^3 + \cdots$$

is an infinite series with a sum to infinity and by the formula just developed:

$$S_\infty = \frac{1}{1 - x} = (1 - x)^{-1}$$

This confirms the binomial expansion in this case, or vice versa, but it is an example which illustrates the fact that there is often more than one way of looking at things.

The definition of arithmetic means is similarly applied to **geometric means.**

  Find the four geometric means of 2 and 195.3125.

In this series $a = 2$ and $ar^5 = 195.3125$.

$$\therefore r^5 = \frac{195.3125}{2} \Rightarrow r = 2.5$$

and the means are 5 12.5 31.25 78.125.

In detail, $r = \left(\dfrac{195{\cdot}3125}{2}\right)^{1/5}$ and the calculator sequence is:

Press	Display	
195·3125	195·3125	
÷	195·3125	
2	2	
=	97·65625	
x^y	97·6525	
(	[1 0	
1	1	
÷	1	
5	5	
)	0·2	
=	2·5	*the value of r*

and then the sequence as on page 226.

EXERCISE 13.3

(*Answers on page 230*)

1. The third and fifth terms of an AP are 6 and -4 respectively. Find the tenth term and the sum of ten terms.

2. The first term of a GP is 10 and the seventh term is $\frac{5}{32}$. Find the common ratio and the minimum number of terms for which the total exceeds 99% of the sum to infinity.

3. Evaluate $\displaystyle\sum_{r=1}^{20} (3 + 2r)$.

4. A ball falls from a height of 10 m and after each bounce reaches a height of three-quarters of the height from which it last fell. How far does it travel?

5. Find the five arithmetic means of 8 and -6.

6. The third and seventh terms of a GP are 18 and $91\frac{1}{8}$ respectively. Find the common ratio, the first term and the sum of 20 terms.

7. The first, second and third terms of a GP are respectively the first, third and ninth terms of an AP. If the first term is 6 find the common ratio and the common difference.

8. Sum the series: $1 - 3 + 5 - 7 + 9 - 11 \cdots$ to 20 terms.

Σ – capital Greek letter s, pronounced *sigma*. Used throughout mathematics to stand for **sum** (meaning addition) of a number of **discrete** (separate) terms. Often used as symbol or logo for the subject.

$\displaystyle\sum_{r=1}^{20} (3+2r)$ means 'add together all the terms obtained by putting $r=1$, 2 successively up to 20'.

9. In an infinite GP the first term is three times the sum of all the subsequent terms. Find the common ratio.

10. For what values of θ is the series: $1 \quad \sin^2\theta \quad \sin^4\theta \quad \cdots$ convergent? When it is, show that its sum is $\sec^2\theta$.

Answers to exercises

ANSWERS TO EXERCISE 13.1

1. $(1 + 2x)^{15} = 1 + 15(2x) + \dfrac{15.14}{2}(2x)^2 + \dfrac{15.14.13}{3.2.1}(2x)^3 + \cdots$

$\qquad = 1 + 30x + 420x^2 + 3640x^3 + \cdots$

2. $\sin 3x = (3x) - \dfrac{(3x)^3}{3!} + \dfrac{(3x)^5}{5!} - \dfrac{(3x)^7}{7!} + \cdots (-1)^{n+1}\dfrac{(3x)^{2n-1}}{(2n-1)!} + \cdots$

> nth term: a term expressed using n so that as n takes the values 1, 2, 3 ... the series is generated.

3. $\dfrac{1}{\sqrt{9-x}} = (9-x)^{-1/2} = 9^{-1/2}\left(1 - \dfrac{x}{9}\right)^{-1/2} = \dfrac{1}{3}\left(1 - \dfrac{x}{9}\right)^{1/2}$

$\qquad = \dfrac{1}{3}\left\{1 + \left(-\dfrac{1}{2}\right)\left(-\dfrac{x}{9}\right) + \left(-\dfrac{1}{2}\right)\left(-\dfrac{3}{2}\right)\left(-\dfrac{x}{9}\right)^2\dfrac{1}{2} + \cdots\right\} = \dfrac{1}{3}\left(1 + \dfrac{x}{18} + \dfrac{3x^2}{648} + \cdots\right)$

$\qquad = \dfrac{1}{3} + \dfrac{x}{54} + \dfrac{x^2}{648} + \cdots$

4. $\dfrac{(1+x)^5}{(2-x)^3} = (1+x)^5(2-x)^{-3} = 2^{-3}(1+x)^5\left(1 - \dfrac{x}{2}\right)^{-3}$

$\qquad = \dfrac{1}{8}(1 + 5x + 10x^2 + \cdots)\left(1 + \dfrac{3x}{2} + \dfrac{(-3)(-4)}{2}\left(-\dfrac{x}{2}\right)^2 + \cdots\right)$

$\qquad = \dfrac{1}{8}(1 + 5x + 10x^2 + \cdots)\left(1 + \dfrac{3x}{2} + \dfrac{3}{2}x^2 + \cdots\right) = \dfrac{1}{8} + \dfrac{13x}{16} + \dfrac{19}{8}x^2 + \cdots$

5. Let $\dfrac{7x + 2}{(x+2)^2(x-2)} \equiv \dfrac{A}{x+2} + \dfrac{B}{(x+2)^2} + \dfrac{C}{x-2}$

$\qquad \Rightarrow 7x + 2 \equiv A(x+2)(x-2) + B(x-2) + C(x+2)^2 \qquad x = 2 \Rightarrow C = 1$

$\qquad\qquad\qquad\qquad\qquad\qquad\qquad\qquad\qquad\qquad\qquad x = -2 \Rightarrow B = 3$

$\qquad\qquad\qquad\qquad\qquad\qquad\qquad\qquad\qquad\qquad\qquad \text{c.f. } x^2 \Rightarrow A = -1$

$$\therefore \frac{7x + 2}{(x + 2)^2(x - 2)} \equiv -1(x + 2)^{-1} + 3(x + 2)^{-2} + (x - 2)^{-1}$$

$$= -2^{-1}\left(1 + \frac{x}{2}\right)^{-1} + 3.2^{-2}\left(1 + \frac{x}{2}\right)^{-2} - 2^{-1}\left(1 - \frac{x}{2}\right)^{-1}$$

$$= -\frac{1}{2}\left(1 + \frac{x}{2}\right)^{-1} + \frac{3}{4}\left(1 + \frac{x}{2}\right)^{-2} - \frac{1}{2}\left(1 - \frac{x}{2}\right)^{-1}$$

$$= -\frac{1}{2}\left\{1 - \frac{x}{2} + \frac{x^2}{4} - \frac{x^3}{8} + \frac{x^4}{16} - \cdots\right\}$$

$$+ \frac{3}{4}\left\{1 - x + \frac{3x^2}{4} - \frac{x^3}{2} + \frac{5x^4}{16} - \cdots\right\}$$

$$- \frac{1}{2}\left\{1 + \frac{x}{2} + \frac{x^2}{4} + \frac{x^3}{8} + \frac{x^4}{16} + \cdots\right\}$$

$$= -\frac{1}{4} - \frac{3x}{4} + \frac{5x^2}{16} - \frac{3x^3}{8} + \frac{11x^4}{64} - \cdots$$

6. $\dfrac{1}{1 + x + x^2} = (1 + x + x^2)^{-1} = 1 + (-1)(x + x^2) + \dfrac{(-1)(-2)(x + x^2)^2}{2!} + \dfrac{(-1)(-2)(-3)(x + x^2)^3}{3!}$

$$= 1 - x - x^2 + x^2 + 2x^3 + \cdots - x^3 \cdots$$

$$= 1 - x + x^3 \cdots$$

Notice this method of apparently converting a trinomial into a binomial.

An easier way with this question would be:

$$\frac{1}{1 + x + x^2} = \frac{1 - x}{(1 - x)(1 + x + x^2)} = \frac{1 - x}{1 - x^3} = (1 - x)(1 - x^3)^{-1}$$

$$(1 - x)(1 - x^3)^{-1} = (1 - x)(1 + x^3 + x^6 + x^9 + \cdots) = 1 - x + x^3 + \cdots$$

7. $16 \cdot 32^{-1/4} = (16 + 0 \cdot 32)^{-1/4} = 16^{-1/4}(1 + 0 \cdot 02)^{-1/4} = \frac{1}{2}(1 + 0 \cdot 02)^{-1/4}$

$$\Rightarrow \frac{1}{2}\left\{1 + \left(-\frac{1}{4}\right)(0 \cdot 02) + \left(-\frac{1}{4}\right)\left(-\frac{5}{4}\right)\frac{(0 \cdot 02)^2}{2} + \left(-\frac{1}{4}\right)\left(-\frac{5}{5}\right)\left(-\frac{9}{4}\right)\frac{(0 \cdot 02)^3}{3!} + \cdots\right\}$$

$$= \frac{1}{2}(1 - 0 \cdot 005 + 0 \cdot 000\,062\,5 - 0 \cdot 000\,000\,937 + \cdots) = 0 \cdot 497\,531$$

> Using the calculator is obviously quicker but here we are testing the method.

8. $\sqrt{\dfrac{(1 + x)}{(1 - x)}} = (1 + x)^{1/2}(1 - x)^{-1/2}$

$$= \left\{1 + \frac{1}{2}x + \left(\frac{1}{2}\right)\left(-\frac{1}{2}\right)\frac{x^2}{2} + \cdots\right\}\left\{1 + \left(-\frac{1}{2}\right)(-x) + \left(-\frac{1}{2}\right)\left(-\frac{3}{2}\right)\frac{(-x)^2}{2!} + \cdots\right\}$$

$$= \left(1 + \frac{x}{2} - \frac{x^2}{8} + \cdots\right)\left(1 + \frac{x}{2} + \frac{3x^2}{8} + \cdots\right)$$

$$= 1 + x + \frac{x^2}{2} + \cdots$$

Series for cos$x$: $\cos x = 1 - \dfrac{x^2}{2} + \dfrac{x^4}{4!} - \dfrac{x^6}{6!} + \dfrac{x^8}{8!} - \cdots$

ANSWERS TO EXERCISE 13.2

1. $(2x + 3y)^5 = (2x)^5 + 5(2x)^4(3y)^1 + 10(2x)^3(3y)^2 + 10(2x)^2(3y)^3 + 5(2x)(3y)^4 + (3y)^5$

        $= 32x^5 + 240x^4y + 720x^3y^2 + 1080x^2y^3 + 810xy^4 + 243y^5$

2. $(3a - 2b)^4 = (3a)^4 + 4(3a)^3(-2b)^1 + 6(3a)^2(-2b)^2 + 4(3a)(-2b)^3 + (-2b)^4$

        $= 81a^4 - 216a^3b + 216a^2b^2 - 96ab^3 + 16b^4$

3. Required term contains $(4p)^3(-3q)^5$ and from row 9 of Pascal's triangle the coefficient is 56.

    $\therefore$ the term is: $56(4p)^3(-3q)^5 = -870\,912\,p^3q^5$

4. $\left(a - \dfrac{1}{a^2}\right)^9$

   The term independent of a is the one containing $a^6\left(\dfrac{1}{a^2}\right)^3$

   $\therefore \dfrac{a^6}{a^6} = 1$ *as cancel out*

   The term is: $84 . a^6\left(-\dfrac{1}{a^2}\right)^3 = -84$

5. $(a + b)^8 = a^8 + 8a^7b + 28a^6b^2 + \cdots$

   $8a^7b = 28a^6b^2 \Rightarrow 2a = 7b \Rightarrow \dfrac{a}{b} = \dfrac{7}{2}$, so $a:b = 7:2$.

ANSWERS TO EXERCISE 13.3

1. Terms are: $a \quad a+d \quad a+2d \quad \cdots$

   $\therefore$ 3rd term: $a + 2d = 6$

      5th term: $a + 4d = -4$ $\Big\}$ $\Rightarrow$ $2d = -10, d = -5$ $\Rightarrow$ $a = 16$

   Then: 10th term is: $a + 9d = 16 - 45 = -29$

   and $S_{10} = \dfrac{10}{2}(16 - 29)$ using $S_n = \dfrac{n}{2}(a + l)$

      $= -65$

2. $a = 10$ and $ar^6 = \dfrac{5}{32}$ $\therefore r^6 = \dfrac{5}{32 \times 10} = \dfrac{1}{64} = \dfrac{1}{2^6}$ $\therefore r = \tfrac{1}{2}$

$S_\infty = \dfrac{10}{1 - \frac{1}{2}} = 20$

99% of $S_\infty = 19{\cdot}8$

Hence $\dfrac{10(1 - \frac{1}{2}^n)}{1 - \frac{1}{2}} > 19{\cdot}8$

Consider $20(1 - \tfrac{1}{2}^n) > 19{\cdot}8$

$\Rightarrow \quad 0{\cdot}2 > 20 \times \tfrac{1}{2}^n$

$\therefore \tfrac{1}{2}^n < \dfrac{0{\cdot}2}{20} = 0{\cdot}01 \quad \Rightarrow \quad n = 7$

3. $\displaystyle\sum_{r=1}^{20} (3 + 2r) = 3 + 2.1 + 3 + 2.2 + 3 + 2.3 + \cdots + 3 + 2.20$

$\qquad\qquad = 5 + 7 + 9 + \cdots + 43$ *an AP*

$S_{20} = \dfrac{20}{2}(5 + 43) = 480$

4. Height reached after 1st bounce $10 \times \dfrac{3}{4}$

Height reached after 2nd bounce $10 \times \left(\dfrac{3}{4}\right)^2$

Height reached after 3rd bounce $10 \times \left(\dfrac{3}{4}\right)^3$ *a convergent GP*

Total distance travelled $= 2 \times \{10 + 10 \times \tfrac{3}{4} + 10 \times \tfrac{9}{16} + \cdots\} - 10$

$\qquad\qquad = 2 \times \dfrac{10}{1 - \frac{3}{4}} - 10 = 70\,\text{m}$

5. If there are five arithmetic means between 8 and -6 $\Rightarrow$ $8 + 6d = -6$ $\Rightarrow$ $d = -2\tfrac{1}{3}$

$\therefore$ the means are: $5\tfrac{2}{3}$ $3\tfrac{1}{3}$ 1 $-1\tfrac{1}{3}$ $-3\tfrac{1}{3}$ -6

6. $ar^2 = 18$ and $ar^6 = 91\tfrac{1}{8}$ $r^4 = \dfrac{91\frac{1}{8}}{18}$ $\dfrac{ar^6}{ar^2} = r^4$

$\therefore r = \left(\dfrac{91\frac{1}{8}}{18}\right)^{1/4} = 1{\cdot}5$ $\boxed{91{\cdot}125} \boxed{\div} \boxed{18} \boxed{=} \boxed{x^y} \boxed{(} \boxed{1} \boxed{\div} \boxed{4} \boxed{)} \boxed{=}$

Then $a = \dfrac{18}{1{\cdot}5^2} = 8$ and $S_{20} = 8\dfrac{(1 - 1{\cdot}5^{20})}{1 - 1{\cdot}5} = 53\,188{\cdot}1$

7.

GP	a	ar^2	ar^2
AP	a	$a + 2d$	$a + 8d$

$\Rightarrow$

6	$6r$	$6r^2$
6	$6 + 2d$	$6 + 8d$

$$\left. \begin{array}{l} 6r = 6 + 2d \\ \text{and } 6r^2 = 6 + 8d \end{array} \right\} \Rightarrow 6r^2 - 24r = -18$$

$$\Rightarrow r^2 - 4r + 3 = 0$$
$$\Rightarrow r = 1 \text{ or } 3$$

$r = 1$ is impossible $\quad \therefore r = 3 \quad \Rightarrow \quad d = 6$

8. $S_{20} = 1 - 3 + 5 - 7 + 9 - 11 \ldots 20$ terms

> *Look for some APs we can sum!*

At first this looks like an **AP** but it is not, as the sign is alternating.
However $S_{20} = 1 + 3 + 5 + 7 + 9 \cdots$ to 20 terms

$$-2(3 + 7 + 11 \cdots \text{ to 10 terms})$$

$$= \frac{20}{2}\{2.1 + 19.2\} - 2 \cdot \frac{10}{2}\{2.3 + 9.4\}$$

$$= -20$$

9. $a = 3\dfrac{ar}{1 - r} \quad \Rightarrow \quad 1 - r = 3r \quad \Rightarrow \quad r = \frac{1}{4}$

10. The series is convergent if $|\sin^2\theta| < 1$ which is all θ except $\dfrac{\pi}{2}, \dfrac{3\pi}{2}, \dfrac{5\pi}{2}$

etc.

$$S_\infty = \frac{1}{1 - \sin^2\theta} = \frac{1}{\cos^2\theta} = \sec^2\theta$$

Now try worksheets 15 and 16.

Chapter 14

EXPONENTIAL AND LOGARITHMIC FUNCTIONS

Aims and objectives

Having worked through this chapter you will:

know what logarithms and exponents are

be able to differentiate log $_a x$

$$\frac{d}{dx}(\log_a x) = \frac{1}{x} \times \log_a e$$

know the definition of e,

$$e = 2{\cdot}718\ldots$$

be able to integrate using logs

$$\int \frac{2x}{x^2 + 1}dx = \ln(x^2 + 1)$$

be able to integrate by parts

$$\int x^2 e^x dx$$

be able to differentiate and integrate a^x.

know the series for e^x

$$e^x = 1 + x + \frac{x^2}{2!} + \frac{x^3}{3!} + \ldots$$

and ln(1 + x)

$$\ln(1 + x) = x - \frac{x^2}{2} + \frac{x^3}{3} + \ldots$$

Definitions

Many of the natural laws of the universe are of an exponential type, for example the loss of heat of a body, growth and decay of matter, statistical functions, and there are many more. Mathematically they are represented as $y = a^x$.

The features of this function are that a is a constant and the independent variable x is in the exponent of a.

> **Remember**
>
> index, power, exponent mean the same.

If $y = a^x$ then $\log_a y = x$

The words **exponential** and **logarithm (log)** are the basis of this chapter.

> Revise if necessary from chapter 6.

Now if $f(x) = a^x$ what is $f^{-1}(x)$?

From above, we can see that $f^{-1}(x) = \log_a x$.

Investigation

Sketch the graphs, on the same diagram, of $f(x)$ and $f^{-1}(x)$ when $f(x) = 2^x$.

Your calculator probably will not work out $\log_2 x$ directly but you can do it if you change the base – see chapter 6 if necessary.

On another diagram sketch $f(x) = 2^{x+1}$ and $f^{-1}(x)$, and on yet another

$f(x) = 2^x + 5$ and $f^{-1}(x)$.

Check your results with those overleaf.

Differentiation of $\log_a x$

These functions are closely involved with calculus and we shall now consider this, working firstly on the log function.

Let $\quad y = \log_a x$

then $\quad y + \delta y = \log_a(x + \delta x)$

$$\Rightarrow \quad \delta y = \log_a(x + \delta x) - \log_a x = \log_a\left(\frac{x + \delta x}{x}\right)$$

$$\therefore \frac{\delta y}{\delta x} = \frac{1}{\delta x}\log\left(1 + \frac{\delta x}{x}\right) = \log\left(1 + \frac{\delta x}{x}\right)^{1/\delta x}$$

To make things easier we now make a substitution.

Let $\quad \dfrac{\delta x}{x} = t \quad \Rightarrow \quad \dfrac{1}{tx} = \dfrac{1}{\delta x}$

and we then have

$$\frac{\delta y}{\delta x} = \log_a(1 + t)^{1/tx} = \frac{1}{x}\log_a(1 + t)^{1/t}$$

From the substitution it follows that as $\delta x + 0$ then $t \rightarrow 0$. We now digress a little to look at the function $(1 + t)^{1/t}$ particularly as $t \rightarrow 0$.

Using a calculator now to evaluate the function for t values of

2 $\quad$ 1 $\quad$ 0·5 $\quad$ 0·2 $\quad$ 0·1 $\quad$ 0·01 $\quad$ 0·001 $\quad$ 0·0001 $\quad$ 0·000 000 1

we get:

1·7   2   2·25   2·49   2·59   2·70   2·7169   2·718   2·718

Now referring back to our differentiation we have:

$$\lim_{\delta x \to 0} \frac{\delta y}{\delta x} = \frac{dy}{dx} = \frac{1}{x} \log_a 2\!\cdot\!718$$

It follows that if we make $a = 2\!\cdot\!718$ then $\dfrac{dy}{dx} = \dfrac{1}{x}$.

This value 2·718 is an approximation because it runs to many decimal places, just as 3·142 is a common approximation for π.

This value 2·718 is one of the most important constants in the world of mathematics and its applications, and it is represented by the letter e.

> This is the definition of e.

A scientific calculator has two logarithmic buttons, one marked $\boxed{\text{log}}$ which gives logarithms to the base 10, and one marked $\boxed{\text{ln}}$ which gives them to the base e. There are also two exponential function buttons. One is 10^x and the other is e^x. There are many exponential functions and we did some work with some on page 234 but the particular exponential function e^x is of such importance that it is referred to as *the* **exponential function.**

If we now return to the calculus we have established that:

> **Investigation**
>
> Look up the work of John Napier.

if $y = \ln x$ then $\dfrac{dy}{dx} = \dfrac{1}{x}$

> **Remember**
>
> $\ln x = \log_e x$

and consequently:

$$\int \frac{1}{x}\, dx = \ln x$$

This apparently simple result opens up another area of differentiation and integration.

e.g. Find $\dfrac{dy}{dx}$ if $y = \ln(x^2 + x)$.

Using the function of a function rule:

$$\frac{dy}{dx} = \frac{1}{x^2 + x} \times (2x + 1) = \frac{2x + 1}{x^2 + x}$$

    ↑   ↑

  differential × *differential*
  of the ln *of* $(x^2 + x)$

e.g. $\quad y = \ln\sin 2\theta. \quad \text{Find } \dfrac{dy}{d\theta}.$

$$\frac{dy}{d\theta} = \underset{\substack{\uparrow}}{\frac{1}{\sin 2\theta}} \times \cos 2\theta \times 2 = \frac{2\cos 2\theta}{\sin 2\theta} = 2\cot 2\theta$$

differential　*differential*　*differential*
of ln　　　　*of sin*　　　　*of 2θ*

EXERCISE 14.1

(*Answers on page 243*)

Find $\dfrac{dy}{dx}$ in each question.

Group A	Group B
1. $y = \ln 5x$	1. $y = 5\ln x$
2. $y = \ln(x^3 + 1)$	2. $y = \ln(x + 1)$
3. $y = \ln\tan x$	3. $y = \ln\sec x$
4. $y = \log_{10} x$	4. $y = \log_5 x$
5. $y = (\ln\cos 3x)^2$	5. $y = (\ln\tan 2x)^{1/2}$

Integration involving logarithms

In the exercise on differentation of log functions we found the pattern of the differential in each case was a fraction consisting of:

$$\frac{\text{the differential of the denominator}}{\text{the function whose log we started with}}.$$

> If $y = \ln z$ then $\dfrac{dy}{dx} = \dfrac{\text{differential of } z}{z}$

When we are faced with an integration of a fraction this is a common type to look out for, one where the top is the differential of the bottom.

e.g. Integrate $\dfrac{3x^2 + 1}{x^3 + x}$ w.r.t. x.

Inspection shows $3x^2 + 1$ to be the differential of $x^3 + x$ and hence the integral is $\ln(x^3 + x) + A$.

e.g. $\displaystyle\int \frac{\cos x}{\sin x}\,dx = \ln \sin x + A$

EXERCISE 14.2

(*Answers on page 244*)

Decide in each case if the integral is a ln type and, if so, do it.

1. $\displaystyle\int \frac{2x - 1}{x^2 - x}\,dx$

2. $\displaystyle\int \frac{3x^2}{x^3 - x^2}\,dx$

3. $\displaystyle\int \frac{4x}{x^2 + 1}\,dx$

4. $\displaystyle\int \frac{\sec^2 x}{\tan x}\,dx$

5. $\displaystyle\int \frac{3x^2 + 1}{x^3}\,dx$

Now for some harder examples.

EXERCISE 14.3

(*Answers on page 244*)

Integrate the following functions w.r.t. x.

Group A

1. $\dfrac{3}{4x + 2}$

2. $\dfrac{4x + 6}{x^2 + 3x}$

3. $\dfrac{1}{2 + 2x + x^2}$

4. $\dfrac{2}{\sqrt{4 - x^2}}$

5. $\dfrac{5}{1 + x}$

Group B

1. $\dfrac{3x}{x^2 + 1}$

2. $\dfrac{3}{x^2 + 1}$

3. $\dfrac{2x - 5}{(2x - 3)^2}$

4. $\dfrac{2x}{\sqrt{(1 - x^2)}}$

5. $\dfrac{5x^2 - x + 2}{(1 - x)(1 + x)^2}$

Integration by parts

So far we have considered the differential of $\ln x$. How about the integral of $\ln x$, $\int \ln x \, dx$?

Before we tackle this we must consider a little more theory.

From page 234 we have the rule for differentiating products.

$$\frac{d(uv)}{dx} = v\frac{dx}{dx} + u\frac{dv}{dx} \quad \text{where } u \text{ and } v \text{ are functions of } x$$

Integrating both sides gives:

$$uv = \int v\frac{du}{dx}dx + \int u\frac{dv}{dx}dx$$

and this may be written:

$$\int u\frac{dv}{dx}dx = uv - \int v\frac{du}{dx}dx$$

This can be used to solve, particularly, integrations of products. It is a very powerful method and much integration is derived from it, including that at levels beyond A level. The method we are going to use is known as integration by parts.

Look again at the rule and follow through firstly u, and then v.

$$\int u\frac{dv}{dx}dx = uv - \int v\frac{du}{dx}dx$$

u *appears here*   *and here*   *and its differential here.*

The function u is *not* integrated on the RHS. In the case of the function v:

$$\int u\frac{dv}{dx}dx = uv - \int v\frac{du}{dx}dx$$

v *appears here as differential,*   *here, and here integrated.*

The function v *is* integrated on the RHS. We shall bear these ideas in mind as we look at an example.

e.g. $I = \int x\sin x \, dx$. Find I.

$x\sin x$ is the product of two functions of x which are not linked in any way that we have considered previously. Neither is the differential of the other, or anything like that.

We make $\int x\sin x\,\mathrm{d}x$ match the LHS of the rule and we have to decide whether x is to be u or $\dfrac{\mathrm{d}v}{\mathrm{d}x}$ and vice versa for $\sin x$. It does usually matter.

$$\text{Let } x = \frac{\mathrm{d}v}{\mathrm{d}x} \qquad \text{and} \quad \sin x = u$$

Integrating: $\dfrac{x^2}{2} = v$ Differentiating: $\cos x = \dfrac{\mathrm{d}u}{\mathrm{d}x}$

Substituting in the rule:

$$\int x\sin x\,\mathrm{d}x = \frac{x^2}{2}\sin x - \int \frac{x^2}{2}\cos x\,\mathrm{d}x$$

This integral is worse than the one we started with. We shall try again!

$$x = u \qquad \text{and} \quad \sin x = \frac{\mathrm{d}v}{\mathrm{d}x}$$

$$\therefore 1 = \frac{\mathrm{d}u}{\mathrm{d}x} \qquad \therefore -\cos x = v$$

Substituting now gives:

$$\int x\sin x\,\mathrm{d}x = -x\cos x + \int 1.\cos x\,\mathrm{d}x$$

This integral is easy.

$$\therefore \int x\sin x\,\mathrm{d}x = -x\cos x + \sin x + A$$

So the integration is done and the importance of the correct initial substitution is demonstrated. In the correct substitution we have made the function x into the one which 'disappears' by differentiation. The function $\sin x$ would never 'disappear'.

The ideas in this integration are not the easiest to grasp but we shall have to persevere. Many students at first consider the method to be a bit of a cheat because, of the two functions of the original product to be integrated, one is in fact differentiated, but all is in order.

e.g.

$$\int x^2\sin x\,\mathrm{d}x = -x^2\cos x + \int 2x\cos x\,\mathrm{d}x \quad \textit{making } x^2 = v \textit{ and } \sin x = \frac{\mathrm{d}u}{\mathrm{d}x}$$

$$= -x^2\cos x + 2\{+x\sin x - \int \sin x\,\mathrm{d}x\}$$

$$= -x^2\cos x + 2x\sin x + 2\cos x + A$$

> Note integration by parts is used twice in this question; firstly to create $\int x\cos x$ from $\int x^2\sin x$, secondly to create $\int \sin x$ from $\int x\cos x$.

EXERCISE 14.4

(*Answers on page 245*)

Integrate w.r.t. x.

1. $x\cos x$
2. $x^3\sin x$
3. $x\ln x$
4. $x\tan^{-1}x$
5. $\dfrac{1}{x^2}\ln x$

The integral of ln$x$

We can now look at the problem of $\int\ln x\,dx$.

$$\int\ln x\,dx = \int 1 \cdot \ln x\,dx \qquad using\ the\ simple\ fact\ that\ lnx = 1 \times lnx$$

$$= x\ln x - \int x\cdot\frac{1}{x}dx \qquad\qquad \ln x = u,\ 1 = \frac{dv}{dx}$$

$$= x\ln x - x + A$$

EXERCISE 14.5

(*Answers on page 246*)

Integrate w.r.t. x.

1. $\tan^{-1}x$
2. $\sin^{-1}x$

Differentiation and integration of a^x

We now turn our attention to the exponential function, a^x.

If $\qquad y = a^x$

$\qquad\quad \log_a y = x$

$\Rightarrow \qquad \dfrac{\ln y}{\ln a} = x$

Differentiating w.r.t. x:

$$\frac{1}{\ln a}.\frac{1}{y}.\frac{dy}{dx} = 1$$

$$\therefore \frac{dy}{dx} = y\ln a = a^x\ln a$$

Now if $a = e$ then $y = e^x$

$$\text{and } \frac{dy}{dx} = e^x$$

Many find this hard to believe!

It means quite simply that the gradient of the function e^x is equal to the function. So at the point where e^x has the value 2 its gradient is 2, and so on.

EXERCISE 14.6

(*Answers on page 247*)

1. If $y = e^{ax}$ find (a) $\dfrac{dy}{dx}$ (b) $\displaystyle\int y\,dx$.

2. If $y = e^x\sin x$ find $\dfrac{dy}{dx}$.

3. If $y = a^{cx}$ find $\dfrac{dy}{dx}$.

4. If $y = xe^x$ find $\displaystyle\int y\,dx$.

5. *If $y = e^{x\sin x}$ find $\dfrac{dy}{dx}$.*

Finally in this chapter we shall investigate the link between the exponential and logarithmic functions and series.

Exponential series

Remember Maclaurin's theorem?

If not see page 213.

$f(x) = e^x$ $f(0) = 1$
$f'(x) = e^x$ $f'(0) = 1$
$f''(x) = e^x$ $f''(0) = 1$

and so on.

Hence

$$e^x = 1 + x + \frac{x^2}{2!} + \frac{x^3}{3!} + \frac{x^4}{4!} + \cdots$$

This is valid for all values of x.

Logarithmic series

$f(x) = \ln x \qquad f(0) = \text{impossible} \qquad$ *See the sketch on page 243*

$f'(x) = \dfrac{1}{x} \qquad f'(0) = \infty$

$f''(x) = -\dfrac{1}{x^2} \quad f''(0) = \infty$

This is an impossible situation and there is no series for $\ln x$.

However, if we consider:

$f(x) = \ln(1 + x) \qquad\qquad f(0) = 0$

$f'(x) = \dfrac{1}{1 + x} \qquad\qquad f'(0) = 1$

$f''(x) = -1(1 + x)^{-2} \qquad f''(0) = -1$

$f'''(x) = +2(1 + x)^{-3} \qquad f'''(0) = 2$

$f^{iv}(x) = -3.2(1 + x)^{-4} \quad f^{iv}(0) = -3.2$

$f^{v}(x) = 4.3.2(1 + x)^{-5} \quad f^{v}(0) = 4.3.2$

Hence $\quad \ln(1 + x) = x - \dfrac{x^2}{2} + \dfrac{2x^3}{3!} - \dfrac{3.2x^4}{4!} + \dfrac{4!x^5}{5!} - \cdots$

$\therefore \ln(1 + x) = x - \dfrac{x^2}{2} + \dfrac{x^3}{3} - \dfrac{x^4}{4} + \dfrac{x^5}{5} - \cdots$

Valid for
$-1 < x \leqslant 1$

and $\quad \ln(1 - x) = -x - \dfrac{x^2}{2} - \dfrac{x^3}{3} - \dfrac{x^4}{4} - \dfrac{x^5}{5} - \cdots$

EXERCISE 14.7

(*Answers on page 247*)

Expand the following functions as a series in ascending powers of x giving the first four terms.

1. $\ln(2 + x)$
2. e^{-3x}
3. $e^x\ln(1 - x)$
4. $(3 + x)^2 e^{-x}$
5. $(1 + x)^{-2} e^{3x}$

Now try worksheets 17 and 18.

Answers to exercises

RESULTS OF THE INVESTIGATION ON PAGE 234

By now we have a good idea of the shape of the exponential function, a^x, and its inverse, the logarithmic function, $\log_a x$.

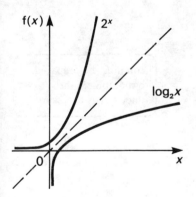
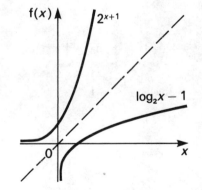
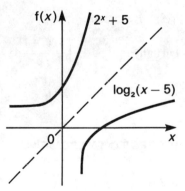

ANSWERS TO EXERCISE 14.1

Group A

1. $\dfrac{dy}{dx} = \dfrac{1}{5x} \times 5 = \dfrac{1}{x}$

2. $\dfrac{dy}{dx} = \dfrac{1}{x^3 + 1} \times 3x^2 = \dfrac{3x^2}{x^3 + 1}$

3. $\dfrac{dy}{dx} = \dfrac{1}{\tan x} \times \sec^2 x = \dfrac{\sec^2 x}{\tan x}$

4. $y = \log_{10}x = \dfrac{\ln x}{\ln 10} \Rightarrow \dfrac{dy}{dx} = \dfrac{1}{\ln 10} \times \dfrac{1}{x} = \dfrac{1}{x\ln 10}$

5. $\dfrac{dx}{dy} = 2(\ln\cos 3x) \times \dfrac{1}{\cos 3x} \times -\sin 3x \times 3 = -6\tan 3x . \ln\cos 3x$

               ↑   ↑   ↖   ↖

    differential of   *differential*   *differential*   *differential*
       $(\quad)^2$ *of ln*   *of cos*   *of 3x*

> An example of a function of a function of a function of a function of x.

Group B

1. $\dfrac{5}{x}$ 2. $\dfrac{1}{x+1}$ 3. $\tan x$ 4. $\dfrac{1}{x\ln 5}$ 5. $\dfrac{\sec^2 2x}{\tan 2x(\ln\tan 2x)^{1/2}}$

ANSWERS TO EXERCISE 14.2

1. Yes. $I = \ln(x^2 - x) + A$

2. No. $\therefore \dfrac{d}{dx}(x^3 - x^2) = 3x^2 - 2x$

3. Yes. $I = \displaystyle\int \dfrac{4x}{x^2+1}\,dx = 2\int \dfrac{2x}{x^2+1}\,dx = 2\ln(x^2+1) + A$

4. Yes. $I = \ln\tan x$

5. Partially ln type $\therefore \displaystyle\int \dfrac{3x^2+1}{x^3}\,dx = \int \dfrac{3x^2}{x^3} + \dfrac{1}{x^3}\,dx = \int \dfrac{3}{x}\,dx + \int x^{-3}\,dx$

$$= 3\ln x - \dfrac{x^{-2}}{2} + A = 3\ln x - \dfrac{1}{2x^2} + A$$

> You must be prepared to manipulate the functions as necessary.

ANSWERS TO EXERCISE 14.3

Group A

1. $\displaystyle\int \dfrac{3}{4x+2}\,dx = \int \dfrac{3}{4}.\dfrac{4}{4x+2}\,dx = \dfrac{3}{4}\ln(4x+2) + A$

2. $\displaystyle\int \dfrac{4x+6}{x^2+3x}\,dx = \int 2.\dfrac{2x+3}{x^2+3x}\,dx = 2\ln(x^2+3x) + A$

3. $\displaystyle\int \dfrac{1}{2+2x+x^2}\,dx = \int \dfrac{1}{1+(1+x)^2}\,dx = \tan^{-1}(1+x) + A$

4. $\displaystyle\int \dfrac{2}{\sqrt{4-x^2}}\,dx = \int \dfrac{2}{2\sqrt{1-\left(\dfrac{x}{2}\right)^2}}\,dx = 2\sin^{-1}\left(\dfrac{x}{2}\right) + A$

5. $\displaystyle\int \frac{5}{1+x}\,dx = \int 5.\frac{1}{1+x}\,dx = 5\ln(1+x) + A$

Group B

1. $\displaystyle\int \frac{3x}{x^2+1}\,dx = \int \frac{3}{2}.\frac{2x}{x^2+1}\,dx = \frac{3}{2}\ln(x^2+1) + A$

2. $\displaystyle\int \frac{3}{x^2+1}\,dx = \int 3.\frac{1}{x^2+1}\,dx = 3\tan^{-1}x + A$

3. $\displaystyle\int \frac{2x-5}{(2x-3)^2}\,dx = \int \frac{2x-3}{(2x-3)^2} - \frac{2}{(2x-3)^2}\,dx = \int\left(\frac{1}{(2x-3)} - \frac{2}{(2x-3)^2}\right)dx$

$\qquad = \frac{1}{2}\ln(2x-3) + (2x-3)^{-1} + A$

4. $\displaystyle\int \frac{2x}{(1-x^2)^{1/2}}\,dx = -2(1-x^2)^{1/2} + A \qquad$ *see Exercise 12.7 question A3 solution*

5. $\displaystyle\int \frac{5x^2+5x+2}{(1-x)(1+x)^2}\,dx = \int\left(\frac{1}{(1+x)^2} - \frac{2}{(1+x)} + \frac{3}{(1-x)}\right)dx \qquad$ *partial fractions*

$\qquad = -\frac{1}{1+x} - 2\ln(1+x) - 3\ln(1-x) + A$

ANSWERS TO EXERCISE 14.4

1. $\displaystyle\int x\cos x\,dx = x\sin x - \int \sin x\,dx$

$\qquad = x\sin x + \cos x + A$

$\boxed{x = u,\ \cos x = \dfrac{dv}{dx}}$

2. $\displaystyle\int x^3\sin x\,dx = -x^3\cos x + \int 3x^2\cos x\,dx$

$\boxed{x^3 = u,\ \sin x = \dfrac{dv}{dx}}$

$\qquad = -x^3\cos x + 3\{x^2\sin x - \int 2x\sin x\,dx\}$

$\boxed{x^2 = u,\ \cos x = \dfrac{dv}{dx}}$

$\qquad = -x^3\cos x + 3x^2\sin x - 6\{-x\cos x + \int\cos x\,dx\}$

$\boxed{x = u,\ \sin x = \dfrac{dv}{dx}}$

$\qquad = -x^3\cos x + 3x^2\sin x + 6x\cos x - 6\sin x + A$

3. $\displaystyle\int x\ln x \, dx = \frac{x^2}{2}\ln x - \int \frac{x^2}{2}\cdot\frac{1}{x}\,dx$

$\ln x = u, \; x = \dfrac{dv}{dx}$

$\displaystyle \qquad = \frac{x^2}{2}\ln x - \frac{x^2}{4} + A \qquad \because \text{we cannot yet integrate } \ln x$

4. $\displaystyle\int x\tan^{-1}x \, dx = \frac{x^2}{2}\tan^{-1}x - \int \frac{x^2}{2}\cdot\frac{1}{1+x^2}\,dx$

$\tan^{-1}x = u, \; x = \dfrac{dv}{dx}$

$\displaystyle \qquad = \frac{x^2}{2}\tan^{-1}x - \frac{1}{2}\int\left(1 - \frac{1}{1+x^2}\right)dx$

$\begin{array}{c} x^2 + 1)x^2 \quad (1 \\ \dfrac{x^2+1}{} \\ -1 \end{array}$

$\displaystyle \qquad = \frac{x^2}{2}\tan^{-1}x - \frac{x}{2} + \frac{1}{2}\tan^{-1}x + A$

5. $\displaystyle\int \frac{1}{x^2}\ln x = -\frac{1}{x}\ln x + \int \frac{1}{x}\cdot\frac{1}{x}\,dx$

$\ln x = u, \; \dfrac{1}{x^2} = \dfrac{dv}{dx}$

$\displaystyle \qquad = -\frac{1}{x}\ln x - \frac{1}{x} + A$

ANSWERS TO EXERCISE 14.5

1. $\displaystyle\int \tan^{-1}x \, dx = \int 1\cdot\tan^{-1}x \, dx$

$\tan^{-1}x = u, \; 1 = \dfrac{dv}{dx}$

$\displaystyle \qquad = x\tan^{-1}x - \int \frac{x}{1+x^2}\,dx \qquad \text{top is differential of bottom hence } \ln$

$\displaystyle \qquad = x\tan^{-1}x - \tfrac{1}{2}\ln(1+x^2) + A$

2. $\displaystyle\int \sin^{-1}x \, dx = \int 1\cdot\sin^{-1}x \, dx$

$\sin^{-1}x = u, \; 1 = \dfrac{dv}{dx}$

$\displaystyle \qquad = x\sin^{-1}x - \int \frac{x}{\sqrt{1-x^2}}\,dx$

$\displaystyle \qquad = x\sin^{-1}x + \sqrt{1-x^2} + A$

ANSWERS TO EXERCISE 14.6

1. $y = e^{ax}$ (a) $\dfrac{dy}{dx} = ae^{ax}$ *applying function of function rule for differential*

       (b) $\displaystyle\int y\,dx = \int e^{ax}\,dx = \dfrac{1}{a}e^{ax}$ *check by differentiating*

2. $y = e^x\sin x$ $\dfrac{dy}{dx} = e^x\sin x + e^x\cos x$ *differential of a product*

3. $y = a^{cx}$ $\dfrac{dy}{dx} = \ln a\,.\,ca^{cx}$ *like question 1 but when the base is other than e there is a multiplying factor of lna*
                                – see working on page 241

4. $y = xe^x$

$$\int xe^x\,dx = xe^x - \int e^x\,dx \quad \text{by parts, } x = u,\ e^x = \dfrac{dv}{dx}$$
$$= xe^x - e^x + A$$

5. $y = e^{x\sin x}$ $\dfrac{dy}{dx} = e^{x\sin x}(\sin x + x\cos x)$ *function of function again – differential of xsinx in brackets*

ANSWERS TO EXERCISE 14.7

1. $\ln(2 + x) = \ln 2\left(1 + \dfrac{x}{2}\right)$ *Changing the appearance of the function to obtain ln(1 + ?)*

$$= \ln 2 + \ln\left(1 + \dfrac{x}{2}\right)$$
$$= \ln 2 + \dfrac{x}{2} - \dfrac{1}{2}\left(\dfrac{x}{2}\right)^2 + \dfrac{1}{3}\left(\dfrac{x}{2}\right)^3 - \cdots$$
$$= \ln 2 + \dfrac{x}{2} - \dfrac{x^2}{8} + \dfrac{x^3}{24} - \cdots$$

2. $e^{-3x} = 1 + (-3x) + \dfrac{(-3x)^2}{2!} + \dfrac{(-3x)^3}{3!} + \cdots$
$$= 1 - 3x + \dfrac{9x^2}{2} + \dfrac{9x^3}{2} + \cdots$$

3. $e^x\ln(1 - x) = \left(1 + x + \dfrac{x^2}{2} + \dfrac{x^3}{3!} + \cdots\right)\left(-x - \dfrac{x^2}{2} - \dfrac{x^3}{3} - \dfrac{x^4}{4}\cdots\right)$
$$= -x - \dfrac{3x^2}{2} - \dfrac{4x^3}{3} - x^4 - \cdots$$

247

4. $(3 + x)^2 e^{-x} = (9 + 6x + x^2)\left(1 - x + \dfrac{x^2}{2} - \dfrac{x^3}{6} + \cdots\right)$

   $= 9 - 3x - \dfrac{x^2}{2} + \dfrac{x^3}{2} - \cdots$

5. $(1 + x)^{-2} e^{3x} = \left(1 + (-2)x + \dfrac{(-2)(-3)}{2}x^2 + \dfrac{(-2)(-3)(-4)}{3!}x^3 + \cdots\right)\left(1 + 3x + \dfrac{(3x)^2}{2} + \dfrac{(3x)^3}{3!} + \cdots\right)$

   $= (1 - 2x + 3x^2 - 4x^3 + \cdots)\left(1 + 3x + \dfrac{9x^2}{2} + \dfrac{9x^3}{2} + \cdots\right)$

   $= 1 + x + \dfrac{3}{2}x^2 + \dfrac{x^3}{2} + \cdots$

Chapter 15

VECTORS

Aims and objectives

Having worked through this chapter you will know:

what are vector quantities

and be able to apply the **scalar, or dot, product** $\quad\quad\quad \mathbf{a} \cdot \mathbf{b} = ab \cos \theta$

$\quad\quad\quad\quad\quad\quad$ the **vector, or cross, product** (briefly)

$$\mathbf{a} \times \mathbf{b} = ab \sin \theta \cdot \mathbf{n}$$

and be able to apply the **vector equation of a line** $\quad\quad \mathbf{r} = \mathbf{a} + \lambda\mathbf{b}$

$\quad\quad\quad\quad\quad\quad$ the **vector equation of a plane** $\quad\quad\quad \mathbf{r} \cdot \mathbf{n} = c$

$$\text{and } \mathbf{r} = \mathbf{a} + \lambda\mathbf{p} + \mu\mathbf{q}$$

In this chapter we shall develop a knowledge of vectors and their applications.

Definitions

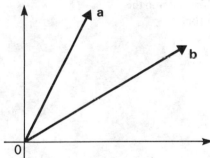

Vectors have the same magnitude but different direction $\therefore \mathbf{a} \neq \mathbf{b}$

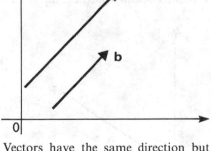

Vectors have the same direction but different magnitude. $\therefore \mathbf{a} \neq \mathbf{b}$ but $\mathbf{a} = n\mathbf{b}$

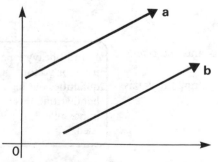

Vectors have the same magnitude and the same direction. $\therefore \mathbf{a} = \mathbf{b}$

> Vector quantities are those in which magnitude and direction matter.

Vector quantities surround us constantly in everyday life. Common examples are velocity, acceleration, force and weight. A good idea of how vector quantities can be combined can be gained from the following example.

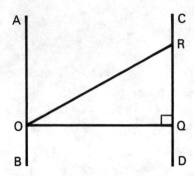

AB and CD represent the banks of a river which is flowing in direction DC at 1 mph. A swimmer who can swim at $1\frac{1}{2}$ mph sets off from O and wishes to get to Q. He swims in the direction OQ. He fails to reach Q but instead finishes up at R. He actually swims the path OR which is the combination of his swimming in the direction OQ added to the movement of the water in the direction CD. Mathematically the diagram would look like this.

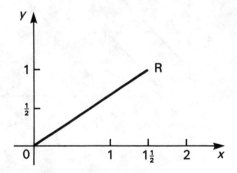

The swimmer's velocity is represented along the x-axis and the river's velocity along the y-axis.

A unit vector along the x-axis is represented by **i** and one along the y-axis by **j**.

The final velocity of the swimmer in this case is:

$1\frac{1}{2}\mathbf{i} + 1\mathbf{j}$ (OQ + QR in the first diagram)

A more simple way of writing this is $\begin{pmatrix} 1\frac{1}{2} \\ 1 \end{pmatrix}$.

> In print heavy type is used for vector quantities but in handwriting this is impossible ∴ i̲, j̲ etc are used.

This is known as a *column vector*.

Although the above diagram represents a very real situation it could also have been a purely geometrical diagram: a diagram of vectors. In this latter case the vector **OR** = **r** is known as the **position vector** of R. There is a close comparison here with the fixing of a point by coordinates.

The system easily extends to three dimensions where the third axis is the z-axis and the unit vector in that direction is usually called **k**.

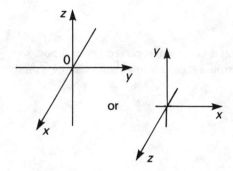

In three dimensions the axes must form a right-handed system; one is shown in this diagram.

Rotating a right-handed screw from Ox to Oy would take it positively along Oz.

Rotating a right-handed screw from Oy to Oz would take it positively along Ox.

Rotating a right-handed screw from Oz to Ox would take it positively along Oy.

EXERCISE 15.1

(*Answers on page 259*)

1. On one diagram draw the vectors (a) $\mathbf{a} = \begin{pmatrix} 1 \\ 5 \end{pmatrix}$ (b) $\mathbf{b} = \begin{pmatrix} 4 \\ 2 \end{pmatrix}$ (c) $\mathbf{a} + \mathbf{b}$
   (d) $\mathbf{a} - \mathbf{b}$. Write (c) and (d) in column vector form.

2. Given that $\mathbf{p} = \begin{pmatrix} 7 \\ 3 \end{pmatrix}$, $\mathbf{q} = \begin{pmatrix} 1 \\ -4 \end{pmatrix}$ and $\mathbf{r} = \begin{pmatrix} 2 \\ 0 \end{pmatrix}$ find, in column form,
   (a) $\mathbf{p} + 2\mathbf{q}$ (b) $2\mathbf{p} - 3\mathbf{q} + \mathbf{r}$ (c) $2\mathbf{q} - 3\mathbf{r}$ (d) $5(\mathbf{p} + 2\mathbf{r}) - 2(\mathbf{r} - 3\mathbf{q})$.

3. Two vectors **a** and **b** are such that $\mathbf{a} + \mathbf{b} = \begin{pmatrix} 6 \\ 2 \end{pmatrix}$ and $2\mathbf{a} - 3\mathbf{b} = \begin{pmatrix} -8 \\ 9 \end{pmatrix}$.
   Find **a** and **b** in column form.

4. The position vectors of A, B and C are $(6\mathbf{i} + 3\mathbf{j} + 2\mathbf{k})$, $(-3\mathbf{i} - 2\mathbf{j} + 6\mathbf{k})$ and $(3\mathbf{i} + 6\mathbf{j} - 2\mathbf{k})$ respectively. Name the solid OABC and any special properties it possesses.

5. A is the point with position vector $\begin{pmatrix} 4 \\ -2 \\ 1 \end{pmatrix}$ and B is the point with

position vector $\begin{pmatrix} 10 \\ 7 \\ 4 \end{pmatrix}$. C is the point which divides AB internally

in the ratio 2:1 and D divides AB externally in the ratio 3:2. Find the position vectors of C and D, the vector **CD** and the length of CD.

Products

We have considered the addition and subtraction of vectors and now we consider products. There are two products concerning vectors and we shall start by defining them.

Scalar product

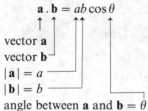

$$\mathbf{a}.\mathbf{b} = ab\cos\theta$$

vector **a**
vector **b**
$|\mathbf{a}| = a$
$|\mathbf{b}| = b$
angle between **a** and **b** = θ

For the scalar product, the result is a scalar quantity. Alternatively, it is called the **dot product**; it is important that this dot is written.

a . b

Vector product
(not required in this book – for information only)

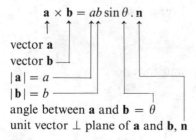

$$\mathbf{a} \times \mathbf{b} = ab\sin\theta.\mathbf{n}$$

vector **a**
vector **b**
$|\mathbf{a}| = a$
$|\mathbf{b}| = b$
angle between **a** and **b** $= \theta$
unit vector $\perp$ plane of **a** and **b**, **n**

For the vector product, the result is a vector quantity. Alternatively, it is called the **cross** or **vec product**; it is important that these signs are written.

a × **b**   or   **a** $_\wedge$ **b**

read 'a cross **b**'   or   '**a** vec **b**'

Now for the good news! In this book we are concerned only with the dot product. The cross product has been defined only to identify the two types of product.

By inspecting the definition of the scalar product,

$\mathbf{a} \cdot \mathbf{b} = ab\cos\theta$

it is not difficult to see that if $\mathbf{a}$ is perpendicular ($\perp$) to $\mathbf{b}$ then $\theta = 90°$ and $\cos\theta = 0$. Then the dot product is zero. Hence the condition for two non-zero vectors to be at right angles to each other is that the dot product is zero.

An important conclusion from this is:

$\mathbf{i} \cdot \mathbf{i} = 1 \times 1 \times \cos 0 = 1 \quad \Rightarrow \quad \mathbf{j} \cdot \mathbf{j} = 1 \quad \text{and} \quad \mathbf{k} \cdot \mathbf{k} = 1$

$\mathbf{i} \cdot \mathbf{j} = 1 \times 1 \times \cos 90° = 0 \quad \Rightarrow \quad \mathbf{j} \cdot \mathbf{i} = 0 \quad \text{and} \quad \mathbf{j} \cdot \mathbf{k} = 0$

$\mathbf{i} \cdot \mathbf{k} = 1 \times 1 \times \cos 90° = 0 \quad \Rightarrow \quad \mathbf{k} \cdot \mathbf{i} = 0 \quad \text{and} \quad \mathbf{k} \cdot \mathbf{j} = 0$

e.g. $(2\mathbf{i} + 3\mathbf{j}) \cdot (3\mathbf{i} + 4\mathbf{k}) = 6\mathbf{i} \cdot \mathbf{i} + 8\mathbf{i} \cdot \mathbf{k} + 9\mathbf{j} \cdot \mathbf{i} + 12\mathbf{j} \cdot \mathbf{k}$
$= 6 + 0 + 0 + 0 = 6$

e.g. $\begin{pmatrix} 2 \\ 3 \\ 4 \end{pmatrix} \cdot \begin{pmatrix} 5 \\ 4 \\ 3 \end{pmatrix} = 2 \times 5 + 3 \times 4 + 4 \times 3$ *all other products are zero as in the example above*
$= 10 + 12 + 12$
$= 34$

e.g. $\begin{pmatrix} 4 \\ 2 \\ -3 \end{pmatrix} \cdot \begin{pmatrix} 1 \\ 2 \\ 2 \end{pmatrix} = 4 + 2 - 6 = 0 \quad \therefore \quad \begin{pmatrix} 4 \\ 2 \\ -3 \end{pmatrix} \perp \begin{pmatrix} 1 \\ 1 \\ 2 \end{pmatrix}$

Vector equation of a line

We can now see that the mechanical operations involved in a scalar product are not difficult and we continue with two more items of theory after which we shall be able to look at various problems on vectors. The first item is the vector equation of a straight line.

From the geometry of the diagram:

$\mathbf{OR} = \mathbf{OA} + \mathbf{AR}$

$\mathbf{r} = \mathbf{a} + \lambda\mathbf{b}$

253

where **a** and **b** are constant and it follows, by inspection, that by varying λ different values of **r** are obtained but R will always be on the line *l*. If λ takes all values from $-\infty$ to $+\infty$ then the line *l* of infinite length will be generated. Since $\mathbf{a} + \lambda\mathbf{b}$ cannot possibly produce the position vector of a point which is not on the line it follows that $\mathbf{r} = \mathbf{a} + \lambda\mathbf{b}$ is unique to the line *l* and hence it is the vector equation of the line.

e.g. Sketch the lines with these vector equations.

(a) $\mathbf{r} = \begin{pmatrix} 5 \\ 1 \end{pmatrix} + \lambda\begin{pmatrix} -2 \\ 4 \end{pmatrix}$

(b) $\mathbf{r} = \begin{pmatrix} 3 + 2\lambda \\ \lambda - 1 \end{pmatrix}$

(c) $\mathbf{r} = (2\lambda - 1)\mathbf{i} + (3 + 4\lambda)\mathbf{j}$

(a) Firstly draw the vector $\begin{pmatrix} 5 \\ 1 \end{pmatrix}$ – OA on the diagram.

From A draw the vector $\begin{pmatrix} -2 \\ 4 \end{pmatrix}$ – AB on the diagram.

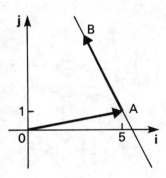

Produce AB and BA to get the required line.

(b) $\mathbf{r} = \begin{pmatrix} 3 + 2\lambda \\ \lambda - 1 \end{pmatrix} = \begin{pmatrix} 3 \\ -1 \end{pmatrix} + \begin{pmatrix} 2\lambda \\ \lambda \end{pmatrix}$

$\qquad = \begin{pmatrix} 3 \\ -1 \end{pmatrix} + \lambda\begin{pmatrix} 2 \\ 1 \end{pmatrix}$

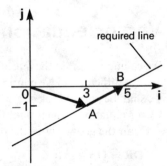

(c) $\mathbf{r} = (2\lambda - 1)\mathbf{i} + (3 + 4\lambda)\mathbf{j}$

$\qquad = (-\mathbf{i} + 3\mathbf{j}) + 2\lambda(\mathbf{i} + 2\mathbf{j})$

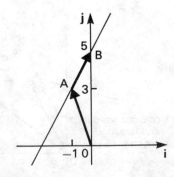

Vector equation of a plane

Before we develop the equation of a plane we need to look at a little problem. How do we define the direction of a plane? A line obviously has direction but how about a plane? What is the direction of a desk top? You may say that it is horizontal but that is not direction. The lines from the centre of it to the corners are horizontal but they are in different directions from each other.

Any plane has many lines at right angles to it but they all have one thing in common. They are in the same direction. If these lines are at right angles to a second plane then the second plane is parallel to the first one. In a room the corners of the walls, the door frames, the window frame verticals are all at right angles to the floor. They are also perpendicular to the ceiling and therefore the ceiling is parallel to the floor (which we knew anyway). It is this line at right angles to the plane, known as the **normal** to the plane, which is used as the basis when referring to the direction of a plane.

We can now look at the equation of a plane.

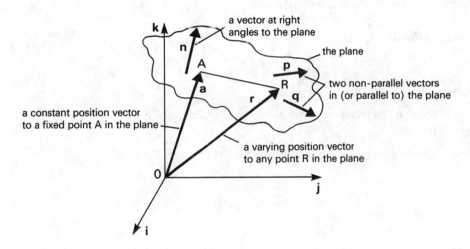

Since **n** is perpendicular to the plane and **AR** is in the plane, then:
AR $\perp$ **n**

$\therefore$ **AR** . **n** = 0   *scalar product of vectors at right angles*

but **AR** = **r** − **a** $\therefore$ (**r** − **a**) . **n** = 0

                 r . **n** − **a** . **n** = 0   *expansion of bracket as in ordinary algebra*

$\Rightarrow$ **r** . **n** = c   *where* **a** . **n** = c, *a constant*

This is one form of the vector equation of a plane.

Consider now two vectors **p** and **q** which are not parallel to each other but are in (or parallel to) the plane.

It is possible to find values of λ and μ so that

$$\mathbf{AR} = \lambda\mathbf{p} + \mu\mathbf{q}$$

and then $\mathbf{r} = \mathbf{a} + \mathbf{AR} = \mathbf{a} + \lambda\mathbf{p} + \mu\mathbf{q}$

> See further note immediately following.

which is another form of the vector equation of a plane.

Suppose we are given vectors $\mathbf{p}$ and $\mathbf{q}$ as shown and from them we wish to create the vector $\mathbf{AB}$.

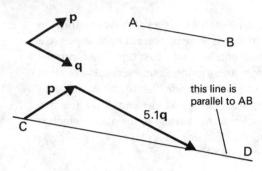

In this case $\mathbf{p} + 5.1\mathbf{q} = \mathbf{CD}$ which is parallel to $\mathbf{AB}$.

But, by measurement, $\mathbf{AB} = \dfrac{5}{12}\mathbf{CD}$

$$\therefore \mathbf{AB} = \frac{5}{12}\mathbf{p} + \frac{25\cdot5}{12}\mathbf{q}$$

Hence $\mathbf{AB}$ is in terms of $\mathbf{p}$ and $\mathbf{q}$ and we can now see the justification of the statement $\mathbf{AR} = \lambda\mathbf{p} + \mu\mathbf{q}$.

e.g. One of the four following vectors is not parallel to the other three. Find which one.

$$\begin{pmatrix} 3 \\ -1 \\ 2 \end{pmatrix} \begin{pmatrix} 1 \\ -\frac{1}{3} \\ \frac{2}{3} \end{pmatrix} \begin{pmatrix} 6 \\ -3 \\ 4 \end{pmatrix} \begin{pmatrix} -9 \\ 3 \\ -6 \end{pmatrix}$$

Let $\mathbf{a} = \begin{pmatrix} 3 \\ -1 \\ 2 \end{pmatrix}$.   Then $\mathbf{b} = \begin{pmatrix} 1 \\ -\frac{1}{3} \\ \frac{2}{3} \end{pmatrix} = \frac{1}{3}\begin{pmatrix} 3 \\ -1 \\ 2 \end{pmatrix} = \frac{1}{3}\mathbf{a}$

$$\mathbf{c} = \begin{pmatrix} 6 \\ -3 \\ 4 \end{pmatrix} = 2\begin{pmatrix} 3 \\ -\frac{3}{2} \\ 2 \end{pmatrix} \neq 2\mathbf{a}$$

$$\mathbf{d} = \begin{pmatrix} -9 \\ 3 \\ -6 \end{pmatrix} = -3\begin{pmatrix} 3 \\ -1 \\ 2 \end{pmatrix} = -3\mathbf{a}$$

Only the vector $\mathbf{c}$ is not a multiple of $\mathbf{a}$ $\therefore$ it is not parallel to $\mathbf{a}$ (or $\mathbf{b}$ or $\mathbf{d}$).

e.g. Show that the lines with vector equations $\mathbf{r} = \begin{pmatrix} 1 + 2\lambda \\ \lambda \\ 5 + 2\lambda \end{pmatrix}$ and $\mathbf{s} - \begin{pmatrix} 5 + \mu \\ -1 + 2\mu \\ 5 + 3\mu \end{pmatrix}$

intersect and state the position vector of their point of intersection.

Equating the **i** component: $1 + 2\lambda = 5 + \mu$ ⎫ Solving simultaneously

Equating the **j** component: $\lambda = -1 + 2\mu$ ⎭ $\Rightarrow \lambda = 3, \mu = 2$

Check these with the **k** component: vector **r**: $(5 + 2\lambda)\mathbf{k} = 11\mathbf{k}$

vector **s**: $(5 + 3\mu)\mathbf{k} = 11\mathbf{k}$

∴ the two lines intersect

and the point of intersection is (7, 3, 11). The point of intersection

has position vector $\begin{pmatrix} 7 \\ 3 \\ 11 \end{pmatrix}$.

e.g. Find the acute angle between the vectors $\begin{pmatrix} 3 \\ 1 \\ -1 \end{pmatrix}$ and $\begin{pmatrix} 1 \\ 5 \\ 3 \end{pmatrix}$.

Using the scalar product:

$$\begin{pmatrix} 3 \\ 1 \\ -1 \end{pmatrix} \cdot \begin{pmatrix} 1 \\ 5 \\ 3 \end{pmatrix} = \sqrt{(3^2 + 1^2 + (-1)^2)}.\sqrt{(1^2 + 5^2 + 3^2)}.\cos\theta$$

$$\Rightarrow \cos\theta = \frac{3 + 5 - 3}{\sqrt{11}\sqrt{35}}$$

$\Rightarrow \quad \theta = 75 \cdot 2°$, the angle between the two vectors.

EXERCISE 15.2

(*Answers on page 260*)

1. $\mathbf{a} = \begin{pmatrix} 1 \\ 2 \\ 3 \end{pmatrix}$, $\mathbf{b} = \begin{pmatrix} 3 \\ \lambda \\ 9 \end{pmatrix}$. Find the values of λ for which:

(a) **a** is parallel to **b** (b) **a** is perpendicular to **b**.

2. Find the vector equation of the line which passes through the point

with position vector $\begin{pmatrix} 2 \\ -1 \\ 3 \end{pmatrix}$ and is parallel to the vector $\begin{pmatrix} 5 \\ 0 \\ -1 \end{pmatrix}$.

3. Find the vector equation of the line which passes through the point

$(3, -2, 1)$ and is parallel to the line $\mathbf{r} = \begin{pmatrix} 1 + 2\lambda \\ \lambda \\ -2 \end{pmatrix}$.

4. Show that the lines with equations $\mathbf{r} = (3 + 2\lambda)\mathbf{i} + (2 + \lambda)\mathbf{j} + 3\lambda\mathbf{k}$ and $\mathbf{r} = (1 + 6\mu)\mathbf{i} + 4\mu\mathbf{j} + (2 + 4\mu)\mathbf{k}$ intersect.

5. Find the angle between the vectors $\begin{pmatrix} 2 \\ 1 \\ -2 \end{pmatrix}$ and $\begin{pmatrix} 3 \\ 2 \\ 0 \end{pmatrix}$.

6. Find the vector equation of the line which passes through the points $(3, 1, 2)$ and $(1, 2, -1)$.

7. Find the angle between the two lines with equations $\mathbf{r} = \begin{pmatrix} 1 + \lambda \\ 2 + 3\lambda \\ -2 \end{pmatrix}$

and $\mathbf{r} = \begin{pmatrix} 2 - \mu \\ 1 + 3\mu \\ 2\mu - 1 \end{pmatrix}$.

8. Find the vector equation of the plane which passes through the point $(3, 1, -2)$ and has as a normal the line with vector equation $\mathbf{r} = (1 + \lambda)\mathbf{i} + (2\lambda - 3)\mathbf{j} + (3 - \lambda)\mathbf{k}$.

9. Find the vector equation of the plane which contains the point $(4, 1, 5)$ and is parallel to the vectors $2\mathbf{i} - \mathbf{j} - 3\mathbf{k}$ and $5\mathbf{i} - 2\mathbf{k}$.

10. Use vector methods to prove the theorem of Pythagoras.

Answers to exercises

ANSWERS TO EXERCISE 15.1

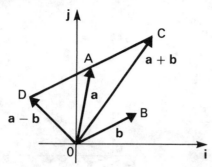

1. (a) $\mathbf{a} = \begin{pmatrix} 1 \\ 5 \end{pmatrix} = \mathbf{OA}$ (b) $\mathbf{b} = \begin{pmatrix} 4 \\ 2 \end{pmatrix} = \mathbf{OB}$

  (c) $\mathbf{a} + \mathbf{b} = \mathbf{OC} = \mathbf{OA} + \mathbf{AC}$ where $\mathbf{AC} = \mathbf{b}$ $\mathbf{a} + \mathbf{b} = \begin{pmatrix} 5 \\ 7 \end{pmatrix}$

  (d) $\mathbf{a} - \mathbf{b} = \mathbf{OD} = \mathbf{OA} + \mathbf{AD}$ where $\mathbf{AD} = -\mathbf{b}$ $\mathbf{a} - \mathbf{b} = \begin{pmatrix} -3 \\ 3 \end{pmatrix}$

2. (a) $\mathbf{p} + 2\mathbf{q} = \begin{pmatrix} 7 \\ 3 \end{pmatrix} + 2\begin{pmatrix} 1 \\ -4 \end{pmatrix} = \begin{pmatrix} 7 \\ 3 \end{pmatrix} + \begin{pmatrix} 2 \\ -8 \end{pmatrix} = \begin{pmatrix} 9 \\ -5 \end{pmatrix}$

  (b) $2\mathbf{p} - 3\mathbf{q} + \mathbf{r} = \begin{pmatrix} 14 \\ 6 \end{pmatrix} - \begin{pmatrix} 3 \\ -12 \end{pmatrix} + \begin{pmatrix} 2 \\ 0 \end{pmatrix} = \begin{pmatrix} 13 \\ 18 \end{pmatrix}$

  (c) $2\mathbf{q} - 3\mathbf{r} = \begin{pmatrix} 2 \\ -8 \end{pmatrix} - \begin{pmatrix} 6 \\ 0 \end{pmatrix} = \begin{pmatrix} -4 \\ -8 \end{pmatrix}$

  (d) $5(\mathbf{p} + 2\mathbf{r}) - 2(\mathbf{r} - 3\mathbf{q}) = 5\begin{pmatrix} 11 \\ 3 \end{pmatrix} - 2\begin{pmatrix} -1 \\ +12 \end{pmatrix} = \begin{pmatrix} 57 \\ -9 \end{pmatrix}$

3. Let $\mathbf{a} = \begin{pmatrix} p \\ q \end{pmatrix}$ and $\mathbf{b} = \begin{pmatrix} r \\ s \end{pmatrix}$. Then $\mathbf{a} + \mathbf{b} = \begin{pmatrix} p + r \\ q + s \end{pmatrix} = \begin{pmatrix} 6 \\ 2 \end{pmatrix}$ $\therefore p + r = 6$ and $q + s = 2$

  and $2\mathbf{a} - 3\mathbf{b} = \begin{pmatrix} 2p - 3r \\ 2q - 3s \end{pmatrix} = \begin{pmatrix} -8 \\ 9 \end{pmatrix}$ $\therefore 2p - 3r = -8$ and $2q - 3s = 9$

  Solving these pairs of equations simultaneously $\Rightarrow p = 2, r = 4, q = 3$ and $s = -1$.

  $\therefore \mathbf{a} = \begin{pmatrix} 2 \\ 3 \end{pmatrix}$ and $\mathbf{b} = \begin{pmatrix} 4 \\ -1 \end{pmatrix}$

4. Any solid with four vertices is a tetrahedron.

  Modulus of $\mathbf{OA} = \sqrt{(6^2 + 3^2 + 2^2)} = \sqrt{49} = 7$

  Modulus of $\mathbf{OB} = \sqrt{((-3)^2 + (-2)^2 + 6^2)} = 7$

  Modulus of $\mathbf{OC} = \sqrt{(3^2 + 6^2 + (-2)^2)} = 7$

5. Three-dimensional situations as in this problem are often very difficult to represent on paper and often a diagram representing two of the dimensions, **i** and **j**, is sufficient to provide a clear insight into the problem. Temporarily ignoring the **k** component we get the diagram shown.

C is such that AC:CB = 2:1.

i component of C = **i** cpt of A + $\frac{2}{3}$ × **i** cpt of **AB**

$\qquad = 4\mathbf{i} + \frac{2}{3} \times (10\mathbf{i} - 4\mathbf{i})$

$\qquad = 4\mathbf{i} + 4\mathbf{i} = 8\mathbf{i}$

Similarly **j** cpt $= -2\mathbf{j} + \frac{2}{3} \times (7\mathbf{j} - -2\mathbf{j}) = 4\mathbf{j}$

and similarly (but not on the diagram)

k cpt $= 1\mathbf{k} + \frac{2}{3}(4\mathbf{k} - 1\mathbf{k})$

$\qquad = 3\mathbf{k}$

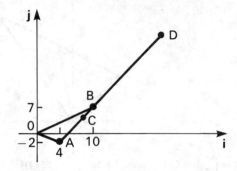

∴ position vector of C is $\begin{pmatrix} 8 \\ 4 \\ 3 \end{pmatrix}$.

For D: **i** cpt $\;=$ **i** cpt of A + 3 × **i** cpt of **AB** $= 4\mathbf{i} + 3 \times (10\mathbf{i} - 4\mathbf{i}) = 22\mathbf{i}$

Similarly **j** cpt $=$ **j** cpt of A + 3 × **j** cpt of **AB** $= -2\mathbf{j} + 3 \times (7\mathbf{j} - -2\mathbf{j}) = 25\mathbf{j}$

and **k** cpt $\quad =$ **k** cpt of A + 3 × **k** cpt of **AB** $= 1\mathbf{k} + 3 \times (4\mathbf{k} - \mathbf{k}) = 10\mathbf{k}$

∴ position vector of D is $\begin{pmatrix} 22 \\ 25 \\ 10 \end{pmatrix}$.

$$\mathbf{CD} = -\mathbf{OC} + \mathbf{OD} = - \begin{pmatrix} 8 \\ 4 \\ 3 \end{pmatrix} + \begin{pmatrix} 22 \\ 25 \\ 10 \end{pmatrix} = \begin{pmatrix} 14 \\ 21 \\ 7 \end{pmatrix} = 7 \begin{pmatrix} 2 \\ 3 \\ 1 \end{pmatrix}$$

Note: $\quad \mathbf{AB} = -\mathbf{OA} + \mathbf{OB} = - \begin{pmatrix} 4 \\ -2 \\ 1 \end{pmatrix} + \begin{pmatrix} 10 \\ 7 \\ 4 \end{pmatrix} = \begin{pmatrix} 6 \\ 9 \\ 3 \end{pmatrix} = 3 \begin{pmatrix} 2 \\ 3 \\ 1 \end{pmatrix}$

which confirms that **CD** is a multiple of **AB**.

$|\mathbf{CD}| = \sqrt{(14^2 + 21^2 + 7^2)} = \sqrt{7^2(2^2 + 3^2 + 1^2)} = 7\sqrt{14}$

ANSWERS TO EXERCISE 15.2

1. (a) If **a** is parallel to **b** then $\mathbf{a} = n\mathbf{b}$.

c.f. **i** and **k** components $n = \dfrac{1}{3}$ i.e. $\mathbf{a} = \dfrac{1}{3}\mathbf{b} \;\Rightarrow\; \lambda = 6$

(b) If **a** is perpendicular to **b** then $\mathbf{a} \cdot \mathbf{b} = 0$

i.e. $3 + 2\lambda + 27 = 0 \Rightarrow \lambda = -15$

2. Considering **i** and **j** components: $\mathbf{r} = \begin{pmatrix} 2 \\ -1 \end{pmatrix} + \lambda \begin{pmatrix} 5 \\ 0 \end{pmatrix}$

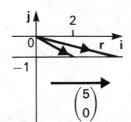

$\therefore$ required equation is $\mathbf{r} = \begin{pmatrix} 2 \\ -1 \\ 3 \end{pmatrix} + \lambda \begin{pmatrix} 5 \\ 0 \\ -1 \end{pmatrix}$

or $\mathbf{r} = \begin{pmatrix} 2 + 5\lambda \\ -1 \\ 3 - \lambda \end{pmatrix}$

3. Here we note the direct comparison between vector algebra and three-dimensional Cartesian geometry. The statements 'a point with coordinates $(3, -2, 1)$' and 'a point with position vector

$\begin{pmatrix} 3 \\ -2 \\ 2 \end{pmatrix}$' say the same thing.

The equation we are after is of the form $\mathbf{r} = \mathbf{a} + \lambda \mathbf{b}$.

We know $\mathbf{a} = \begin{pmatrix} 3 \\ -2 \\ 1 \end{pmatrix}$.

b has to be found from $\mathbf{r} = \begin{pmatrix} 1 + 2\lambda \\ \lambda \\ -2 \end{pmatrix} = \begin{pmatrix} 1 \\ 0 \\ -2 \end{pmatrix} + \begin{pmatrix} 2\lambda \\ \lambda \\ 0 \end{pmatrix}$

i.e. $\mathbf{r} = \begin{pmatrix} 1 \\ 0 \\ -2 \end{pmatrix} + \lambda \begin{pmatrix} 2 \\ 1 \\ 0 \end{pmatrix}$

Since the lines are parallel $\mathbf{b} = \begin{pmatrix} 2 \\ 1 \\ 0 \end{pmatrix}$

and the required equation is $\mathbf{r} = \begin{pmatrix} 3 \\ -2 \\ 1 \end{pmatrix} + \lambda \begin{pmatrix} 2 \\ 1 \\ 0 \end{pmatrix}$

4. At the point of intersection the values of **r** obtained from both equations are the same.

$(3 + 2\lambda)\mathbf{i} + (2 + \lambda)\mathbf{j} + 3\lambda\mathbf{k} = (1 + 6\mu)\mathbf{i} + 4\mu\mathbf{j} + (2 + 4\mu)\mathbf{k}$

$\therefore 3 + 2\lambda = 1 + 6\mu$ *The lines intersect only if there is a pair of values for λ and μ which satisfy all*

$2 + \lambda \quad = 4\mu$ *three equations.*

$3\lambda \quad = 2 + 4\mu$

Solving the first two $\Rightarrow -1 = 1 - 2\mu \Rightarrow \mu = 1, \lambda = 2$

Substituting these values in the third shows that it is satisfied by them $\therefore$ the lines intersect.

5. $\begin{pmatrix} 2 \\ 1 \\ -2 \end{pmatrix} \cdot \begin{pmatrix} 3 \\ 2 \\ 0 \end{pmatrix} = \sqrt{2^2 + 1^2 + (-2)^2} \cdot \sqrt{3^2 + 2^2 + 0^2} \cos\theta$ *definition of scalar product*

$\therefore 6 + 2 + 0 = \sqrt{9} \cdot \sqrt{13} \cdot \cos\theta$

$\therefore \theta = \cos^{-1}\left(\dfrac{8}{3\sqrt{13}}\right) = 42\cdot3°$

6. Again it will probably help if we consider a two-dimensional diagram first.
   The equation of the line is of the form:

   $\mathbf{r} = \mathbf{OB} + \lambda\mathbf{BA}$ or $\mathbf{r} = \mathbf{OB} + \lambda\mathbf{AB}$

   or $\mathbf{r} = \mathbf{OA} + \lambda\mathbf{BA}$ or $\mathbf{r} = \mathbf{OA} + \lambda\mathbf{AB}$

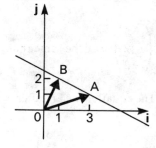

There is an element of choice but basically all these equations are the same.

$\therefore$ the required equation is: $\mathbf{r} = \begin{pmatrix} 3 \\ 1 \\ 2 \end{pmatrix} + \lambda \begin{pmatrix} 3 - 1 \\ 1 - 2 \\ 2 - -1 \end{pmatrix} = \begin{pmatrix} 3 \\ 1 \\ 2 \end{pmatrix} + \lambda \begin{pmatrix} 2 \\ -1 \\ 3 \end{pmatrix}$

i.e. $\mathbf{r} = \begin{pmatrix} 3 + 2\lambda \\ 1 - \lambda \\ 2 + 3\lambda \end{pmatrix}$

7. To find the angle between the lines we first need to know the direction vectors of the lines.

$\mathbf{r} = \begin{pmatrix} 1 + \lambda \\ 2 + 3\lambda \\ -2 \end{pmatrix} = \begin{pmatrix} 1 \\ 2 \\ -2 \end{pmatrix} + \lambda \begin{pmatrix} 1 \\ 3 \\ 0 \end{pmatrix}$ and $\mathbf{r} = \begin{pmatrix} 2 - \mu \\ 1 + 3\mu \\ 2\mu - 1 \end{pmatrix} = \begin{pmatrix} 2 \\ 1 \\ -1 \end{pmatrix} + \mu \begin{pmatrix} -1 \\ 3 \\ 2 \end{pmatrix}$

and the direction vectors are $\begin{pmatrix} 1 \\ 3 \\ 0 \end{pmatrix}$ and $\begin{pmatrix} -1 \\ 3 \\ 2 \end{pmatrix}$ respectively.

If θ is the angle between the lines $\cos\theta = \dfrac{\begin{pmatrix} 1 \\ 3 \\ 0 \end{pmatrix} \cdot \begin{pmatrix} -1 \\ 3 \\ 2 \end{pmatrix}}{\sqrt{10} \cdot \sqrt{14}}$

$\Rightarrow \theta = \cos^{-1}\left(\dfrac{8}{\sqrt{10}\sqrt{14}}\right) = 47 \cdot 5°$

8. The equation of the line is $\mathbf{r} = \begin{pmatrix} 3 \\ -3 \\ 3 \end{pmatrix} + \lambda \begin{pmatrix} 1 \\ 2 \\ -1 \end{pmatrix}$

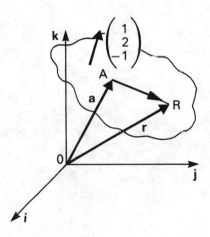

$\therefore$ the direction vector of the line is $\begin{pmatrix} 1 \\ 2 \\ -1 \end{pmatrix}$.

A is the fixed point with position vector $\begin{pmatrix} 3 \\ 1 \\ -2 \end{pmatrix}$.

then $\qquad \mathbf{AR} \cdot \begin{pmatrix} 1 \\ 2 \\ -1 \end{pmatrix} = 0$

$\therefore \left(\mathbf{r} - \begin{pmatrix} 3 \\ 1 \\ -2 \end{pmatrix}\right) \cdot \begin{pmatrix} 1 \\ 2 \\ -1 \end{pmatrix} = 0$

$\Rightarrow \mathbf{r} \cdot \begin{pmatrix} 2 \\ 2 \\ -1 \end{pmatrix} = 7 \qquad$ *the equation of the plane*

9. $\qquad \mathbf{r} = 4\mathbf{i} + \mathbf{j} + 5\mathbf{k} + \lambda(2\mathbf{i} - \mathbf{j} + 3\mathbf{k}) + \mu(5\mathbf{i} - 2\mathbf{k})$
$\therefore \mathbf{r} = (4 + 2\lambda + 5\mu)\mathbf{i} + (1 - \lambda)\mathbf{j} + (5 + 3\lambda - 2\mu)\mathbf{k}$

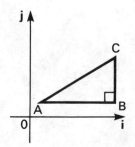

10. $\mathbf{AB} = c\mathbf{i}$, $\mathbf{BC} = a\mathbf{j}$, $\mathbf{AC} = c\mathbf{i} + a\mathbf{j}$, $|\mathbf{AC}| = b$

$$\mathbf{AC}.\mathbf{AC} = \begin{pmatrix} c \\ a \end{pmatrix} \cdot \begin{pmatrix} c \\ a \end{pmatrix} = c^2 + a^2$$

but $\mathbf{AC}.\mathbf{AC} = b \times b \times \cos 0 = b^2$

$\therefore b^2 = c^2 + a^2$ 　　　　*Pythagoras' theorem*

Now try worksheets 19 and 20.

Chapter 16

COMPLEX NUMBERS

Aims and objectives

Having worked through this chapter you will:

know what a complex number is $i = \sqrt{-1}, \; a + ib$

be able to draw and use an Argand diagram

know the basic algebra of complex numbers $a + bi$

know the r, θ form of a complex number $r \cos \theta + ir \sin \theta$

know the geometric representation of products and quotients

be able to solve problems on loci.

Definition of i

On pages 48 and 50 a brief reference was made to complex numbers. In this chapter this work is developed a little further.

We have already met the definition of i.

$$\sqrt{-1} = i$$

It follows that $i^2 = (\sqrt{-1})^2 = -1$

$$i^3 = i^2 \times i = -1 \times i = -i$$
$$i^4 = i^2 \times i^2 = -1 \times -1 = 1$$
$$i^5 = i^4 \times i = 1 \times i = i$$
$$i^6 = i^4 \times i^2 = 1 \times -1 = -1$$

and so a cycle develops for successive integer powers of i:

$i \quad -1 \quad -i \quad 1 \quad i \quad -1 \quad -i \quad 1 \quad i \quad -1 \quad -i \quad 1$

and so on.

EXERCISE 16.1

(*Answers on page 271*)

Evaluate these.

1. i^{11}

2. $3i \times (2 + 5i)$

3. i^{69}

4. i^{-7}

5. $2i^3 \times 3i^8 \times 5i^5$

Argand diagrams and conjugate numbers

Complex numbers can be represented diagrammatically.

OA represents the complex number $z = a + bi$

OC represents the complex number $\bar{z} = a - bi$

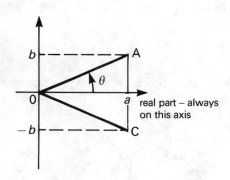

imaginary part – always on this axis (this is why physicists use j – it corresponds with the **j**-axis in vector work)

real part – always on this axis

Investigation

Find out about Jean Argand (Swiss) 1768–1822.

Now $\bar{z}$ is the **conjugate** of z. It has the same real part but a change of sign on the imaginary part.

Modulus of z: The length OA $= |z| = \sqrt{a^2 + b^2}$

Argument of z: The angle θ is the argument of $z = \arg z = \tan^{-1}\left(\dfrac{b}{a}\right)$.

Basic complex number algebra

Addition and subtraction of complex numbers is exactly the same as for vectors. The real parts are added and the imaginary parts are added.

  $(a + bi) + (c + di) = a + c + (b + d)i$

Multiplication follows the usual rules of algebra.

  $(a + bi) \times (c + di) = ac + adi + bci + bdi^2$
$$= ac - bd + (ad + bc)i$$

Division is dealt with as follows.

$$\frac{a + bi}{c + di} = \frac{(a + bi)(c - di)}{(c + di)(c - di)}$$ *the usefulness of the difference*
of two squares once more

$$= \frac{ac + bd + (bc - ad)i}{c^2 - i^2d^2}$$

$$= \frac{(ac + bd) + i(bc - ad)}{c^2 + d^2}$$

$$= A + Bi$$ *a normal complex number*

The (r, θ) form

OR represents a complex number of modulus r and argument θ. From the diagram OP $= r\cos\theta$ and PR $= r\sin\theta$.

Hence the number OR may be written

$$r\cos\theta + i \cdot r\sin\theta = r(\cos\theta + i\sin\theta) \qquad real + imaginary$$

This is known as the (r, θ) or **modulus, argument** form. We shall now consider multiplication and division of complex numbers in the (r, θ) form.

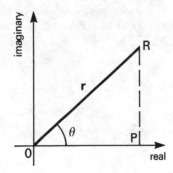

Investigation

Try these yourself first, by the same method as above.

$$p(\cos\alpha + i\sin\alpha) \times q(\cos\beta + i\sin\beta)$$

$$\frac{p(\cos\alpha + i\sin\alpha)}{q(\cos\beta + i\sin\beta)}$$

You should develop a certain pattern about the results. Read on when you are stuck or as a check.

Multiplication

$p(\cos\alpha + i\sin\alpha) \times q(\cos\beta + i\sin\beta)$

$\quad = pq(\cos\alpha\cos\beta + i\cos\alpha\sin\beta + i\sin\alpha\cos\beta + i^2\sin\alpha\sin\beta)$

$\quad = pq\{(\cos\alpha\cos\beta - \sin\alpha\sin\beta) + i(\sin\alpha\cos\beta + \cos\alpha\sin\beta)\}$

$\quad = pq(\cos(\alpha + \beta) + i\sin(\alpha + \beta))$ *using the compound angle formulae*

The result is a complex number of which the modulus is the product of the moduli and the argument is the sum of the arguments.

P and Q represent (p, α) and (q, β) *using the (r, θ) form*

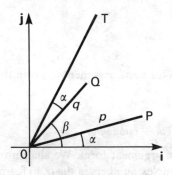

From above if $Q\hat{O}T = \alpha$ then $x\hat{O}T = \alpha + \beta$ and R (where OR $= pq$) lies on OT.

Now if PS (where S is at $(1, 0)$) is drawn and then $O\hat{S}P = \theta$ transferred to $O\hat{Q}R$ we have similar triangles ORQ and OPS in which:

$$\frac{OR}{OP} = \frac{OQ}{OS}$$

$$\Rightarrow \frac{OR}{p} = \frac{q}{1}$$

$$\Rightarrow OR = pq$$

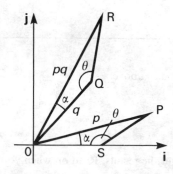

and hence OR represents the product of OQ and OP.

Division

$$\frac{p(\cos\alpha + \sin\alpha)}{q(\cos\beta + i\sin\beta)} = \frac{p(\cos\alpha + i\sin\alpha)(\cos\beta - i\sin\beta)}{q(\cos\beta + i\sin\beta)(\cos\beta - i\sin\beta)}$$

$$= \frac{p\{(\cos\alpha\cos\beta + \sin\alpha\sin\beta) + i(\sin\alpha\cos\beta - \cos\alpha\sin\beta)\}}{q(\cos^2\beta + \sin^2\beta)}$$

$$= \frac{p}{q}(\cos(\alpha - \beta) + i\sin(\alpha - \beta))$$

The result is a complex number of which the modulus is the division of the moduli, and the argument is the subtraction of the arguments.

Using a similar method of the one we used for multiplication, we form two similar triangles with p, α, q and β as shown and again OS = 1.

Then $\dfrac{OR}{OS} = \dfrac{OP}{OQ}$

$\Rightarrow\quad r = \dfrac{p}{q}$

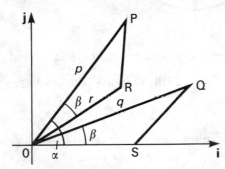

Hence OR represents the division of OP by OQ.

e.g. If $x + iy = 2(3 + 2i) + 3(1 - 2i)$, find the values of x and y.

$x + iy = 6 + 4i + 3 - 6i = 9 - 2i$

$\Rightarrow x = 9$ and $y = -2$

This follows from the method of equating the real parts and equating the imaginary parts.

It must be remembered here that if one complex number is equal to another they must have the same modulus and the same argument so it follows that they have the same real components and the same imaginary components.

e.g. Express $\dfrac{5}{3 + 2i}$ in the form $a + ib$.

$$\frac{5}{3 + 2i} = \frac{5}{(3 + 2i)} \cdot \frac{(3 - 2i)}{(3 - 2i)} = \frac{15 - 10i}{9 - 4i^2} = \frac{15 - 10i}{13}$$

This is now in the form $a + ib$ where $a = \dfrac{15}{13}$ and $b = -\dfrac{10}{13}$.

e.g. On a diagram shade the region covering all possibilities of the complex number z given that $2 < |z| < 4$ and $\dfrac{\pi}{6} < \arg z < \dfrac{\pi}{2}$.

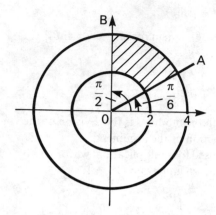

If $2 < |z| < 4$ then z lies between the two circles, radii 2 and 4. And if $\dfrac{\pi}{6} < \arg z < \dfrac{\pi}{2}$ then z lies between OA and OB. To satisfy both conditions z lies in the region shaded.

e.g. Show that the reciprocal of a complex number is equal to its conjugate divided by its modulus squared.

Let the complex number be $p + iq$.

Its reciprocal is $\dfrac{1}{p + iq} = \dfrac{1}{(p + iq)} \cdot \dfrac{(p - iq)}{(p - iq)}$

$$= \dfrac{p - iq}{p^2 + q^2} = \dfrac{\text{the conjugate}}{\text{the modulus squared}}$$

> This is the sort of question where the wording may frighten you – don't let it!

e.g. A complex number z and its conjugate $\bar{z}$ are such that $z\bar{z} + 2z = 12 + 6i$. Find the two possible values of z.

Let $z = x + iy$.

Then $(x + iy)(x - iy) + 2(x + iy) = 12 + 6i$

$\Rightarrow \quad x^2 + y^2 + 2x + 2yi \qquad = 12 + 6i$

$\therefore 2y = 6 \qquad$ *equating imaginary parts*

$\quad y = 3$

$\Rightarrow \quad x^2 + 3^2 + 2x = 12 \qquad$ *equating real parts and substituting for y*

$\therefore \quad x^2 + 2x - 3 = 0$

$\Rightarrow \quad x = -3 \quad \text{or} \quad 1$

$\therefore$ the values of z are $-3 + 3i \quad$ and $\quad 1 + 3i$.

EXERCISE 16.2

(*Answers on page 272*)

1. Find the value of $\dfrac{1 + 3i}{2 + i}$ by a geometrical method. Outline your method.

   This is more important than geometrical accuracy. Check your answers by calculation.

2. Express $1 - \sqrt{3}i$ in (r, θ) form.

3. $z = \dfrac{5 - 3i}{2 + i}$. Find $\arg z$, in radians.

   Write down $\arg z^2$ and find $|z^2|$.

4. Investigate the connection between the roots of a quadratic equation given that it has complex roots.

5. If $3 + i$ is a root of $x^2 + bx + c = 0$ find b and c given that they are real.

6. $z_1 = p + 2i$ and $z_2 = q + pi$. $z_1 + z_2 = 5$. Find p and q and find $z_1{}^2 - z_2{}^2$ in the form $a + ib$.

7. Given that $z = x + yi$ find z if $z^2 = 4i$ (x and y are real).

8. Find the square root of (a) $5 - 12i$ (b) $8i$.

9. Express the product $(5 + 4i)(3 + 2i)$ in the form $p + iq$. Similarly write down $(5 - 4i)(3 - 2i)$. Deduce the prime factors of $7^2 + 22^2$.

10. Given that x and y are real solve $\dfrac{7}{x + iy} = 1 - \dfrac{3}{5 - 2i}$ for x and y.

Answers to exercises

ANSWERS TO EXERCISE 16.1

1. $i^{11} = i^8 \times i^3 = (i^4)^2 \times i^3 = 1 \times -i = -i$
2. $3i(2 + 5i) = 6i + 15i^2 = 6i - 15$
3. $i^{69} = i^{68} \times i = (i^4)^{17} \times i = 1 \times i = i$
4. $i^{-7} = \dfrac{1}{i^7} = \dfrac{1}{i^4 \times i^3} = \dfrac{1}{-i} = -\dfrac{1}{i} \times \dfrac{i}{i} = -\dfrac{i}{-1} = i$

   > You have met this idea before – rationalising the denominator

5. $30i^{16} = 30(i^4)^4 = 30$

ANSWERS TO EXERCISE 16.2

1. Draw OQ and OP to represent $2 + i$ and $1 + 3i$ respectively.
   Measure $X\hat{O}Q \ (=25°)$ and make $P\hat{O}T$ the same.
   Join QS, measure $O\hat{Q}S \ (=19\cdot2°)$ and make $O\hat{P}R$ the same.

   Then OR represents $\dfrac{OP}{OQ}$ and OR $= 1\cdot04 + 1\cdot1i$.

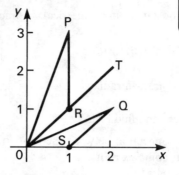

> Technical drawing/ engineering students should seek to produce a better diagram than the one given here!

   By calculation:

   $$\frac{1 + 3i}{2 + i} = \frac{(1 + 3i)(2 - i)}{(2 + i)(2 - i)} = \frac{5 + 5i}{5} = 1 + i.$$

2. $|1 - \sqrt{3}i| = \sqrt{1^2 + \sqrt{3}^2} = 2 \quad \Rightarrow r = 2$

   Then $1 - \sqrt{3}i = 2\left(\dfrac{1}{2} - \dfrac{\sqrt{3}i}{2}\right)$

   We are now looking for an angle θ where $\cos\theta = \frac{1}{2}$ and $\sin\theta = -\dfrac{\sqrt{3}}{2}$.

   By considering the signs we find the angle is in the 4th quadrant and by inspection of the values $\theta = \dfrac{5\pi}{3}$ or $-\dfrac{\pi}{3}$.

   Hence $1 - \sqrt{3}i = 2\left(\cos\left(\dfrac{-\pi}{3}\right) + i\sin\left(\dfrac{-\pi}{3}\right)\right)$

> It is normal for $-\pi < \arg z < \pi$

3. $z = \dfrac{(5 - 3i)}{(2 + i)}\dfrac{(2 - i)}{(2 - i)} = \dfrac{7 - 11i}{5}$

   Then $\arg z = \tan^{-1}\left(\dfrac{-11}{7}\right) = -1\cdot00$ rad (or $5\cdot284$ rad)

   $\arg z^2 = \arg z + \arg z = -2\cdot00$ rad

   $|z^2| = |z| \times |z| = |z|^2 = \left(\dfrac{7}{5}\right)^2 + \left(-\dfrac{11}{5}\right)^2 = \dfrac{170}{25} = 6\cdot8$

4. $ax^2 + bx + c = 0$ where a, b and c are real.
   If one root is $p + iq$ the other is $p - iq$.

   $\therefore$ *sum of roots* $= -\dfrac{b}{a}$ *which is real (no imaginary part)*

   Alternatively, $x = \dfrac{-b \pm \sqrt{b^2 - 4ac}}{2a}$ and since $b^2 < 4ac$

   the roots are $\dfrac{-b + \sqrt{b^2 - 4ac}}{2a}$ and $\dfrac{-b - \sqrt{b^2 - 4ac}}{2a}$.

   The roots are the conjugates of each other.

> Care must be taken to observe in which quadrant the complex number lies.
>
> Carelessly evaluating the $\tan^{-1}\left(-\dfrac{11}{7}\right)$ could give $2\cdot142$ rad which, whilst numerically correct, would indicate a number with a negative real part and a positive imaginary part, i.e. in the second quadrant. Our number here clearly lies in the 4th quadrant hence the answers given. When the words 'write down' appear in a question as in this one they must be taken literally. They imply that the answer can be written down directly without any working out.

5. One root is $3 + i$ so the other is $3 - i$.

   The sum of the roots $= 6 = -b \quad \therefore b = -6$

   Product of roots $= (3 + i)(3 - i) = 10 = c \quad \therefore c = 10$

6. $z_1 + z_2 = (p + q) + (p + 2)i = 5$

> This question can also be done by substituting $3 + i$ for x, equating real and imaginary parts and solving the simultaneous equations. Try it and see which way you prefer!

Equating imaginary parts: $\Rightarrow p + 2 = 0 \quad \therefore p = -2$

Equating real parts: $\Rightarrow p + q = 5 \quad \therefore q = 7$

$z_1{}^2 - z_2{}^2 = (z_1 + z_2)(z_1 - z_2) = 5(-9 + 4i) = -45 + 20i$

7. $(x + yi)^2 = x^2 - y^2 + 2xyi = 4i$

Equating imaginary parts: $xy = 2 \Rightarrow y = \dfrac{2}{x}$

Equating real parts: $x^2 - \dfrac{4}{x^2} = 0$

$$x^4 = 4$$
$$x^2 = 2 \quad \text{or} \quad x^2 = -2$$
$$x = \pm\sqrt{2} \quad x = \pm\sqrt{2}.i$$

x is real $\quad \therefore z = \pm\left(\sqrt{s} + \dfrac{2}{\sqrt{2}}i\right) = \pm\sqrt{2}(1 + i)$

8. (a) Let the square root be $p + iq$.

Then $(p + iq)^2 = 5 - 12i$

$\Rightarrow p^2 - q^2 + 2pqi = 5 - 12i$

$\Rightarrow p^2 - q^2 = 5 \quad \text{and} \quad pq = -6$

$\therefore p^2 - \dfrac{36}{p^2} = 5$

$\Rightarrow p^4 - 5p^2 - 36 = 0$

$(p^2 - 9)(p^2 + 4) = 6$

$\Rightarrow p = \pm 3 \quad \text{or} \quad p = \pm 2i$

$q = \mp 2$

$\therefore$ the square root is $\pm(3 - 2i)$

(b) Similarly:

$p^2 - q^2 + 2pqi = 8i$

$\Rightarrow \left.\begin{array}{l} p^2 - q^2 = 0 \\ pq = 4 \end{array}\right\} \Rightarrow p^2 - \dfrac{16}{p^2} = 0 \Rightarrow p = \pm 2, q = \pm 2$

$\therefore$ the square root is $\pm(2 + 2i)$

9. $(5 + 4i)(3 + 2i) = 15 - 8 + 12i + 10i = 7 + 22i$

$(5 - 4i)(3 - 2i) = 7 - 22i$

$7^2 + 22^2 = 7^2 - 22^2i^2$

$= (7 - 22i)(7 + 22i) = (5 - 4i)(3 - 2i)(5 + 4i)(3 + 2i)$

$= (5^2 - 4^2i^2)(3^2 - 2^2i^2)$

$= 41 \times 13$

10. $\dfrac{7}{x + iy} = 1 - \dfrac{3}{5 - 2i}$

$\Rightarrow \dfrac{7}{x + iy} + \dfrac{3}{5 - 2i} = 1 \Rightarrow 35 - 14i + 3x + 3yi = (x + iy)(5 - 2i)$

$\Rightarrow 35 + 3x + i(3y - 14) = 5x + 2y + i(5y - 2x)$

$\Rightarrow \left.\begin{array}{r} 35 + 3x = 5x + 2y \\ 3y - 14 = 5y - 2x \end{array}\right\} \Rightarrow \left.\begin{array}{r} 35 = 2x + 2y \\ -14 = 2y - 2x \end{array}\right\} \Rightarrow y = 5\tfrac{1}{4},\ x = 12\tfrac{1}{4}$

A good example of the use of imaginary numbers to solve a real problem:
- starting with $7^2 + 22^2$ which is real
- using complex factors
- finishing with 41×13 which is real.

Now try worksheets 21 and 22.

Chapter 17

DIFFERENTIAL EQUATIONS AND INTEGRATION BY SUBSTITUTION

Aims and objectives

Having worked through this chapter you will:

know what a differential equation is

be able to solve simple differential equations

be able to solve differential equations of the variables separable type

$$\frac{dy}{dx} = xy$$

$$\Rightarrow \int \frac{1}{y} \cdot dy = \int x dx$$

be able to integrate by substitution.

$$\int \frac{\sqrt{x}}{1-x} \cdot dx$$

Differential equations

An equation of the type $\dfrac{dy}{dx} = k$ is a differential equation, so called because it contains a differential, $\dfrac{dy}{dx}$.

Further examples of differential equations are:

$$\frac{d^2y}{dx^2} = -w^2x$$

$$\frac{dV}{dt} = a(V^2 - v)^2$$

$$\frac{d^2y}{dx^2} + 5\frac{dy}{dx} + 6y = ae^{3x}$$

because they contain differentials.

If we now take the first one:

$$\frac{dy}{dx} = k$$

$$\Rightarrow \quad y = kx + A$$

At this stage the differential equation has been solved. The differential has been 'removed'. This is the **general solution.**

If in addition we had further information which enabled us to be more precise about the solution and led us to say:

$$y = 2x + 1$$

we then have a **particular solution**.

Graphically $\dfrac{dy}{dx} = k$ tells us the gradient of y is constant.

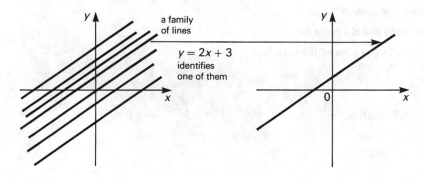

We have already met many differential equations, although they were not identified as such, and solving them inevitably means integration.

e.g. Solve the differential equation $\dfrac{dy}{dx} = 4x + 3$ given that $y = 6$ when $x = 1$.

$$\frac{dy}{dx} = 4x + 3$$

$$\Rightarrow y = 2x^2 + 3x + A \qquad \textit{integrating both sides w.r.t. x.}$$
$$\textit{This identifies a family of parabolas.}$$

Substituting: $\Rightarrow 6 = 2 + 3 + A$

$$\Rightarrow y = 2x^2 + 3x + 1 \quad \textit{A specific one from the family.}$$

After this we should be able to deal with differential equations of the type $\dfrac{dy}{dx} = f(x)$.

Separable variables

How would we deal with an equation of the form

$$\frac{dy}{dx} = f(y) \quad \text{such as} \quad \frac{dy}{dx} = y^2?$$

Rearranging:

$$\Rightarrow \frac{1}{y^2} \cdot \frac{dy}{dx} = 1$$

Integrating both sides:

$$\int \frac{1}{y^2} \cdot \frac{dy}{dx} \cdot dx = \int 1 \cdot dx$$

$$\Rightarrow \int \frac{dy}{y^2} = \int 1 \, dx$$

Note at this stage that we have one variable, y, appearing *only* on the LHS and the other variable, x, appearing *only* on the RHS.

An equation where this can be done is said to be of the **separable variables** type.

Continuing: $\quad -\frac{1}{y} = x + A$

$$\Rightarrow \quad xy + Ay + 1 = 0$$

There are no longer any differentials and the equation has been solved, in this case in the general form.

Separable variables differential equations occur frequently, particularly in mechanics and physics.

e.g. If $\dfrac{dv}{dt} = 3(5 - v)$ express v in terms of t given that $v = 0$ when $t = 0$.

$$\frac{dv}{dt} = 3(5 - v)$$

$$\Rightarrow \int \frac{dv}{5 - v} = \int 3 \, dt \longleftarrow \text{variables separated}$$

$$\Rightarrow -\ln(5 - v) = 3t + A \longleftarrow \text{integration done} \quad \left.\begin{array}{c} \\ \\ \\ \end{array}\right\} \text{the usual}$$

$$\therefore -\ln 5 = A \longleftarrow \text{given values substituted} \quad \text{routine}$$

$$\Rightarrow \ln 5 - \ln(5 - v) = 3t \longleftarrow \text{particular solution}$$

$$\ln\left(\frac{5}{5 - v}\right) = 3t$$

$$\frac{5}{5 - v} = e^{3t}$$

$$5e^{-3t} = 5 - v$$

$$\therefore v = 5(1 - e^{-3t}) \qquad \text{\textit{v in terms of t, as required}}$$

e.g. Solve the differential equation $\dfrac{dy}{dx} = xy - 3y + 2x - 6$.

$$\dfrac{dy}{dx} = xy - 3y + 2x - 6$$ *At first glance this question seems to have no distinctive features!*

$$\Rightarrow \dfrac{dy}{dx} = (x-3)(y+2)$$ *Inspection and perseverance produce this line which follows simple factorising.*

$$\Rightarrow \int \dfrac{dy}{y+2} = \int (x-3)\,dx$$

$$\therefore \ \ln(y+2) = \dfrac{x^2}{2} - 3x + A$$ *It is possible to go only as far as this general solution in this case.*

e.g. Solve the equation $\dfrac{d^2x}{dt^2} = -16x$ given that $\dfrac{dx}{dt} = 5$ when $x = 0$ and $x = 0$ when $t = 0$.

$\dfrac{d^2x}{dt^2}$ is the acceleration and

$$\dfrac{d^2x}{dt^2} = \dfrac{dv}{dt}$$

also $\dfrac{dv}{dt} = \dfrac{dv}{dx} \times \dfrac{dx}{dt} = v\dfrac{dv}{dx} \quad \left(\because \dfrac{dx}{dt} = v \right)$

$\therefore$ original equation is $v\dfrac{dv}{dx} = -16x$

$$\Rightarrow \int v\,dv = \int -16x\,dx \quad \textit{separating the variables}$$

$$\dfrac{v^2}{2} = -\dfrac{16x^2}{2} + A$$

Substituting $v = 5$, $x = 0$: $\quad \Rightarrow A = \dfrac{25}{2}$

$$\Rightarrow v^2 = 25 - 16x^2 \quad \textit{a useful equation, v in terms of x}$$

i.e. $\quad v = \sqrt{(25 - 16x^2)}$

$$\dfrac{dx}{dt} = \sqrt{(25 - 16x^2)}$$

$$\int \dfrac{dx}{\sqrt{(25 - 16x^2)}} = \int dt \quad \textit{separating the variables}$$

$$\Rightarrow \int \dfrac{1}{5} \dfrac{dx}{\sqrt{\left(1 - \left(\dfrac{4x}{5}\right)^2\right)}} = \int dt$$

$$\Rightarrow \dfrac{1}{4}\sin^{-1}\left(\dfrac{4x}{5}\right) = t + B$$

For mechanics students: this is SHM and the example is particularly useful.

Acceleration in differential form three ways: in terms of (a) x, t (b) v, t (c) v, x.

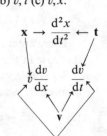

these two forms are particularly significant for mechanics students.

Substituting $x = 0$, $t = 0$: $\Rightarrow$ $B = 0$

$$\therefore \frac{4x}{5} = \sin 4t$$

$$x = \frac{5}{4}\sin 4t \qquad \textit{the solution required, x in terms of t}$$

EXERCISE 17.1

(*Answers on page 283*)

1. Solve the differential equation $\dfrac{dy}{dx} = y(2x + 1)$ given $y = 1$ when $x = 0$.

2. Solve the equation $\dfrac{1}{x}.\dfrac{dy}{dx} = 2$, given that the minimum value of the solution is 3.

3. The gradient of a curve is three times the ordinate of the point in question. Find the equation of the curve if it passes through $(0, e^2)$.

4. Given $y.\dfrac{dy}{dx} - (x + 1) = 0$ and $y = 0$ when $x = 0$ find the value of y when $x = 3$.

5. The area of the surface of a body increases at a rate which is twice the reciprocal of the time. If, when $t = 1$ second the area A is $1\ \text{cm}^2$ find A as a function of t.

Integration by substitution

From time to time during the course we have considered the matter of integration; first in chapter 11, trigonometry and inverse trigonometry in chapter 12, exponential, logarithmic and integration by parts in chapter 14. Now we come to the final section on integration.

In these questions the **integrand** does not readily fit into any of the types we have looked at so far. The **method of substitution** comes to the rescue.

As usual we shall tackle the problem by looking at some examples. As we do them, have constantly in mind that we are looking for substitutions which convert the integrand into a type we *can* deal with.

> Integrand: the bit you are trying to integrate; the bit between $\int$ and dx

e.g. $\quad I = \int x(x + 2)^7\,dx \qquad$ *this could be done by expanding the bracket and creating an eight term polynomial*

It is easier to let $u = x + 2$ $\Rightarrow$ $\dfrac{du}{dx} = 1$

$$\text{i.e.} \quad \int du = \int dx$$

Substituting: $\Rightarrow \displaystyle\int x\,(x + 2)^7\,dx \quad = \quad \int (u - 2).u^7\,du$

Hence $I = \int (u^8 - 2u^7)\,du$

$$= \frac{u^9}{9} - \frac{2u^8}{8} + A$$

$$\therefore I = \frac{1}{9}(x+2)^9 - \frac{1}{4}(x+2)^8 + A$$

Must convert back into the original variable in the case of an indefinite integral.

e.g. $I = \int \frac{\sqrt{x}}{1-x}\,dx$

Let $x = u^2 \Rightarrow \sqrt{x} = u$

$$\Rightarrow \frac{dx}{du} = 2u \quad \Rightarrow \int dx = \int 2u\,du$$

The awkward bit here is the $\sqrt{x}$ in the numerator $\Rightarrow$ if $x = u^2$ the root would disappear and $1 - u^2$ in the denominator would not be a problem; so try it!

$$\sqrt{x} = u$$

$$dx = 2u\,du$$

Substituting: $\Rightarrow \int \frac{\sqrt{x}}{1-x}\,dx \quad \Rightarrow \quad \int \frac{u \cdot 2u}{1-u^2}\,du$

$$x = u^2$$

and hence the integral is $I = \int \frac{2u^2}{1-u^2}\,du = \int \left(-2 + \frac{2}{1-u^2} \right) du$

$$I = \int \left(-2 + \frac{1}{1-u} + \frac{1}{1+u} \right) du \qquad \textit{using partial fractions}$$

$$= -2u - \ln(1-u) + \ln(1+u) + A$$

$$= -2u + \ln\left(\frac{1+u}{1-u} \right) + A$$

$$I = -2\sqrt{x} + \ln\left(\frac{1+\sqrt{x}}{1-\sqrt{x}} \right) + A$$

In a case like this, an indefinite integral, we must give our answer in terms of the variable in which the question was given. Hence the final stage of changing from u back to x.

e.g. $I = \int \frac{x^3}{(x+2)^2}\,dx$

We could already do this example; expand the denominator, divide etc.

Let $x + 2 = u \quad \Rightarrow \quad \int dx = \int du$

$$\therefore I = \int \frac{(u-2)^3}{u^2} du$$

$$= \int \frac{u^3 - 6u^2 + 12u - 8}{u^2} du$$

$$= \int \left(u - 6 + \frac{12}{u} - \frac{8}{u^2} \right) du$$

$$= \frac{u^2}{2} - 6u + 12\ln u + \frac{8}{u} + A$$

$$\int \frac{x^3}{(x+2)^2} dx = \frac{1}{2}(x+2)^2 - 6(x+2) + 12\ln(x+2) + \frac{8}{x+2} + A$$

Most people would say that in this case substitution makes the solution easier.

> You decide for yourself.

$$I = \int \frac{x}{\sqrt{(1-x^2)}} dx$$

> This has a familiar look about the denominator but it is confounded by the x in the numerator: so what?

Let $x = \sin\theta \quad \Rightarrow \quad \int dx = \int \cos\theta \, d\theta$

then $\quad I = \int \frac{\cos\theta . \sin\theta}{\sqrt{(1 - \sin^2\theta)}} d\theta$

> Remember that $\sqrt{(1-x^2)}$ is much simplified if $x = \sin\theta$, so try that.

$$= \int \frac{\cos\theta . \sin\theta}{\cos\theta} d\theta$$

$$= -\cos\theta + A$$

$$= -\sqrt{(1 - \sin^2\theta)} + A$$

$$= A - \sqrt{(1-x^2)}$$

> Remember that the suggestion of what to substitute was vague at the outset, it was just an idea. Expect this to happen often.

Change of limits

If we have a definite integral, changing our function may cause us to change our limit values.

$$I = \int_0^1 \frac{1}{e^x + e^{-x}} dx$$

$$\therefore I = \int_0^1 \frac{e^x}{e^{2x} + 1} dx$$

Let $\quad u = e^x$

$$\therefore \int du = \int e^x\,dx$$

$$\therefore I = \int_{x=0}^{x=1} \frac{du}{1+u^2} \quad \text{or} \quad \int_1^e \frac{du}{1+u^2}$$ *At this stage care must be taken with the limits.*

Here the limits are unchanged and since the integrand is now in terms of u they have to be specified as values of x.

In this version the limits have been changed according to the substitution:
when $x = 0$ $u = e^0 = 1$
and $x = 1$ $u = e^1 = e$
Usually this is the preferred (easier) method.

$$\therefore I = \left[\tan^{-1}u\right]_1^e$$
$$= \tan^{-1}e - \tan^{-1}1$$
$$= 0{\cdot}43$$

> The advantage of changing the limits can be seen here; there is no need to change back to the original variable.

e.g. $$I = \int_0^{\pi/4} \sin^5x\,dx$$ *a rather special type – odd powers of sin or cos functions*

Let $u = \cos x$

$$\Rightarrow \int du = \int -\sin x\,dx \quad \text{and} \quad \text{when } x = 0 \quad u = 1$$
$$x = \frac{\pi}{4} \quad u = \frac{1}{\sqrt{2}}$$

$$\therefore I = -\int_1^{1/\sqrt2} (1-u^2)^2\,du \qquad \because\ \sin^4x = (\sin^2x)^2 = (1-\cos^2x)^2$$

$$= -\int_1^{1/\sqrt2} (1 - 2u^2 + u^4)\,du$$

$$= -\left[u - \frac{2u^3}{3} + \frac{u^5}{5}\right]_1^{1/\sqrt2}$$

$$= -\left(\frac{1}{\sqrt2} - \frac{1}{3\sqrt2} + \frac{1}{20\sqrt2}\right) + \left(1 - \frac{2}{3} + \frac{1}{5}\right)$$

$$= -\frac{43}{60\sqrt2} + \frac{8}{15}$$

$$= 0{\cdot}0266$$

EXERCISE 17.2

(*Answers on page 285*)

1. Find y in terms of x given that $\dfrac{dy}{dx} = xe^{-2y}$ and $y = 1$ when $x = 0$.

2. Find $\displaystyle\int_0^1 \frac{1}{1 + e^x}\,dx$.

3. Find $\displaystyle\int \frac{e^x}{9 - e^{2x}}\,dx$.

4. The tangent to a curve has gradient equal to twice the ordinate of the point of contact. Find the equation of the curve given that it passes through the point $(1, 1)$.

5. A rectangular oil tank has a square base, of edge 50 cm, and at any time t the depth of the oil is h. If oil is being used at a rate equal to $25h^2$ find a differential equation connecting h and t. Also find the time it takes to empty from full, $h = 100$ cm, to quarter-full.

6. Evaluate $\displaystyle\int_0^2 \sqrt{(16 - x^2)}\,dx$.

7. Newton's law of cooling states that $\dfrac{d\theta}{dt} = -k(\theta - \theta_A)$ where θ is the temperature of the body, θ_A the temperature of the air which is constant, k is a constant and t is the time. If $\theta_A = 18°C$ and the body cools from $100°C$ to $60°C$ in 10 minutes how much longer will it take to cool to $20°C$?

8. Find $\int x\sqrt{(1 - x^4)}\,dx$.

9. Find $\displaystyle\int \frac{(1 + e^x)^2}{1 + e^{2x}}\,dx$

> Expand the numerator and be prepared for heavy going.

10. A mechanics problem results in the equation $\dfrac{dv}{dt} = g - v^2$, where v is the velocity and t is time. Find v in terms of t given that when $t = 0$, $v = 0$.

Answers to exercises

ANSWERS TO EXERCISE 17.1

1.
$$\frac{dy}{dx} = y(2x + 1)$$

$$\Rightarrow \int \frac{dy}{y} = \int (2x + 1)\,dx \qquad \textit{separating the variables}$$

$$\therefore \ln y = x^2 + x + A \qquad \textit{integrating}$$
$$\ln 1 = 0 + A \Rightarrow A = 0 \qquad \textit{substituting for x and y}$$
$$\therefore \ln y = x^2 + x$$

2.
$$\frac{1}{x}\cdot\frac{dy}{dx} = 2$$
$$\Rightarrow \int dy = \int 2x\,dx$$
$$\Rightarrow y = x^2 + A$$

Minimum when $x = 0$ $\therefore A = 3$ *from quadratic theory*

Solution is $y = x^2 + 3$

3.
$$\frac{dy}{dx} = 3y \qquad \textit{gradient equals three times ordinate}$$
$$\int \frac{dy}{y} = \int 3\,dx \qquad \textit{separating the variables}$$
$$\ln y = 3x + A$$
$$\Rightarrow y = e^{(3x+A)}$$
$$\Rightarrow y = e^{(3x+2)}$$

4. $y\cdot\dfrac{dy}{dx} - (x+1) = 0$
$$\Rightarrow \int y\,dy = \int (x+1)\,dx \qquad \textit{separating the variables}$$
$$\frac{y^2}{2} = \frac{x^2}{2} + x + A \qquad \textit{integrating}$$

$x = 0, y = 0 \Rightarrow A = 0.$

Then $x = 4 \Rightarrow y^2 = 4^2 + 2.4 = 24$
$$y = 4\cdot 9.$$

5.
$$\frac{dA}{dt} = \frac{2}{t} \qquad \textit{rate of increase of area } \left(\frac{dA}{dt}\right) = 2 \times \textit{reciprocal of t}$$
$$\therefore A = 2\ln t + c \qquad \textit{integrating}$$

When $t = 1, A = 1 \Rightarrow c = 1$
$$\therefore A = 2\ln t + 1$$

ANSWERS TO EXERCISE 17.2

1. $\dfrac{dy}{dx} = xe^{-2y}$

$\Rightarrow \displaystyle\int \dfrac{dy}{e^{-2y}} = \int x\,dx$ *separating the variables*

$\displaystyle\int e^{2y}\,dy = \int x\,dx$

$\dfrac{1}{2}e^{2y} = \dfrac{x^2}{2} + A$ *integrating*

$\dfrac{1}{2}e^2 = 0 + A \quad \therefore A = \dfrac{e^2}{2}$ *substituting*

$\Rightarrow e^{2y} = x^2 + e^2$

$2y = \ln(x^2 + e^2)$

$y = \dfrac{1}{2}\ln(x^2 + e^2) = \ln\sqrt{(x^2 + e^2)}$

2. $I = \displaystyle\int_0^1 \dfrac{1}{1 + e^x}\,dx$ *no obvious simplifying substitutions ∴ try $u = e^x$*

Let $u = e^x \Rightarrow \displaystyle\int du = \int e^x dx \Rightarrow \int dx = \int \dfrac{du}{e^x} = \int \dfrac{du}{u}$

$\therefore I = \displaystyle\int_1^e \dfrac{du}{u(1 + u)} = \int_1^e \left(\dfrac{1}{u} - \dfrac{1}{1 + u}\right) du$ *by partial fractions*

$\therefore I = \Big[\ln u - \ln(1 + u)\Big]_1^e$

$= (\ln e - \ln(1 + e)) - (\ln 1 - \ln 2)$

$= 1 + \ln\left(\dfrac{2}{1 + e}\right)$

3. $I = \displaystyle\int \dfrac{e^x}{9 - e^{2x}}\,dx$

Let $u = e^x \Rightarrow \displaystyle\int du = \int e^x dx$

$\therefore I = \displaystyle\int \dfrac{du}{9 - u^2} = \int \dfrac{du}{(3 - u)(3 + u)} = \dfrac{1}{6}\int \left(\dfrac{1}{3 - u} + \dfrac{1}{3 + u}\right) du$

$\therefore I = \dfrac{1}{6}\ln\left(\dfrac{3 + u}{3 - u}\right) + A$

$= \dfrac{1}{6}\ln\dfrac{(3 + e^x)}{(3 - e^x)} + A$

4. Gradient of tangent is $\dfrac{dy}{dx}$.

$$\therefore \dfrac{dy}{dx} = 2y$$

$$\Rightarrow \int \dfrac{dy}{y} = \int 2\,dx \qquad \textit{separating the variables}$$

$$\therefore \ln y = 2x + A$$

substituting $(1, 1) \Rightarrow 0 = 2 + A \quad \therefore A = -2$

and then $\ln y = 2x - 2 \quad$ or $\quad ye^2 = e^{2x}$

5. Volume of oil at any time: $\quad V = 2500\,h \qquad \textit{setting out the given information}$

Flow of oil $\qquad\qquad\qquad \dfrac{dV}{dt} = -25h^2 \qquad V \textit{ decreasing } \therefore \dfrac{dV}{dt} \textit{ is negative}$

> This is a busy question and an organised approach is required.

$$\dfrac{dV}{dt} = \dfrac{dV}{dh}\cdot\dfrac{dh}{dt} \quad \text{and} \quad \dfrac{dV}{dh} = 2500$$

$$\therefore -25h^2 = 2500\cdot\dfrac{dh}{dt}$$

$$\therefore \dfrac{dh}{dt} = -\dfrac{h^2}{100}$$

$$\Rightarrow \int dt = -\int \dfrac{100}{h^2}\,dh \quad \textit{a differential equation for h and t}$$

$$\Rightarrow \quad t = \dfrac{100}{h} + A$$

Substituting $t = 0,\ h = 100$: $\quad \Rightarrow A = -1$

$$\therefore t = \dfrac{100}{h} - 1 \qquad \textit{an equation for h and t}$$

When quarter-full $h = 25\,\text{cm}$ and then:

$$t = \dfrac{100}{25} - 1 = 3\,s$$

6. $I = \displaystyle\int_0^2 \sqrt{(16 - x^2)}\,dx \qquad \textit{not of recognisable type except that a trigonometric substitution is suggested}$

$$\therefore \text{let } x = 4\sin\theta \quad \int dx = \int 4\cos\theta\,d\theta$$

then $I = \int_0^{\pi/6} 4\cos\theta\sqrt{(16 - 16\sin^2\theta)}\,d\theta = \int_0^{\pi/6} 16\cos^2\theta\,d\theta$

$\Rightarrow I = \int_0^{\pi/6} 8(\cos2\theta + 1)\,d\theta \qquad using\ 2\cos^2\theta = \cos2\theta + 1$

$= 8\left[\frac{1}{2}\sin2\theta + \theta\right]_0^{\pi/6}$

$= 8\left(\frac{1}{2}\cdot\frac{\sqrt{3}}{2} + \frac{\pi}{6}\right) - 8(0 + 0)$

$= 2\sqrt{3} + \frac{4\pi}{3}$

7. $\qquad \dfrac{d\theta}{dt} = -k(\theta - \theta_A)$

$\Rightarrow \int\dfrac{d\theta}{\theta - \theta_A} = \int -k\,dt \qquad separating\ the\ variables$

Integrating $\Rightarrow \ln(\theta - \theta_A) = -kt + A$

Substituting $\theta = 100$, $t = 0 \Rightarrow \ln(100 - 18) = A \quad \therefore A = \ln82$

Substituting $\theta = 60$, $t = 10 \Rightarrow \ln(60 - 18) = -10k + \ln82$

$\therefore k = \dfrac{1}{10}\ln\left(\dfrac{82}{42}\right)$

Substituting $\theta = 20 \Rightarrow \ln(20 - 18) = -\dfrac{1}{10}\ln\left(\dfrac{82}{42}\right)\cdot t + \ln82$

$\Rightarrow \qquad t = \dfrac{10\ln\left(\dfrac{82}{2}\right)}{\ln\left(\dfrac{82}{42}\right)} = 55\cdot5\ \text{min}$

> This is a typical exponential result: cooling the first 40° taking 10 min and cooling the second 40° taking 45·5 min: these are realistic values.

$\therefore$ further time required $= 55\cdot5 - 10 = 45\cdot5\,\text{min}$

8. $\quad I = \int x\sqrt{(1 - x^4)}\,dx$

Let $x^2 = \sin\theta \quad \Rightarrow \quad \int 2x\,dx = \int\cos\theta\,d\theta$

$\therefore I = \int\frac{1}{2}\cos\theta\cdot\cos\theta\,d\theta$

$= \frac{1}{2}\int\frac{1}{2}(\cos2\theta + 1)\,d\theta \qquad\qquad using\ rule\ \mathbf{8}\ on\ page\ 185$

$= \frac{1}{4}\cdot\frac{1}{2}\sin2\theta + \frac{\theta}{4} + A \qquad\qquad sin2\theta = 2sin\theta\ cos\theta$

$$\therefore \ \Rightarrow \frac{1}{4}\sin\theta\cos\theta + \frac{\theta}{4} + A$$

$$= \frac{1}{4}x^2\sqrt{1-x^2} + \frac{1}{4}\sin^{-1}x^2 + A$$

Now $\sin\theta = x^2 \Rightarrow$

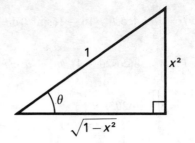

9. $\displaystyle I = \int \frac{(1 + e^x)^2}{(1 + e^{2x})}\,dx = \int\left(\frac{1}{1 + e^{2x}} + \frac{2e^x}{1 + e^{2x}} + \frac{e^{2x}}{1 + e^{2x}}\right)dx$

$\displaystyle \therefore I = \int \frac{1}{1 + e^{2x}}\,dx \quad + \int \frac{2e^x}{1 + e^{2x}}\,dx \quad + \int \frac{e^{2x}}{1 + e^{2x}}\,dx \qquad$ *three integrals*

$\displaystyle = I_1 \qquad\qquad\qquad + I_2 \qquad\qquad\qquad + I_3$

$$\text{Let } u = e^x$$

$$\int du = \int e^x\,dx \qquad I_3 = \frac{1}{2}\ln(1 + e^{2x})$$

$$I_1 = \frac{1}{2}\ln\left(\frac{e^{2x}}{1 + e^{2x}}\right) \qquad\qquad I_2 = \int \frac{2\,du}{1 + u^2}$$

$$\qquad\qquad\qquad\qquad\qquad\qquad = 2\tan^{-1}u$$

(as for question 2) $\qquad\qquad\qquad = 2\tan^{-1}(e^x)$

$$\therefore I = \frac{1}{2}\ln(e^{2x}) - \frac{1}{2}\ln(1 + e^{2x}) + 2\tan^{-1}(e^x) + \frac{1}{2}\ln(1 + 3^{2x}) + A$$

$$= x + 2\tan^{-1}(e^x) + A$$

10. $$\frac{dv}{dt} = g - v^2$$

$$\therefore \int \frac{dv}{g - v^2} = \int dt$$

$$\Rightarrow \frac{1}{\sqrt{2\sqrt{g}}}\int\left(\frac{1}{\sqrt{g} - v} + \frac{1}{\sqrt{g} + v}\right)dv = \int dt$$

$$\Rightarrow \frac{1}{2\sqrt{g}}\left[-\ln(\sqrt{g} - v) + \ln(\sqrt{g} + v)\right] = t + A \quad \textit{using } g - v^2 = (\sqrt{g} - v)(\sqrt{g} + v) \textit{ and partial fractions}$$

Substituting $t = 0$, $v = 0 \Rightarrow A = 0$

$$\therefore \ln\left(\frac{\sqrt{g} + v}{\sqrt{g} - v}\right) = 2\sqrt{g} \cdot t$$

$$\Rightarrow \quad \sqrt{g} + v = (\sqrt{g} - v)e^{2t\sqrt{g}}$$

$$v(1 + e^{2t\sqrt{g}}) = \sqrt{g}(e^{2t\sqrt{g}} - 1)$$

$$\therefore v = \frac{\sqrt{g}(e^{2t\sqrt{g}} - 1)}{(e^{2t\sqrt{g}} + 1)} \qquad v \text{ in terms of } t$$

Now try worksheets 23 and 24.

Chapter 18

COORDINATE GEOMETRY

Aims and objectives

Having worked through this chapter you will:

know the geometry of the straight line

$$y = mx + c$$
$$y - y_1 = m(x - x_1)$$

know the geometry of the conics

   parabola

   ellipse

   hyperbola

   circle

$$y^2 = 4ax$$
$$\frac{x^2}{a^2} + \frac{y^2}{b^2} = 1$$
$$xy = c^2$$
$$(x - f)^2 + (y - g)^2 = r^2$$

know the cartesian and parametric forms
be able to recognise curves by looking at their equations.

This chapter is about coordinate or analytical geometry which is distinct from Euclidean geometry. Euclidean geometry is the geometry of GCSE: angles in triangles, Pythagoras' theorem, angle properties of circles etc.

We have already met coordinate geometry under the heading 'Graphs' and what we are really about is looking at some particular functions.

Straight line geometry

Firstly the straight line, easily recognisable by its equation. All terms are of degree 1 or 0. It is usually written as:

$$ax + by + c = 0$$

or $\qquad y = mx + c$

This is a useful form because

$m =$ gradient

$c \;=\; y$-axis intercept.

Angle between lines

If two lines have gradients m_1 and m_2 the angle between them, θ, is given by:

$$\tan\theta = \frac{m_1 - m_2}{1 + m_1 m_2}$$

and if $\theta = 90°$, $\tan\theta = \infty$ $\quad \Rightarrow 1 + m_1 m_2 = 0 \quad \Rightarrow m_1 m_2 = -1$

Distance between points

If two points A and B have coordinates (x_A, y_A) and (x_B, y_B) then the distance between them is:

$$\sqrt{(x_A - x_B)^2 + (y_A - y_B)^2}$$

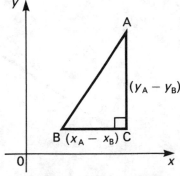

Distance of point from a line

We now find a formula for the distance (perpendicular) of any point (h, k) from the line $ax + by + c = 0$.

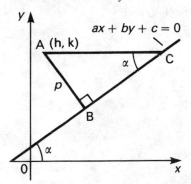

The x-coordinate of C is obtained by substituting $y = k$ in the equation $ax + by + c = 0$.

$$\Rightarrow \quad x_C = -\frac{(bk + c)}{a}$$

Now $p = \text{AC} \sin\alpha \qquad \tan\alpha = m = -\frac{a}{b} \Rightarrow$

$$= \left(-\frac{(bk + c)}{a} - h \right) \frac{a}{\sqrt{(a^2 + b^2)}}$$

i.e. $\quad p = \dfrac{ah + bk + c}{\sqrt{(a^2 + b^2)}}$

The negative sign is ignored because we are interested only in the modulus of p. In practice distances on one side of a base line are considered positive and those on the other are negative.

It is the usual convention to take the origin side of a line as positive.

e.g. Find the equation of the straight line passing through $(8, 6)$ and $(2, 3)$.
X is any point on the line and no matter where it is:

gradient XB = gradient AB

$$\therefore \quad \frac{y-3}{x-2} = \frac{6-3}{8-2} = \frac{3}{6} \text{ or } \frac{1}{2}$$

$$\Rightarrow \quad 2y - 6 = x - 2$$

$$2y = x + 4$$

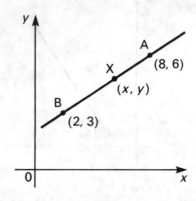

e.g. Find the equation of the straight line passing through the point $(1, 4)$ and with gradient $-\frac{3}{4}$.

Again X is any point (x, y) on the line and:

gradient XA = gradient of line

$$\therefore \frac{y-4}{x-1} = -\frac{3}{4}$$

$$\Rightarrow 4y - 16 = -3x + 3$$

$$\Rightarrow 4y + 3x = 19$$

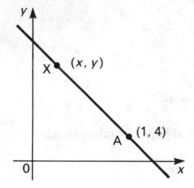

Formulae for equations of lines

It is useful to find formulae for the above examples. Using x_A, y_A as coordinates of A and x_B, y_B as coordinates of B, we have from the first example:

$$\frac{y - y_A}{x - x_A} = \frac{y_B - y_A}{x_B - x_A} \qquad \textit{use this if two points are given}$$

and from the second

$$\frac{y - y_A}{x - x_A} = m \qquad \textit{use this if one point and gradient are given}$$

Show that the points A(1, 1), B(4, 3) and C(3, −2) are the vertices of a square. Find the fourth vertex, D, and find the area of the square.

A, B and C are vertices of a square if AB = AC and AB ⊥ AC.

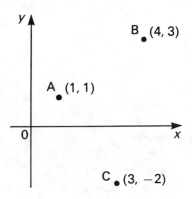

$$AB = \sqrt{(4-1)^2 + (3-1)^2} = \sqrt{13}$$
$$AC = \sqrt{(3-1)^2 + (-2-1)^2} = \sqrt{13} \quad \Rightarrow AB = AC$$
$$m_{AB} \times m_{AC} = \frac{(3-1)}{(4-1)} \times \frac{(-2-1)}{(3-1)} = -1 \quad \therefore AB \perp AC$$

So A, B and C are vertices of a square.

For D: $x_D - x_C = x_B - x_A$
$$\Rightarrow x_D - 3 = 4 - 1 \quad \Rightarrow \quad x_D = 6$$
and $y_D - y_C = y_B - y_A$
$$\Rightarrow y_D - -2 = 3 - 1 \quad \Rightarrow \quad y_D = 0$$
∴ D is the point (6, 0).

Area of ABCD = $AB^2 = \sqrt{13}^2 = 13$

Straight line approximations

Straight line graphs are often used, particularly in scientific experiments, to find out information about relationships between two variables when the relationships are not actually linear. An example or two will make this clear.

The table gives a set of readings obtained from an experiment.

x	1	2	3	4	5
y	2	2·5	2·67	2·75	2·8

x and y satisfy a relationship of the form $y + \dfrac{a}{x} = b$. By drawing a suitable linear graph find a and b and hence the specific relationship.

$y + \dfrac{a}{x} = b$ *may be written in the form*

$y + ax^{-1} = b$ *which is linear form for the variables*
                        y and x^{-1}, not y and x.

Hence we draw up a fresh table.

x^{-1}	1	0·5	0·3	0·25	0·2
y	2	2·5	2·67	2·75	2·8

and this leads to the following graph.

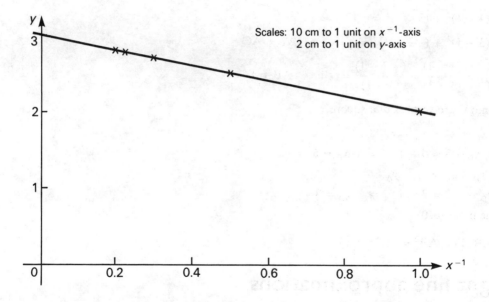

Scales: 10 cm to 1 unit on x^{-1}-axis
2 cm to 1 unit on y-axis

From the graph: slope $= \dfrac{3-2}{0-1} = -1$

and intercept $= 3$

$\Rightarrow$ equation is: $y = -x^{-1} + 3$

$$y + \frac{1}{x} = 3$$

It would have been a simple matter to draw the graph $y \propto x$ but it would not be easy to find a and b from it.

e.g. By drawing a linear graph determine the values of a and b in the equation $y = ab^x$ given that it is satisfied by the values in this table.

x	1	2	3	4
y	6·3	11·34	20·4	36·7

$y = ab^x$

This is an exponential variation. It can be converted to a linear form by taking logs throughout.

$$\Rightarrow \ln y = \ln(ab^x)$$
$$\ln y = \ln a + \ln b^x$$
$$\Rightarrow \ln y = x\ln b + \ln a$$

So a graph of $\ln y$ against x should give a straight line of gradient $\ln b$ and intercept $\ln a$.

The table of values becomes:

x	1	2	3	4
$\ln y$	1·8	2·4	3·0	3·6

and the graph is like this.

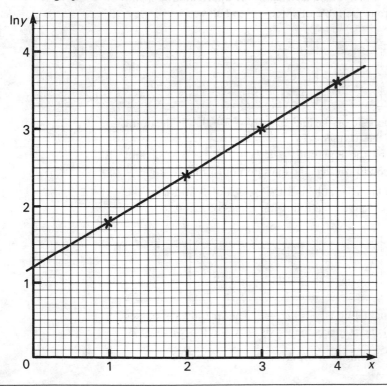

The scales are 2 cm to 1 unit on each axis. Intercept (on $\ln y$ axis) $= 1\cdot23$

$\Rightarrow 1\cdot23 = \ln a \quad \therefore a = 3\cdot4$

$\text{Gradient} = \dfrac{3\cdot6 - 1\cdot8}{4 - 1} = 0\cdot6$

$\therefore 0\cdot6 = \ln b \quad \Rightarrow \quad b = 1\cdot8$

Hence equation is:
$y = 3\cdot4 \,.\, 1\cdot8^x$

EXERCISE 18.1

(*Answers on page 304*)

1. Find the equation of the perpendicular bisector of the line joining the points $(10, 8)$ and $(4, 1)$.

2. Find the equation of the line which divides AB in the ratio 3:2 and makes an angle of $45°$ with AB where A is $(-4, -6)$ and B is $(6, -1)$, given that both lines have positive gradients.

3. The points $(1, 0)$, $(9, 7)$ and (p, q) are collinear. Find a relation between p and q. Deduce the equation of the line containing the points.

4. An experiment is performed with a view to finding the values of a and b in the equation $ay^2 + bx^2 = 24$. Using a straight line approximation find the values of a and b from the table of values given below.

x	1	1·5	2	2·5	3
y	4·7	4·4	4	3·4	2·4

5. A $(2, 1)$ and B $(-1, 3)$ both lie on the line $2x + 3y - 7 = 0$. C is the point $(5, 2)$. Find the area of the triangle ABC.

6. Three lines are given by the equations $y = 2x + 1$, $2y = 5 - 3x$ and $y = mx + 2$. Find the condition that the lines do not form a triangle.

7. By drawing a suitable linear graph find the values of p and q in the relationship $y = p + qx^{1/3}$ given the following values of x and y.

x	1	2	3	4	5
y	3	2·5	2·1	1·8	1·6

8. The equation of a straight line is $y = mx + c$. The line always passes through the point $(3, 4)$ and it meets the y-axis at A and the x-axis at B. Show that the locus of the midpoint of AB is $\dfrac{4}{y} + \dfrac{3}{x} = 2$.

Conics

We now consider the definitions of certain curves. The framework on which these definitions are based consists of a fixed point, the **focus**, and a fixed line, the **directrix.**

We can consider the path traced out by a moving point, P, which is obeying a particular rule. We study the **locus** of P.

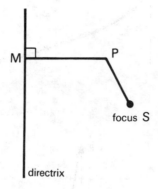

The rule is that:

$$\frac{\text{the distance of P from the focus}}{\text{the distance of P from the directrix}} = \text{a constant, } e.$$

$$\frac{\text{PS}}{\text{PM}} = e$$

e is the eccentricity.

The value of e determines the shape of the curve produced. It falls into one of three categories.

If $e < 1$ an **ellipse** is produced.

Cartesian equation: $\dfrac{x^2}{a^2} + \dfrac{y^2}{b^2} = 1$

> This is the second use of the letter e in a standard sense, the other was in logarithm and exponential work. For those doing mechanics it is used for the coefficient of restitution in impact problems.

Parametric form: $x = a\cos\theta,\ y = b\sin\theta$

Tangent equation: $ay\sin\theta + bx\cos\theta = ab$

Normal equation: $by\cos\theta - ax\sin\theta = (b^2 - a^2)\sin\theta\cos\theta$

Focus at $(\pm ae, 0)$

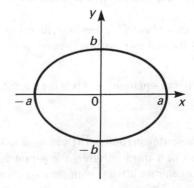

If $e = 1$ a **parabola** is produced.

Cartesian equation: $y^2 = 4ax$

Parametric form: $x = at^2, y = 2at$

Tangent equation: $ty = x + at^2$

Normal equation: $y + tx = 2at + at^3$

Focus at $(a, 0)$

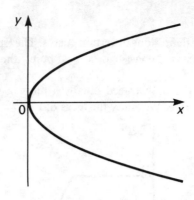

If $e > 1$ a **hyperbola** is produced.

Cartesian equation: $xy = c^2$

Parametric form: $x = ct, y = c/t$

Tangent equation: $t^2y + x = 2ct$

Normal equation: $y = t^2x + \dfrac{c}{t} - ct^3$

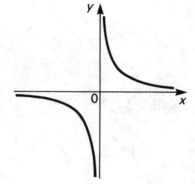

Cartesian and parametric forms

The information is given here, in this form, for easy reference later. We must now look at some of the details.

Cartesian equation: This is the equation of the function connecting x and y.

Parametric equation: In these equations x and y are expressed separately in terms of a third variable, the **parameter**. In each case if we eliminate the parameter we are left with the cartesian equation.

> It is a rewarding exercise to research Descartes.

Tangent and normal equations

Tangent and normal equations: These are given in terms of the parameter of the point of contact.

Equations of tangents and normals are all found in the same way. In the case of the parabola, substitute $x = at^2$, $y = 2at$.

At any point the gradient $= \dfrac{dy}{dx} = \dfrac{dy/dt}{dx/dt} = \dfrac{2a}{2at} = \dfrac{1}{t}$

∴ the equation of the **tangent** is:

$$\frac{y - 2at}{x - at^2} = \frac{1}{t} \quad \Rightarrow \quad ty = x + at^2 \quad using \; \frac{y - y_1}{x - x_1} = m \left(y_1 = 2at, \; x_1 = at^2, \; m = \frac{1}{t} \right)$$

For the **normal** the gradient is $-t$ and the equation is:

$$\frac{y - 2at}{x - at^2} = -t \quad \Rightarrow \quad y + tx = 2at + at^3$$

> The normal is the line passing through the point of contact of the tangent, ⊥ to the tangent or curve.

We have covered here the bare essentials of this work. The full study of these curves is a large and complex matter. The hyperbola mentioned here is a special case in that it is a **rectangular hyperbola** because its asymptotes are at right angles. The axes are also asymptotes and only thus does the equation become as simple as $xy = c^2$.

Sections of a cone

These curves are collectively known as the **conics**, short for conic sections, because they can be obtained by taking sections of a cone.

The diagram shows a cone of semi-vertical angle α. AB is a cross-section of the cone and AB makes angle β with the vertical. Different shapes are revealed as β takes different values.

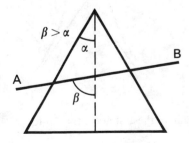

View ⊥ plane AB

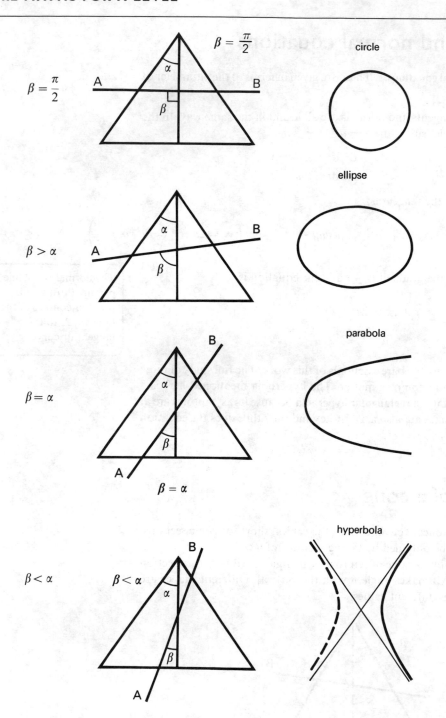

It would be time well spent to investigate where these shapes, the conics, occur. Consider, for starters:

the parabola: reflectors, radio telescopes

the ellipse: orbits (Kepler)

the hyperbola: gas laws (Boyle).

The circle

Finally in this section we must pay some attention to the **circle**. It can be considered as a special case of the ellipse, when $a = b$, and then the equation is:

$x^2 + y^2 = a^2$
or $x = a\cos\theta, y = a\sin\theta$.

Consider the circle shown, which has its centre at C (g, h). Then

$$CN^2 + NP^2 = CP^2$$
$$(x - g)^2 + (y - h)^2 = r^2$$
$$\Rightarrow \quad x^2 + y^2 - 2gx - 2hy + g^2 + h^2 - r^2 = 0$$

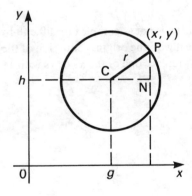

Now $(g^2 + h^2 - r^2)$ is constant in value, say c, and the standard equation of the circle is:

$x^2 + y^2 - 2gx - 2hy + c = 0$

where the centre is at (g, h)

and transforming $c = g^2 + h^2 - r^2 \quad \Rightarrow \quad r = \sqrt{(g^2 + h^2 - c)}$.

Recognition features of the equation of a circle are:

(a) equal coefficients of x^2 and y^2

(b) no xy terms.

The tangent equation

Consider the tangent at the point (x_1, y_1) on the circle.

$$x^2 + y^2 + 2gx + 2hy + c = 0$$

$$\Rightarrow 2x + 2y \cdot \frac{dy}{dx} + 2g + 2h \cdot \frac{dy}{dx} = 0 \qquad \textit{differentiating w.r.t. } x$$

$$\Rightarrow \frac{dy}{dx} = -\frac{(x+g)}{(y+h)}$$

$\therefore$ at (x_1, y_1) the gradient is $-\left(\dfrac{x_1 + g}{y_1 + h}\right)$ $\qquad$ *substituting* (x_1, y_1) *in* $\dfrac{dy}{dx}$

and the equation of the tangent is:

$$\frac{y - y_1}{x - x_1} = -\frac{x_1 + g}{y_1 + h} \qquad \textit{using } \frac{y - y_1}{x - x_1} = m$$

$$\Rightarrow yy_1 - y_1^2 + yh - y_1 h = -xx_1 - xg + x_1{}^2 + x_1 g$$
$$\Rightarrow yy_1 + xx_1 + g(x - x_1) + h(y - y_1) = x_1{}^2 + y_1{}^2$$
$$\Rightarrow xx_1 + yy_1 + g(x + x_1) + h(y + y_1) = x_1{}^2 + y_1{}^2 + 2gx_1 + 2hy_1$$

adding $2gx_1 + 2hy_1$ *to each side*

So $xx_1 + yy_1 + g(x + x_1) + h(y + y_1) + c = 0$
since (x_1, y_1) *is on the circle*

This equation, the tangent in cartesian form, is not as complex or difficult to remember as it at first appears. Compare it with the original equation of the circle. Wherever two xs or two ys appear replace one of the xs or ys with x_1 or y_1.

$$x^2 \rightarrow xx_1 \qquad\qquad y^2 \rightarrow yy_1$$
$$2x \rightarrow x + x_1 \qquad 2y \rightarrow y + y_1$$

> **Investigation**
>
> Can this idea be applied to all the conics equations? You should find it can and hence gives an easily remembered way of writing down the cartesian forms of the tangents.

Recognition of functions

Obviously there has been much algebra in this chapter and that cannot be avoided but it should be kept in perspective. To remember all the equations of curves, tangents, normals etc, that have been mentioned is quite a daunting task. We need to concentrate on the principles by which they are derived, repeatedly applying these principles, which apply to all functions anyway. Then we find that many of the results are automatically committed to memory.

As has been said before it is useful to be able to recognise a function immediately.

1. degree 1 throughout   straight line $ax + by + c = 0$
    $y = mx + c$

2. degree 2 on x or y parabola $(y - p)^2 = 4a(x - q)$
only, otherwise $y^2 = 4ax$
degree 1 $x^2 = cy$

3. degree 2 on x and y ellipse $\dfrac{x^2}{a^2} + \dfrac{y^2}{b^2} = 1$
sum of x^2 and y^2
no product terms

$$\frac{(x - p)^2}{a^2} + \frac{(y - q)^2}{b^2} = 1$$

4. product terms or   hyperbola $xy = c^2$
degree 2 on x and y
difference of x^2 $\dfrac{x^2}{a^2} - \dfrac{y^2}{b^2} = 1$
and y^2

5. degree 2 on x and y circle $x^2 + y^2 + 2gx + 2hy + c = 0$
equal coefficients of $(x - g)^2 + (y - h)^2 = r^2$
x^2 and y^2
no product terms

e.g. By considering the equations (a) to (e) determine which curves they represent.

(a) $y + 1 = \dfrac{1}{x - 1}$ hyperbola $\because (y + 1)(x - 1) = 1$
contains xy as only 2nd degree term (others are of degree 1 or 0)

(b) $2x^2 + 2y^2 + 5x - 7 = 0$ circle $\because$ equal coefficient of x^2 and y^2, no xy term

(c) $2y = x^2 + 1$ parabola $\because$ 2nd degree on x 1st degree on y

(d) $3x = y - 1$ straight line $\because$ degree 1 on x and y

(e) $2(y + 1)^2 = 9 - (x - 2)^2$ ellipse $\because$ degree 2 on x and y x^2 and y^2 terms are added but do not have same coefficient

EXERCISE 18.2

(*Answers on page 308*)

1. Find the equations of the tangents at the points P and Q, with parameters p and q respectively on the curve $y^2 = 4x$. If the tangents meet at R find the cartesian equation of the locus of R given that $p^2 + q^2 = 1$. State the coordinates of the vertex of the locus of R.

This is an 'in at the deep end' question; do not hesitate to turn to the solution.

2. Find the equation of the normal to the curve $\dfrac{x^2}{4} + \dfrac{y^2}{9} = 1$ at the point $(2\cos\theta, 3\sin\theta)$ and state the coordinates of the points where it cuts the axes. Given that $\theta = \dfrac{\pi}{3}$ find the distance between these two points.

3. Find the equation of the normal at the point $(4, 3)$ on the curve with equation $xy + x - 3y = 7$. Also find the coordinates of the point where the normal again meets the curve.

> Don't bother looking for standard results or formulae: it is better done from first principles.

4. $A(6, 2)$ and $B(-2, -4)$ are opposite ends of the diameter of a circle. Find its equation.

5. The circle given by $x^2 + y^2 = 9$ undergoes the transformation:

   $x \rightarrow x - 3$, $y \rightarrow y + 4$, scaling by a factor of 2.

   Find the equation of the new circle. Show both circles on a diagram and find the equation of the axis of symmetry of the two circles.

6. ASB is a focal chord of the parabola $y^2 = 16x$, where S is the focus and A is the point $(1, 4)$. Find the coordinates of B and the angle between the tangents at A and B.

> A challenge is set at the end of the solution to this question.

7. Does the point $(-1, 2)$ lie inside, outside or on the circle with equation $x^2 + y^2 + 6x - 10y + 18 = 0$?

8. Find the equations of the tangent(s) to the curve $2x^2 + y^2 = 12$ which have gradient of 2.

9. AB is a diameter of the hyperbola $xy = c^2$. The tangent at A meets the ordinate through B and P and the abscissa through B and Q. Show that PA = AQ.

10. The points $A(-1, 4)$ and $B(5, -3)$ are opposite ends of the diameter of a circle. Find the equation of the circle.

Answers to exercises

ANSWERS TO EXERCISE 18.1

1. The midpoint of the line from $(4, 1)$ to $(10, 8)$ is $(7, 4\frac{1}{2})$.   *this is* $\left(\dfrac{4 + 10}{2}, \dfrac{1 + 8}{2}\right)$

   Gradient of the line is $\dfrac{8 - 1}{10 - 4} = \dfrac{7}{6}$

   $\therefore$ gradient of $\perp$ line is $-\dfrac{6}{7}$ $m_1 m_2 = -1$ *for $\perp$ lines*

$\therefore$ line has gradient $-\dfrac{6}{7}$ and passes through $(7, 4\frac{1}{2})$.

$\Rightarrow \quad \dfrac{y - 4\frac{1}{2}}{x - 7} = -\dfrac{6}{7} \quad \Rightarrow \quad 7y - 31\frac{1}{2} = -6x + 42 \quad \Rightarrow \quad 7y + 6x = 73\frac{1}{2}$

The equation is: $14y + 12x = 147$

2. $\qquad x_C = x_A + AP = x_A + \dfrac{3}{5}AQ$

$\qquad \therefore x_C = -4 + \dfrac{3}{5}(6 - -4) = 2$

Similarly $y_C = -6 + \dfrac{3}{5}(-1 - -6) = -3 \quad \therefore C$ is $(2, -3)$

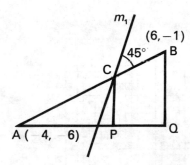

If m_1 is the gradient of the required line and m_2 the gradient of AB then

$\tan 45° = \dfrac{m_1 - m_2}{1 + m_1 m_2}$

$\Rightarrow \quad 1 = \dfrac{m_1 - \frac{1}{2}}{1 + \frac{1}{2}m_1} \quad \Rightarrow \quad m_1 = 3$

The required equation is:

$\qquad \dfrac{y - -3}{x - 2} = 3 \qquad \qquad using \ \dfrac{y - y_C}{x - x_C} = m_1$

$\qquad \Rightarrow y + 3 = 3x - 6$

$\qquad \qquad y = 3x - 9$

3. Slope of line $= \dfrac{7 - 0}{9 - 1} = \dfrac{q - 0}{p - 1}$

$\qquad \qquad \Rightarrow 7p - 7 = 8q$

Equation of line is: $8y = 7x - 7$

> Collinear points are points in the same straight line.

4. $ay^2 + bx^2 = 24$ $\Rightarrow$ $y^2 = -\dfrac{bx^2}{a} + \dfrac{24}{a}$

which will give a straight line if x^2 is plotted as abscissae and y^2 as ordinates.

The y^2 intercept is $\dfrac{24}{a}$ and the slope is $-\dfrac{b}{a}$.

Drawing up the table of values:

x^2	1	2·25	4	6·25	9
y^2	22·1	19·4	16	11·6	5·8

$\text{OA} = \dfrac{24}{a} = 24$ $\therefore a = 1$

$-\dfrac{b}{a} = \dfrac{24}{-12}$ $\Rightarrow$ $b = 2$

$\therefore$ the equation is: $x^2 + 2y^2 = 24$

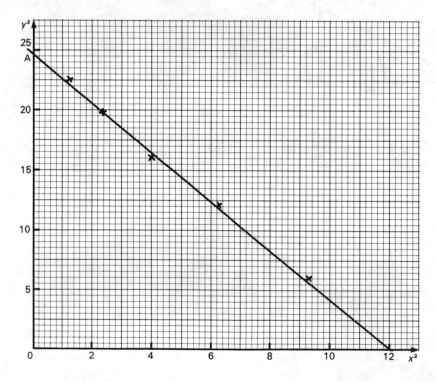

5. If D is the foot of the perpendicular from C to the line then the area $\triangle ABC$ is $\frac{1}{2} \times CD \times AB$.

$$\therefore A = \frac{1}{2} \times \frac{(2 \times 5 + 3 \times 2 - 7)}{\sqrt{2^3 + 3^2}} \times \sqrt{\{(2 - -1)^2 + (1 - 3)^2\}}$$

$$= \frac{1}{2} \times \frac{9}{\sqrt{13}} \times \sqrt{13}$$

$$= 4 \cdot 5 \text{ square units}$$

6. $y = 2x + 1$ and $2y = 5 - 3x$ are not parallel $\therefore$ they intersect. $y = mx + 2$ will not form a triangle with the others if it is parallel to either.

$\therefore$ the condition for no triangle is $m = 2$ or $m = -\frac{3}{2}$.

$y = 2x + 1$ and $2y = 5 - 3x$ meet at $x = \frac{3}{7}$, $y = \frac{13}{7}$ (found by solving simultaneously). If $y = mx + 2$ passes through $\frac{3}{7}, \frac{13}{7}$ then $m = -\frac{1}{3}$.

$\therefore m = -\frac{1}{3}$ is also a condition for no triangle.

7. Drawing up a new table of values:

$x^{1/3}$	1	1·3	1·4	1·6	1·7
y	3	2·5	2·1	1·8	1·6

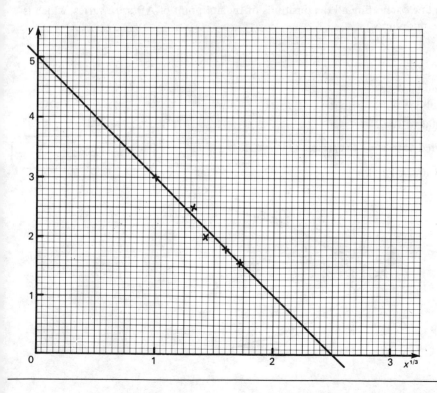

$p = y$-intercept $= 5$

$q = $ slope $= \dfrac{5-0}{0-2\cdot5} = -2$

$\therefore$ the equation is $y = 5 - 2x^{1/3}$

8. $y = mx + c$ contains $(3, 4)$.

$\therefore 4 = 3m + c \quad \Rightarrow \quad m = \dfrac{4-c}{3}$

the line is: $y = \dfrac{(4-c)}{3}x + c \qquad$ *eliminating m*

When $x = 0$, $y = c \quad \Rightarrow \quad$ A is $(0, c)$

When $y = 0$, $x = \dfrac{3c}{c-4} \quad \Rightarrow \quad$ B is $\left(\dfrac{3c}{c-4}, 0\right)$

If the midpoint of AB is $(x, y) \quad \Rightarrow \quad x = \dfrac{3c}{2(c-4)} \quad$ and $\quad y = \dfrac{c}{2}$.

Eliminating c: $\quad \Rightarrow \quad x = \dfrac{3y}{2y-4} \quad \Rightarrow \quad 2xy - 4x = 3y$

$$\text{or} \quad 2 = \dfrac{4}{y} + \dfrac{3}{x}$$

This is the x, y equation of the line connecting all the positions of the midpoint of AB as m varies, which is the equation of the locus of the midpoints.

ANSWERS TO EXERCISE 18.2

1. The first sentence says:

On $y^2 = 4x$ P is the point $(p^2, 2p)$

and Q is the point $(q^2, 2q)$.

NB   When $y^2 = 4x$ is compared with $y^2 = 4ax$ we see that $a = 1$.

See page 298.

Now find the equations of PR and QR.

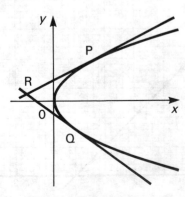

From page 297

      equation of tangent is $ty = x + at^2$

   $\therefore$ the equation of PR is $py = x + p^2$

and the equation of QR is $qy = x + q^2$

See page 298.

Solving these to find where they meet, R, gives:

$y = p + q, \; x = pq$

This is the parametric form of the locus of R.

    For the cartesian form we have to eliminate p and q.

$$y = p + q \;\Rightarrow\; y^2 = (p + q)^2 \qquad\qquad \textit{a common move at this stage}$$

$$= p^2 + q^2 + 2pq$$

$$\therefore y^2 = 1 + 2x \qquad\qquad \because p^2 + q^2 = 1 \text{ and } pq = x$$

This is a parabola.

It has a vertex where $y = 0 \Rightarrow (-\tfrac{1}{2}, 1)$ *equation is* $y^2 = 2(x + \tfrac{1}{2})$

In questions of this type the locus often turns out to be the same type of curve as the original.

2. The curve is an ellipse so the equation of the normal is of the form:

$by\cos\theta - ax\sin\theta = (b^2 - a^2)\sin\theta\cos\theta$

See page 298.

In this case $a = 2, b = 3$

$\therefore$ the normal is $3y\cos\theta - 2x\sin\theta = -5\sin\theta\cos\theta$

Cuts y-axis when $x = 0$, at $\left(0, -\dfrac{5}{3}\sin\theta\right)$

and the x-axis when $y = 0$, at $\left(\dfrac{5}{2}\cos\theta, 0\right)$.

If $\theta = \dfrac{\pi}{3}$ the points are $\left(0, -\dfrac{5\sqrt{3}}{6}\right)$ and $\left(\dfrac{5}{4}, 0\right)$

and the distance between them is $\sqrt{\left(\left(-\dfrac{5\sqrt{3}}{6}\right)^2 + \left(\dfrac{5}{4}\right)^2\right)} = 1\cdot 9$.

3. $xy + x - 3y = 7$ *a hyperbola*

$$\Rightarrow \; y + x\dfrac{dy}{dx} + 1 - 3\dfrac{dy}{dx} = 0$$

i.e. $\dfrac{dy}{dx} = \dfrac{y + 1}{3 - x}$

at $(4, 3)$ $\dfrac{dy}{dx} = \dfrac{3 + 1}{3 - 4} = -4$

$\therefore$ the gradient of the normal is $\dfrac{1}{4}$ and the equation of the normal is:

$$\dfrac{y-3}{x-4} = \dfrac{1}{4} \quad \Rightarrow \quad 4y = x + 8$$

To find where the normal again meets the curve substitute from the normal equation in the curve equation.

i.e. $(4y - 8)y + (4y - 8) - 3y - 7 = 0$

$\Rightarrow 4y^2 - 7y - 15 = 0$ \qquad It is known that $y = 3$ is one solution.

$\therefore (y - 3)(4y - 5) = 0 \quad \Rightarrow \quad y = \dfrac{5}{4}$ is the other solution.

The normal meets the curve again at $\left(-3, \dfrac{5}{4}\right)$.

4. The centre of the circle is at the midpoint of AB, $\left(\dfrac{6-2}{2}, \dfrac{2-4}{2}\right) = (2, -1)$.

The equation is: $(x - 2)^2 + (y - -1)^2 = (6 - 2)^2 + (2 - -1)^2$

$\Rightarrow x^2 + y^2 - 4x + 2y - 20 = 0$

5. $x^2 + y^2 = 9$ has a radius of 3.

$\therefore$ the new circle has a radius of 6 and its equation is:

$$(x - 3)^2 + (y + 4)^2 = 36$$
$$x^2 + y^2 - 6x + 8y - 11 = 0$$

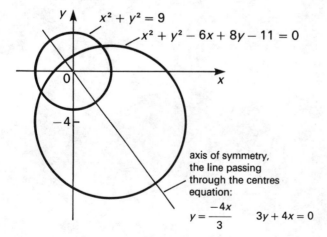

$x^2 + y^2 = 9$

$x^2 + y^2 - 6x + 8y - 11 = 0$

axis of symmetry, the line passing through the centres equation:

$y = \dfrac{-4x}{3} \qquad 3y + 4x = 0$

After these five questions, you will appreciate that questions on conics often seem to be long-winded and frightening, but if you have really tried to understand the principles involved you may be starting to think that they are really not so bad.

6. Compare $y^2 = 16x$ with $y^2 = 4ax$ where the focus is at $(a, 0)$.

Then the coordinates of S are $(4, 0)$ $(4a = 16 \Rightarrow a = 4)$.

A focal chord is one which passes through the focus.

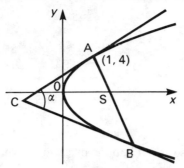

The equation of AB: $\dfrac{y}{x-4} = \dfrac{4}{1-4}$ $\Rightarrow$ $3y + 4x - 16 = 0$

To find B: solve the equation for AB with the equation of the parabola.

$y^2 = 16\dfrac{(16 - 3y)}{4}$ $\Rightarrow$ $y^2 + 12y - 64 = 0$ $\Rightarrow$ $(y - 4)(y + 16) = 0$

$\therefore$ at B $y = -16$ and $x = \dfrac{16 - 3 \cdot -16}{4} = 16$

B is $(16, -16)$.

The diagram shows tangents at A and B. The angle between them is α.

$\tan\alpha = \dfrac{m_1 - m_2}{1 + m_1 m_2}$ $\qquad$ *m, is the gradient of CA, m_2 is the gradient of CB*

$y^2 = 16x$ $\Rightarrow$ $2y\dfrac{dy}{dx} = 16$ $\Rightarrow$ $\dfrac{dy}{dx} = \dfrac{8}{y}$

$\therefore m_1 = \dfrac{8}{4} = 2$ and $m_2 = \dfrac{8}{-16} = -\dfrac{1}{2}$

These two values sound familiar: $\alpha = 90°$ $\quad \because m_1 m_2 = -1$

> **Challenge**
>
> Using $y^2 = 4ax$, focal chord PSQ (P has parameter p, Q has q) show that the tangents at the ends of a focal chord always meet at 90°.

7. The centre of the circle is at $(-3, 5)$ and the radius is $\sqrt{(-3)^2 + 5^2 - 10} = 4$.

The distance of the point from the centre $= \sqrt{\{(-1 - -3)^2 + (2 - 5)^2\}} = \sqrt{13} < 4$

$\therefore$ it is inside the circle.

8. $2x^2 + y^2 = 12$ is an ellipse.

$\therefore$ it will have two tangents of the same slope.

Differentiating $\Rightarrow 4x + 2y\dfrac{dy}{dx} = 0$ $\Rightarrow$ $\dfrac{dy}{dx} = -\dfrac{2x}{y}$

The gradient of the tangent is 2.

$\therefore -\dfrac{2x}{y} = 2$ $\Rightarrow$ $y = -x$ $\qquad$ *this is the connection between the coordinates at the points where the gradient is 2*

Substituting in $2x^2 + y^2 = 12$ $\Rightarrow$ $3x^2 = 12$ $\Rightarrow$ $x = \pm 2, y = \mp 2.$

Then the equations of the tangents are:

$$\frac{y - -2}{x - 2} = 2 \quad \Rightarrow \quad y = 2x - 6$$

and $\dfrac{y - 2}{x - -2} = 2 \quad \Rightarrow \quad y = 2x + 6$

9. The wording of the question, seemingly complex, sorts out into the diagram shown.

A is $\left(ct, \dfrac{c}{t} \right)$ $\therefore$ B is $\left(-ct, \dfrac{-c}{t} \right)$ *by symmetry*

The x-coordinate of P is $-ct$ (same as B).

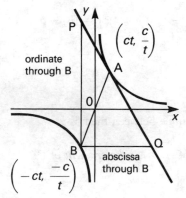

The x-coordinate of Q is where $y = -\dfrac{c}{t}$ meets the tangent $t^2 y + x = 2ct$. *See page 298.*

So $-\dfrac{ct^2}{t} + x_Q = 2ct \quad \Rightarrow \quad x_Q = 3ct$

Then $x_Q - x_A = x_A - x_P = 2ct$

$\therefore$ PA $=$ AQ.

10. Let P be any point (x, y) on the circle.

A$\hat{\text{P}}$B $= 90°$ $\Rightarrow$ gradient of AP $\times$ gradient of PB $= -1$

$$\Rightarrow \left(\frac{y - 4}{x - -1} \right)\left(\frac{y - -3}{x - 5} \right) = -1$$

$\Rightarrow x^2 + y^2 - 4x - y - 17 = 0$ *the equation of the circle*

A longer method would have been to use Pythagoras' theorem: AP^2 + PB^2 = AB^2

Now try worksheets 25 and 26.

WORKSHEETS

The following worksheets enable you constantly to review the work you are doing, and each worksheet should be started according to the table below.

Worksheet	After completion of chapter
1, 2	6
3, 4	8
5, 6, 7	9
8, 9	10
10, 11	11
12, 13, 14	12
15, 16	13
17, 18	14
19, 20	15
21, 22	16
23, 24	17
25, 26	18

WORKSHEET 1

1. Factorise $x + 9y - 6\sqrt{xy} - z$.

Try worksheets 1 and 2 after completing chapter 6.

2. Solve the equation $\dfrac{1}{x + 1} - \dfrac{2}{x + 2} - \dfrac{3}{x - 3} = \dfrac{2}{x^2 + 3x + 2}$.

3. Without using a calculator, evaluate $\left(\dfrac{8}{27}\right)^{-4/3} \times \left(\dfrac{4}{9}\right)^{2\frac{1}{2}}$.

4. Find x if $p^x = qr^x$.

5. $f(x) = x^2 + 8x + 10 + c$. Find the values of c if $f(x) > 0$.

6. Simplify and evaluate: $\dfrac{\sqrt{8} + \sqrt{2}}{\sqrt{8} - \sqrt{2}}$.

7. Solve for x the equation $\sqrt{x} + \sqrt{a} = \sqrt{c}$.

8. Without using a calculator, evaluate $9{\cdot}98^2 - 0{\cdot}02^2$.

9. Solve the equation $10(\log x)^2 - 39 \log x + 14 = 0$.

10. If the equations $x^2 - bx - c = 0$ and $x^2 - 2bx + 2c = 0$, where $c \neq 0$, have a common root, find the relation between b and c. Show that, if b is real, c is positive.

WORKSHEET 2

1. Starting with the graph of x^2 detail and sketch the transformations necessary to sketch $6x - 9 - x^2$.

2. If α and β are the roots of $x^2 - 6x + 4 = 0$ then find the value of
$$\frac{\alpha}{\beta + 1} + \frac{\beta}{\alpha + 1}.$$

3. A cyclist travels from A to B at an average speed of $(u + 5)$ mph and returns from B to A at an average speed of $(u - 5)$ mph. Find the average speed in mph for the whole journey if it is d miles from A to B.

4. Solve simultaneously for x and y the equations $axy = 1$ and $x + \dfrac{1}{y} = b$.
If x and y also satisfy $\dfrac{2}{x} + y = c$ prove that $(a + 1)(2a + 1) = abc$.

5. Express $\log_2 10$ in terms of m and n where $m = \log_3 6$ and $n = \log_6 5$.

6. Solve the equation $3x^2 = 1 + \dfrac{5}{x^2}$.

7. Simplify $\sqrt{288} - \sqrt{27} + 2\sqrt{243} - \sqrt{32}$ leaving your answer in surd form.

8. Solve for x the equation $\dfrac{4}{3^{x-2}} = 3.2^x$.

9. Simplify $\dfrac{3}{\sqrt{2} - 1} - \dfrac{3}{\sqrt{2} + 1}$.

10. Evaluate $81^{1/2} \times 27^{1/3} \times 6^{-2}$ without using a calculator.

WORKSHEET 3

1. Solve the equation $7x = 3x^2$.

2. Eight is the result of subtracting eighteen times a number from five times the square of the number, which is an integer. Find the number.

3. Solve the equation $9^x - 4.3^x + 3 = 0$.

4. Find the range of values of x for which $\dfrac{(x - 1)(3 - x)}{(x + 2)} > 0$.

5. Express $\dfrac{x^2 + 3}{(x + 2)^2(x - 1)}$ in partial fractions.

6. Complete $a - b = (a^{1/2} - b^{1/2})(\quad)$.

7. Given that $p = q^m$ and $q = p^n$ find a relationship between m and n.

8. Find x and y if $x^2 - y^2 = 5$ and $x^2 + xy - 3y^2 = 8$.

> Try worksheets 3 and 4 after completing chapter 8.

9. If α and β are the roots of $2x^2 + 7x - 3 = 0$ form the equation with roots $\alpha^2 + \dfrac{1}{\beta}$ and $\beta^2 + \dfrac{1}{\alpha}$.

10. Express $1 - 5\log_{10}p$ as the log of one number.

WORKSHEET 4

1. Find the range of values of x for which $\dfrac{2x^2 + 3x - 2}{4x - x^2 - 3} > 0$.

2. Find the condition that makes one root of $ax^2 + bx + c = 0$ k times the other.

3. $y = x - \dfrac{1}{x}$. Find $x^2 + \dfrac{1}{x^2}$ in terms of y and use your result to solve the equation $x^4 + 2x^3 - 5x^2 - 2x + 1 = 0$. [A harder question!]

4. Express $\dfrac{x^4}{x^2 - 3x - 10}$ in a form involving partial fractions.

5. Describe the transformations necessary to produce $2x^2 + 8x + 7$ from x^2. Illustrate each one.

6. Simplify $\dfrac{3^{n-2} \times 9^n}{27^{n/3} \times 81^{n/2}}$.

7. Solve the equation $x^3 + \dfrac{8}{x^3} = 9$.

8. Show that $\sqrt{7} - \sqrt{6} = \dfrac{1}{\sqrt{7} + \sqrt{6}}$.

9. Solve the simultaneous equations:
$$3x - 2y + z = 2$$
$$x + 2y + z = 8$$
$$5x - 3y + z = 2.$$

10. Find the quadratic equation with roots which are the cubes of the roots of $2x^2 + 6x - 5 = 0$.

WORKSHEET 5

1. Factorise $x^3 - 7x - 6$.
2. Evaluate $\{125^{2/3}(9^{1/2}.8^{1/3})^2\}^{1/2}$ without using a calculator.
3. Solve the equation $q^{x+1} - 10.3^x + 1 = 0$.

4. Given that $\log_{10}\left(\dfrac{P}{Q}\right) = \lambda t$ express P in terms of Q, λ and t.

Given that $Q = 15$, $\lambda = 0\cdot7$ and $t = 2\cdot9$ evaluate P.

[Try worksheets 5, 6 and 7 after completing chapter 9.]

5. $f(x) = x^2$, $g(x) = x + 2$, $h(x) = -x$. State $hgf(x)$ and sketch it.

6. Sketch $|hgf(x)|$ as defined in question **5**.

7. For which values of x is $\dfrac{4 - x}{6 + x - x^2}$ positive?

   For which values of x has the function no determinate value?

8. Solve the equations $\quad x + \dfrac{1}{y} = 6, \quad y + \dfrac{2}{x} = 1, \quad x, y \in \mathbb{R}$.

9. Resolve $\dfrac{x^2 + 2}{(x^2 + 2x + 3)(2x + 1)}$ into partial fractions.

10. Eliminate t from the equations $x = t^2$, $y = t^3$.
    Draw the graph of your resultant equation in x and y for $0 \leqslant x \leqslant 5$.
    Can you find a transformation which would convert your function into an even one? What would its equation be?

WORKSHEET 6

1. Find the range of values of λ for which $2x^2 + \lambda x + 50 = 0$ has real, different roots.

2. In the functions given in (a) to (e) decide whether they are even, odd or neither, justifying your answers.

   (a) $3x^5 - 4x + 2$ (b) $\dfrac{3x}{x^3 - 4x^5}$ (c) $|x^3|$

   (d) $2x^3 - x$ (e) $\dfrac{x^4 - 1}{x^2}$

3. Find the values of μ for which one root of $3x^2 + \mu x + 2 = 0$ is three times the other.

4. Sketch the graphs of (a) $|x + 2|$ (b) $\left| \dfrac{1}{x + 2} \right|$.

5. If $p + q = \dfrac{1}{(p + \sqrt[3]{r})^2}$ make r the subject.

6. Find a if the remainder when $x^3 + 2x^2 - ax + 7$ is divided by $x - 2$ is 1.

7. Find x if $p^{-x} q^{2x} = r^{x-2}$.

8. State the period of these functions. (a) $\sin 3x$ (b) $\cos 2x$ (c) $\tan x$.

9. α and β are the roots of $x^2 - 5x + 2 = 0$. Form the equation with roots $p\alpha + q\beta$ and $q\alpha + p\beta$.

10. Rationalise the denominator of $\dfrac{1}{1 + \sqrt{2} - \sqrt{3}}$.

WORKSHEET 7

1. Find γ from $pV^\gamma = c$ when $p = 1024$, $V = 468$ and $c = 5.6 \times 10^6$.
2. Find the range of values of k for which $x^2 - x + k = 0$ has real, distinct roots.
3. $f(x) = 5^x$, $g(x) = \log_{10} x$, $h(x) = 2x$. Find gfh(x). Find the value of x when gfh(x) = 3.
4. Draw the graph of $y = (2x - 1)^2(3 - x)$ for values of x from 0 to 3. Use it to find the range of values of k for which $(2x - 1)^2(3 - x) = kx$ has three real, distinct roots.
5. Write $7 - 12x - 3x^2$ in the form $p((x - q)^2 + r)$ and state the maximum or minimum value, identifying which it is. Describe the transformations which would produce the graph of $y = 7 - 12x - 3x^2$ from $y = x^2$.

6. Solve the inequality $\dfrac{x + 1}{x - 2} < 2$.

7. $f(x) = (x + 1)^2$ is defined for $x > 0$. Sketch the function and state its range. Find and sketch $f^{-1}(x)$ stating the domain and range.

8. Express $\dfrac{x}{(x - 1)^3}$ in partial fractions.

9. Simplify $\dfrac{\sqrt{128} - \sqrt{32} + \sqrt{8}}{\sqrt{3}(\sqrt{81} + \sqrt{27})}$ leaving your answer in surd form with a rational denominator.

10. Sketch the reciprocal of $f(x)$ if $f(x) = x^2 + x - 2$.

WORKSHEET 8

1. Differentiate (a) $(x^2 + 3)^3(1 - x)^5$ (b) $\dfrac{(x^2 + 3)^2}{(1 - x)^5}$ w.r.t. x.

> Try worksheets 8 and 9 after completing chapter 10.

2. Differentiate $x^3 - 4x$ from first principles.
3. Find the minimum value of $x^2 + 6x + 13$ by two quite different methods.
4. Sketch the curve $y = x^3 + 3x^2 - 9x - 3$ showing all important features.
5. The two functions, h and g are defined as $h(x) = \dfrac{1}{x}$ and $g(x) = x + 2$.

   Find gh(x) and the inverse of gh(x). Investigate the gradients of both of these composite functions and sketch them.
6. Find the maximum area which can be contained by 200 metres of fencing arranged in a rectangle.

7. Water is being poured into a hemispherical bowl at the rate of 5 litres per minute. If the depth of water at any instant is h the volume of water in the bowl is given by $V = \dfrac{\pi h^2}{3}(3r - h)$ where r is the radius, in this case 10 cm. Find the rate at which the water level is rising when $h = 5$ cm.

8. The formula for the perimeter of a rectangle is $P = 2(l + b)$. l is measured accurately but b is subject to an error of 2 mm. Use calculus methods to find the error in P. (This is not in the text; treat it as an investigation. **Hint:** Use basic definitions of calculus, δp etc.)

9. Differentiate $\dfrac{x^3(x^5 + 1)^5}{(x + 2)(x - 3)}$ w.r.t. x.

10. The velocity of a car is given by $v = 15 + \dfrac{10}{t}$. Find the acceleration when $t = 3$. (v in $\mathrm{m\,s^{-1}}$, t in s.)

WORKSHEET 9

1. Find the differential coefficient of $f^{-1}(x)$ where $f(x) = (x - 3)^2$ for $x > 3$.

2. Find the mean of the roots of $3x^2 + 5x - 2 = 0$.

3. The distance travelled by a particle is given by $x = \dfrac{t^3}{3} - \dfrac{5t^2}{2} + 6t$, where x is in metres from O (where $x = 0$ and $t = 0$). Find the distance from O when the velocity is zero and find the velocity when the acceleration is zero. Describe fully the first six seconds of the motion.

4. Use calculus to find the percentage change in the area of a circle if the radius changes by 0·5%.

5. Differentiate $\dfrac{1}{x(x - 1)(x + 1)}$ w.r.t. x.

6. Two cars approach a cross-roads (90°) at speeds of 40 mph and 50 mph. Find the rate at which the distance between them is changing when they are 1 mile and $\frac{1}{2}$ mile respectively from the junction.

7. Solve the inequality $\dfrac{12}{x + 1} > x + 2$.

8. Find $\dfrac{dy}{dx}$ if $y = \dfrac{\sqrt[3]{(x^3 - 1)}}{\sqrt{(1 - x)}}$.

9. Given that $z = \sqrt{1 + y^2}$ and $y = (x + 2)^5$ find $\dfrac{dz}{dx}$ when $x = -1$, $y = 1$, leaving your answer in surd form.

10. Solve the equation $8x^3 + 26x^2 - 24x = 0$.

WORKSHEET 10

Try worksheets 10 and 11 after completing chapter 11.

1. Water is being poured into a conical vessel (vertex downwards) at a constant rate. The diameter of the top is 20 cm and the height is 15 cm. Find the rate at which the vessel is being filled if the level is rising at $2\,\text{cm}\,\text{s}^{-1}$ when the depth of the water is 3 cm.

2. Evaluate $\displaystyle\int_0^4 \frac{2x}{\sqrt{x^2+9}}\,dx$.

3. Find the mean value of $y = x^2 + x + 1$ over the domain $1 \leqslant x \leqslant 4$.

4. Find $\displaystyle\int (x^2+1)(x^3+3x)^5\,dx$.

5. Find the area between the curve $y = 2 + x - x^2$ and the x-axis.

6. The slope of a curve is given by $ax + b$, where a and b are constants. When $x = 1$ the slope is 8 and when $x = 4$ it is 17. Find the equation of the curve given that it passes through (2, 18).

7. Find the area between the curve $y = x^2 - 7x + 10$, the x-axis and the ordinates $x = 1$ and $x = 3$. (The answer is not $\frac{2}{3}$.)

8. Find the value of $\dfrac{dy}{dx}$ for $2x^2 + 5xy - 3y^2 = 8$ when $x = 1$ and $y = 2$.

9. Integrate: (a) $\dfrac{(x+3)^2}{\sqrt{x}}$ (b) $(x+1)(x-1)(x+2)$.

10. The velocity of a bicycle is given by $v = 3t(t-2)$, $3 < t < 6$, t is time of travel in seconds. Find the distance travelled in the fifth second.

WORKSHEET 11

1. Find the mean value of $2x - 6$ between $x = 1$ and $x = 5$.

2. Evaluate $\displaystyle\int_0^2 (x-2)(x^2-4x)^3\,dx$.

3. A cuboid measures $6x$ by $3x$ by $2x$. Its volume is increasing at the rate of $2\,\text{m}^3/\text{min}$. Find the rate of increase of the surface area when $x = 3\,\text{m}$.

4. Find $\displaystyle\int \frac{x}{(5x^2+1)^2}\,dx$.

5. Evaluate $\displaystyle\int_4^9 \left(\frac{1}{\sqrt{x}} + \sqrt{x}\right)dx$.

6. Find the area enclosed between the curves $y = 2 - x^2$ and $y = x^2$ and the y-axis, $x > 0$.

7. The arc of the curve $y^2 + (x-5)^2 = 25$ between $x = 0$ and $x = 4$ is rotated through 2π about the x-axis. Calculate the volume generated.

Further explanation in solution.

Use $\displaystyle V = \pi\int_0^4 y^2\,dx$.

8. A particle has initial velocity $3\,\mathrm{m\,s}^{-1}$ and the acceleration $2t + 1\,\mathrm{m\,s}^{-2}$. Find the distance travelled in the second second.

9. Find the area enclosed between the curve $y = (x - 1)^3$, the y-axis and the ordinates $y = 0$, $y = 1$.

10. Use calculus to show that the volume of a cone is $V = \dfrac{\pi}{3}r^2h$.

WORKSHEET 12

1. Solve the equation $2\sin\dfrac{\theta}{4} = 1$ for $0 \leqslant \theta < 360°$.

2. Differentiate $x\sin x$ w.r.t. x stating the necessary condition.

3. Determine whether $2\cos^2 x$ is an odd function, an even function or neither.

4. Evaluate $\displaystyle\int_0^{\pi/6} \sin^5 x \cos x\,dx$.

5. The distance travelled by a particle in time t is given by $x = a\sin kt$. Express the acceleration as a function of the distance.

6. Prove that $\sin 5\theta + \sin 3\theta + \sin\theta = \sin 3\theta(4\cos^2\theta - 1)$.

7. Solve the equation $\sin 3\theta(4\cos^3\theta - 1) = 1$ for $0 \leqslant \theta \leqslant \pi$.

8. Ship A leaves port P simultaneously with ship B. A travels at 5 knots on a bearing of 030°; B goes at 4 knots on a bearing of 310°. Find the distance and bearing of A from B after one hour.

9. Solve the equation $\tan 2\theta + 1 = 0$ for $0 \leqslant \theta < 2\pi$. Give the general solution.

10. From A, 50 feet to the west, the top of a tree has an elevation of 40°. From B, due south, the elevation is 28°. Find the maximum elevation of the tree from any point on the line AB.

> Try worksheets 12, 13 and 14 after completing chapter 12.

WORKSHEET 13

1. Solve the equation $\cos 2x + 3\cos x - 1 = 0$ giving all solutions between 0 and 2π, and the general solution.

2. Evaluate $\displaystyle\int_0^{\pi/2} \sin^5 x\,dx$. **Hint:** $\sin^5 x = \sin x \sin^4 x$

> A statement of the obvious but very useful.

3. Show that $\dfrac{d(\tan\theta)}{d\theta} = \sec^2\theta$.

4. Find $\displaystyle\int \dfrac{2}{\sqrt{(9 - 4x^2)}}\,dx$.

5. Determine whether the function $\tan 3x$ is odd, even or neither. If it is periodic state the period.

6. Sketch the function $|\cos 2x|$ and describe it as fully as possible.

7. Evaluate $\displaystyle\int_0^1 \frac{1}{2 + 2x + x^2}\,dx$.

8. Solve the equation $5\sin x + 12\cos x = 5$ for $-\pi < x \leqslant \pi$.

9. Differentiate $\dfrac{\sqrt{\sin\theta}\,\cos\theta}{\sin\dfrac{\theta}{2}\cos\dfrac{\theta}{2}}$ w.r.t. θ.

10. Find the maximum value of $f(x)$ where $f(x) = 2 + \sin x - \sin^2\dfrac{x}{2}$. Leave your answer in surd form.

WORKSHEET 14

1. Find $\displaystyle\int \frac{3}{2x^2 + 12x + 20}\,dx$.

2. By drawing suitable graphs solve the equation $x = 5\sin 2x$ for $x > 0$.

3. Find $\dfrac{dy}{dx}$ from $\sin^2 x + \sin x\cos y + \cos^2 y = 1$.

4. Find $\displaystyle\int \cos^2(2x + 1)\,dx$.

5. Solve the equation $2\tan^2 x + \sec x + 1 = 0$ giving the general solution.

6. Find $\displaystyle\int \frac{1}{\sqrt{(3 + 2x - x^2)}}\,dx$.

7. Find $\displaystyle\int \cos^3 x\,dx$.

8. Find the maximum and minimum value of $7\sin 2x + 24\cos 2x + 3$.

9. Without using a calculator, evaluate $\cos 50° - \tan 40° \sin 50°$.

10. Without using a calculator show that $\tan 15° = 2 - \sqrt{3}$.

> **Hint:** $2 \times 15 = 30$

WORKSHEET 15

1. Express $\dfrac{1}{(1 - x)(2 + x)}$ in partial fractions and then express in a series of ascending powers of x as far as the term in x^3.

> Try worksheets 15 and 16 after completing chapter 13.

2. Find the sum of the series: $2 - \dfrac{2}{3} + \dfrac{2}{9} - \dfrac{2}{27} \cdots$.

3. Find the term in $x^3 y^4$ in the expansion of $(3x + 2y)^7$.

4. Evaluate $\displaystyle\int_0^1 \frac{2x}{\sqrt{1-x^2}}\,dx$.

5. Solve the equation $7.2^x = \dfrac{5}{3^{x-1}}$.

6. Evaluate $\displaystyle\sum_{r=1}^{50} (\log_{10} 2^r)$.

7. Write down the coefficient of x^{10} in the expansion of $(1 + 2x)^{30}$.

8. Find the term independent of x in the expansion of $\left(2x - \dfrac{1}{x^2}\right)^{21}$.

9. Solve the equation $x^{2/3} + 3x^{1/3} - 2 = 0$.

10. Two plane mirrors face each other at a distance $2a$ apart. A torch is held midway between them so that it shines directly into one mirror. Form a series for the distance of successive images from the torch and find the distance of the twelfth image. (Images are formed as far behind a plane mirror as objects are in front.)

WORKSHEET 16

1. Find the minimum value of k so that $2x^2 + 12x + k > 0$.

2. The function y is defined as $y = \tan^2\theta - 2\tan\theta$ for $0 \pm \theta < \dfrac{\pi}{2}$. Find the minimum value of y.

3. Express the roots of the equation $x^2 + 3x + c = 0$ as a series in ascending powers of c up to the term in c^2.

4. Find three numbers with sum of 42 and product of 1728, given that they form a geometric progression.

5. Express $0\cdot\dot{1}$ as a fraction.

6. Without using a calculator, evaluate $\sqrt{0\cdot98}$ correct to 3 decimal places.

7. Express $\dfrac{1}{(1 + x)(1 + x + x^2)}$ as a series in ascending powers of x as far as the term in x^3.

8. Find the nine arithmetic means of 10 and -5.

9. Given that $f(x) = 2x$, $g(x) = \sqrt{x}$, $h(x) = x + 1$ find $ghf(x)$ as a series in ascending x up to x^4.

10. Find the ratio of $a:b$ if in the expression of $(2a + 5b)^{12}$ the term in a^7 is equal to the term in a^8.

WORKSHEET 17

1. If $y = e^x \sin x$ find $\dfrac{d^2y}{dx^2}$ in terms of $\dfrac{dy}{dx}$ and y.

2. Given $y = \log_{10}(2x + 1)$ find $\dfrac{dy}{dx}$.

Try worksheets 17 and 18 after completing chapter 14.

3. $f(x) = x^2$, $g(x) = e^x$, $h(x) = fg(x)$, $k(x) = gf(x)$.

Is $h(x)$ the same function as $k(x)$? Justify your answer.

Find $h^{-1}(x)$ and sketch $h(x)$ and $h^{-1}(x)$ on the same graph.

4. The portion of the curve $y = e^{-2x}$ between $x = -2$ and $x = 1$ is rotated through one revolution about the x-axis. Find the volume of the shape generated.

5. Evaluate $\int_0^1 x^2 e^x \, dx$.

6. Solve the equation $e^x(e^x + 1) = 2$.

7. If $e^x = y$ and $e^y = z$ express x in terms of z.

8. Find $\int e^x \sin x \, dx$.

> **Hint:** It does not matter which is u and which dv to begin: you will have to apply the 'by parts' technique twice.

9. Form the equation with roots $\alpha^3 + \dfrac{1}{\beta}$, $\beta^3 + \dfrac{1}{\alpha}$ given that α and β are the roots of $2x^2 - 6x - 1 = 0$.

10. If $y = a^x$ express y as a power of e.

WORKSHEET 18

1. Find the area enclosed between $y = \ln x$, the x-axis and the ordinates $x = 2$ and $x = 3$.

2. Find $\int \dfrac{3}{\sqrt{5 - x^2}} \, dx$.

3. Sketch the function given by:

$f(x) \to x$ $0 \leqslant x < 1$

$g(x) \to 1 - (x - 1)^2$ $1 \leqslant x < 2$

with period 2.

4. Sketch $y = e^{-x} - 2$ and the inverse of y, if it exists, on the same diagram.

5. If $y = e^{2x} \ln(1 + x)$ find $\dfrac{dy}{dx} - 2y$ in terms of x.

6. y, x and z are variables dependent on t. $y = 3e^x + x^2$ and $z = \ln(2x^3 + x)^2$. Find $\dfrac{dy}{dt}$ when $x = 1$, given $\dfrac{dz}{dt} = 7$ when $x = 1$.

7. Evaluate $\int_1^4 \dfrac{3x + 1}{3x^2 + 2x} \, dx$.

8. State the range of values of the constant k if $e^{(2x-k)} > e^x$ when $x > 0$.

9. Find $\displaystyle\int \frac{2x+1}{1+x^2}\,dx$.

10. Evaluate $\displaystyle\int_0^{\pi/2} \sin3x \cos2x \, dx$.

WORKSHEET 19

1. Find the angle between the vectors $2\mathbf{i} + 3\mathbf{j} - \mathbf{k}$ and $5\mathbf{i} - 2\mathbf{j} + 3\mathbf{k}$.

2. Solve the equation $5(1 - \sec x) = \tan^2 x$ for $0 \leqslant x \leqslant 180°$.

3. Find the angle between the lines with vector equations:
   $\mathbf{r} = (1+2\lambda)\mathbf{i} + 3\lambda\mathbf{j} + (2-\lambda)\mathbf{k}$ and $\mathbf{r} = (3+\mu)\mathbf{i} + (1+2\mu)\mathbf{j} + (8\mu-2)\mathbf{k}$.

4. Show that the lines with vector equations

   $$\mathbf{r} = \begin{pmatrix} \lambda \\ 2\lambda \\ 4-\lambda \end{pmatrix} \quad \text{and } \mathbf{r} = \begin{pmatrix} 2-\mu \\ 1+\mu \\ 1+2\mu \end{pmatrix}$$

   intersect and find the position vector of the point of intersection. Find a vector equation of the plane containing the two lines.

5. Evaluate $\displaystyle\int_{\pi/6}^{\pi/3} (\cot x + \tan x)\,dx$.

6. Use vector methods to prove the midpoint theorem.

7. Find the vector equation of the plane containing the point with

   position vector $\begin{pmatrix} 4 \\ 1 \\ -2 \end{pmatrix}$ and perpendicular to the vector $\begin{pmatrix} 2 \\ -1 \\ -1 \end{pmatrix}$.

8. Express $\sqrt{(1 - x - 12x^2)}$ as a series in ascending powers of x as far as the term in x^3. State the values of x for which your answer is valid.

9. The position vector of a particle at any time t is $t^2\mathbf{i} + 2t\mathbf{j} + 3\mathbf{k}$. Find the velocity and acceleration vectors of the particle.

10. Solve the equations: $2x + 3y = z$
    $$3x = 6y + 5z + 7$$
    $$4x + z = 9y + 18.$$

> Try worksheets 19 and 20 after completing chapter 15.

WORKSHEET 20

1. Find the sum of the multiples of three greater than 700 but less than 800.

2. Explain why the elevation of the midpoint of a factory chimney is not half the elevation of the top of the chimney.

3. A is the point with position vector $\begin{pmatrix} 1 \\ 4 \end{pmatrix}$ and B has position vector $\begin{pmatrix} 3 \\ 1 \end{pmatrix}$.
   P is on AB such that $AP:PB = 2:1$. Find the position vector of P.

Q divides AB externally in the ratio $3:2$. Find the vector **PQ** in component form, $\begin{pmatrix} s \\ t \end{pmatrix}$.

4. Express $2x^4 + 3x^3 - 4x^2 - 3x + 2$ as a product of four linear factors.

5. If $y = e^{-t}(\cos 2t + \sin 2t)$ find the value of $\dfrac{d^2y}{dt^2} + 2\dfrac{dy}{dt} + 5y$.

6. If the lines $\mathbf{r} = 1\begin{pmatrix} -\lambda \\ 2\lambda \\ 1+\lambda \end{pmatrix}$ and $\mathbf{r} = \begin{pmatrix} \mu \\ 5+\mu \\ 1-2\mu \end{pmatrix}$ intersect find the position vector of their point of intersection. Find the angle between the lines.

7. Find $\displaystyle\int \dfrac{6}{7 + 4x + x^2}\,dx.$

8. For what values of x is this inequality true?
$12(x^2 + x + 1) > 17x + 14$

9. Solve the equation $12\sin x - 5\cos x = 13$, giving the general solution.

10. A particle has velocity vector $\mathbf{v} = 2t\mathbf{i} + 3t^2\mathbf{j} + \mathbf{k}$. Find its position vector at time t given that initially its position vector is $\begin{pmatrix} 2 \\ 1 \\ 3 \end{pmatrix}$.

WORKSHEET 21

1. Solve the equation $x^4 - 5x^2 - 36 = 0$, giving all four roots.

Try worksheets 21 and 22 after completing chapter 16.

2. Express $\dfrac{1}{1 + 2i} + \dfrac{3}{3 - i}$ as a single fraction with a rational denominator.

3. z_1 and z_2 are the numbers $1 + i$ and $1 + \sqrt{3}i$ respectively. Find $z_1 z_2$ and $\dfrac{z_1}{z_2}$, in the form $a + ib$. Express z_1, z_2, $z_1 z_2$ and $\dfrac{z_1}{z_2}$ in the (r, θ) form.

4. The height and radius of a cone vary in such a way that the volume remains constant at $300\pi\,\text{cm}^3$. Find the rate at which the height is changing when $h = 9$ cm and the radius is increasing at $2\,\text{cm s}^{-1}$.

5. Evaluate $\displaystyle\int_{\pi/6}^{\pi/3} \dfrac{\cos\theta - \sin\theta}{\cos\theta + \sin\theta}\,d\theta.$

6. Verify that the point, A(6, 4, 5) lies on the line $\mathbf{r} = \begin{pmatrix} 1 \\ 3 \\ 1 \end{pmatrix} + \lambda\begin{pmatrix} 5 \\ 1 \\ 3 \end{pmatrix}$

and that the point B(11, 3, 9) does not. Find the angle between AB and the line. C is on AB produced so that AB = BC. State the coordinates of C.

7. z is a complex number such that $|z| < 2$ and $\dfrac{\pi}{2} < \arg z < \pi$. On an Argand diagram shade the area representing possible values of z.

8. Evaluate $\displaystyle\int_1^2 \dfrac{(2x-1)^2}{x}\,dx$.

9. Express $\ln(2+x)$ in a series of ascending powers of x, stating the validity.

10. Express $\dfrac{i^5+1}{i^3}$ with a rational denominator.

WORKSHEET 22

1. Express $z = \dfrac{3-2i}{2+3i}$ in the form $a+ib$. Hence give the modulus and argument of z.

2. Find the area between the curve $y = (x-2)^5$, the y-axis and the ordinates $y = 0$, $y = 1$.

3. By expressing e^{ix} as a series in x find e^{ix} in terms of $\cos x$ and $\sin x$. Repeat for e^{-ix}. Hence find $\cos x$ and $\sin x$ in terms of e^{ix}.

4. The area of an ellipse is given by $A = \pi ab$ where a and b are the semi-axes. a and b vary but A remains constant. Find the rate of change of a in terms of a, b and $\dfrac{db}{dt}$.

5. The roots of a cubic equation $x^3 + bx^2 + cx + d = 0$ are α, β and γ. Find b, c and d in terms of α, β and γ.

6. Find the complex number z which satisfies $z\bar{z} + 3z = 56 + 12i$, where $\bar{z}$ is the conjugate of z. (Two answers.)

7. Use calculus to show that $y = 10 - 12x + 6x^2 - x^3$ is a decreasing function for all values of x.

8. Evaluate $\displaystyle\int_0^{\pi/2} e^x \cos x\,dx$.

9. In the expansion of $\dfrac{1}{1+ax} - \dfrac{2}{2-x}$ in ascending powers of x the term in x^2 is zero. Find a.

10. Find the values of $\cos\theta$ for which the curve $y = 4\cos^3\theta - \cos^2\theta - \cos\theta$ has zero gradient.

WORKSHEET 23

1. Solve the equation $\dfrac{dy}{dx} = \dfrac{2x}{y}$ given that when $x = 1$, $y = 1$.

2. Evaluate $\displaystyle\int_0^3 \sqrt{9-x^2}\,dx$.

> Try worksheets 23 and 24 after completing chapter 17.

3. Solve the equation $\dfrac{dy}{dx} = e^y \sin x$ expressing y in terms of x, given that when $x = 0$ $y = 0$.

4. Solve the equation $4z - 3z\bar{z} = -7 - 4i$.

5. Find $\displaystyle\int \dfrac{x^2}{\sqrt{1 - x^2}}\,dx$.

6. The acceleration of a particle is proportional to $1 + v^2$ where v is the velocity. When $t = 0$, $v = 1$. Express v in terms of k and t where k is the constant of proportionality.

7. Find the relationship between a, b and c if the planes given by the

    equations $\mathbf{r} . \begin{pmatrix} 2 \\ 5 \\ 1 \end{pmatrix} = 12$ and $\mathbf{r} . \begin{pmatrix} a \\ b \\ c \end{pmatrix} = 7$ are perpendicular to each other.

8. Evaluate $\displaystyle\int_1^2 x^2 e^x\,dx$, giving your answer to the nearest whole number.

9. In an electrical circuit the link between voltage and time is given by

    $V\dfrac{dV}{dt} = e^{V^2} . \ln(2t + \varepsilon)$, where ε is a constant.

    Show that $(2t + \varepsilon)\ln(2t + \varepsilon) - 2t + e^{-V^2} = c$, a constant.

10. Find the three geometric means of -2 and -162.

WORKSHEET 24

1. The portion of the curve $y = xe^x$ between $x = 0$ and $x = 2$ is revolved through $360°$ about the x-axis. Find the volume swept out.

2. Find the value of a if the coefficients of x and x^2 in the expansion of $(1 + ax)^{-3}$ are equal.

3. Solve the differential equation $(x^2 y + xy - 12y)\dfrac{dy}{dx} = 1$.

4. Evaluate $\displaystyle\int_2^6 x^2\sqrt{12 - x^2 - 4x}\,dx$

    A hard one.

5. Find the link between p and q if one root of $px^2 + qx + r = 0$ is the reciprocal of the other.

6. Find x in terms of t given $\dfrac{dx}{dt} = x^2 e^{3t}$ and $x = 1$ when $t = 1$. Find x when $t = 0$.

7. Find the term independent of x in the expansion of $\left(2x^3 - \dfrac{1}{x}\right)^{20}$.

8. $z_1 = 24 - 7i$, $z_2 = -5 + 12i$. Express z_1, z_2 and $z_1 z_2$ in (r, θ) form.

9. Find $\dfrac{dy}{dx}$ if $y = \ln(\ln \sin^2 x)$.

10. The vector equations of two lines are $\mathbf{r} = \begin{pmatrix} 1 \\ 2 \\ 3 \end{pmatrix} + \lambda \begin{pmatrix} 2 \\ -1 \\ 2 \end{pmatrix}$ and

$\mathbf{r} = \begin{pmatrix} 2 \\ 0 \\ 1 \end{pmatrix} + \mu \begin{pmatrix} a \\ b \\ c \end{pmatrix}$. Find a, b and c given that the lines intersect
when $\lambda = 2$, $\mu = 3$.

WORKSHEET 25

1. Find the equation of the normal to the curve $xy = 16$ at the point where $x = 2$.

2. The point A (2, 1) is on the line $3y + 4x = 11$. B is the point (3, 4) and C is the foot of the perpendicular from B to the line. Find the length of AC.

3. The line $y + 2 = 3x$ intersects the parabola $(y + 1)^2 = 6(x + 2)$. Find the coordinates of the midpoint of AB where A and B are the points of intersection.

4. On an Argand diagram sketch the area representing the complex number z where $|z - i| \leqslant 2$ and $\dfrac{\pi}{4} \leqslant \arg z \leqslant \dfrac{2\pi}{3}$.

5. Find the equation of the line perpendicular to $4y + 5x = 2$ and having an intercept of 4 on the y-axis.

6. A parabola has its vertex at $x = 1$, its focus at (3, 0) and it is symmetrical about the x-axis. Find the area enclosed by the part of the curve in the first quadrant, the x-axis and the line $x = 5$.

7. The tangents to the parabola $y^2 = 4ax$ at the points P and Q with parameters p and q respectively meet at R. If the tangents are at right angles to each other find the locus of R.

8. For what values of x is $\dfrac{3 - 5x - 2x^2}{6 - 11x + 4x^2}$ positive?

9. Differentiate $\sin 2x$ w.r.t. x from first principles.

10. Express $\ln\left(\dfrac{1 + x}{1 - x}\right)$ as a series in ascending powers of x.

> Try worksheets 25 and 26 after completing chapter 18.

WORKSHEET 26

1. Find the equation of the median AM of the triangle ABC where A is $(-1, 4)$, B is (3, 5) and C is $(1, -3)$. Write down the coordinate of the centroid of the triangle. (**Hint**: at G, on AM where AG $= \frac{2}{3}$AM.) Hence find the equation of the median BG.

2. Name the curve given by $y^2 = x^3$. Find the equation of the tangent to the curve at (1, 1). Find at which other points this tangent cuts the curve.

3. The acceleration of a particle is given by $a = c(1 + v^2)$ where v is the velocity. Find v in terms of x given that when $x = 0$, $v = 0$.

4. Find the values of m if $y = mx$ is a tangent to $(x - 4)^2 + y^2 = 4$.

5. Find the equation of the normal to the curve $x^2 + 2y^2 = 9$ at the point $(1, 2)$. Find also the coordinates of the point where it again cuts the curve.

6. Find the angle between the two lines $y = 5x$ and $2y + 6x = 3$.

7. Sketch the graph of $y = \operatorname{cosec}(x - 45°)$ for $45° < x < 135°$.

8. By diagram solve the inequality $|x| < |x + 2|$.

9. Find the values of c so that $3x + 4y + c = 0$ is a tangent to the circle $x^2 + y^2 - 2x - 4y - 20 = 0$.

10. z is the complex number with (r, θ) form $(3, \frac{\pi}{6})$.

   Find (a) z^2 (b) $\dfrac{z}{\bar{z}}$, where $\bar{z}$ is the conjugate.

Answers to worksheets

ANSWERS TO WORKSHEET I

1. $x + 9y - 6\sqrt{xy} - z = (x^{1/2})^2 - 6x^{1/2}y^{1/2} + 9(y^{1/2})^2 - (z^{1/2})^2$

$$= (x^{1/2} - 3y^{1/2})^2 - (z^{1/2})^2 \quad \text{differences of two squares}$$

$$= (x^{1/2} - 3y^{1/2} - z^{1/2})(x^{1/2} - 3y^{1/2} + x^{1/2})$$

$$= (\sqrt{x} - 3\sqrt{y} - \sqrt{z})(\sqrt{x} - 3\sqrt{y} + \sqrt{z})$$

2. $\dfrac{1}{x + 1} - \dfrac{2}{x + 2} - \dfrac{3}{x - 3} = \dfrac{2}{x^2 + 3x + 2}$

$\Rightarrow \dfrac{(x + 2)(x - 3) - 2(x + 1)(x - 3) - 3(x + 1)(x + 2)}{(x + 1)(x + 2)(x - 3)} = \dfrac{2}{(x + 1)(x + 2)}$

$\Rightarrow \dfrac{-4x^2 - 6x - 6}{(x + 1)(x + 2)(x - 3)} = \dfrac{2}{(x + 1)(x + 2)}$

$\Rightarrow -2(2x^2 + 3x + 3)(x + 1)(x + 2) = 2(x + 1)(x + 2)(x - 3)$

$\Rightarrow x + 1 = 0 \quad \text{or} \quad x + 2 = 0 \quad \text{or} \quad -2x^2 - 3x - 3 = x - 3$

$\Rightarrow x \quad\quad = -1 \quad\quad\quad x = -2 \quad\quad\quad 2x^2 + 4x = 0$

$\Rightarrow x = 0 \quad \text{or} \quad x = -2$

Be careful not to lose solutions at this stage.

$\therefore$ solutions are $x = -1$, $x = -2$ (twice), $x = 0$.

3. $\left(\dfrac{8}{27}\right)^{-4/3} \times \left(\dfrac{4}{9}\right)^{5/2} = \left(\dfrac{27}{8}\right)^{4/3} \times \left(\dfrac{2}{3}\right)^{5}$

$$= \dfrac{81}{16} \times \dfrac{32}{243} = \dfrac{2}{3}$$

4. $p^x = qr^x \Rightarrow \log p^x = \log qr^x$

$\therefore \ \log p^x = \log q + \log r^x$

$\therefore \ x\log p = \log q + x\log r$

$$\Rightarrow x = \dfrac{\log q}{\log p - \log r} = \dfrac{\log q}{\log p/r}$$

5. $f(x) = x^2 + 8x + 10 + c$

$\quad x^2 + 8x + 10 + c > 0$

$\Rightarrow (x + 4)^2 + c - 6 > 0 \qquad$ *completing the square*

$\therefore f(x) > 0 \quad$ if $\quad c - 6 > 0 \quad \because (x + 4)^2 > 0$

$$c > 6$$

6. $\dfrac{\sqrt{8} + \sqrt{2}}{\sqrt{8} - \sqrt{2}} = \dfrac{\sqrt{4} + 1}{\sqrt{4} - 1} \qquad$ *divide throughout by $\sqrt{2}$*

$$= \dfrac{3}{1} = 3$$

or $\dfrac{(\sqrt{8} + \sqrt{2})(\sqrt{8} + \sqrt{2})}{(\sqrt{8} - \sqrt{2})(\sqrt{8} + \sqrt{2})} = \dfrac{8 + 2 + 2\sqrt{16}}{8 - 2}$

$$= \dfrac{18}{6} = 3$$

7. $\sqrt{x} + \sqrt{a} = \sqrt{c}$

$\therefore \sqrt{x} = \sqrt{c} - \sqrt{a}$

$\Rightarrow x = (\sqrt{c} - \sqrt{a})^2 = c + a - 2\sqrt{ac}$

8. $9{\cdot}98^2 - 0{\cdot}02^2 = (9{\cdot}98 - 0{\cdot}02)(9{\cdot}98 + 0{\cdot}02)$

$$= 9{\cdot}96 \times 10$$

$$= 99{\cdot}6$$

9. $10(\log x)^2 - 39\log x + 14 = 0$

$\Rightarrow (5\log x - 2)(2\log x - 7) = 0$

$\Rightarrow \log x = \dfrac{2}{5} \quad$ or $\quad \log x = \dfrac{7}{2}$

$\quad x = 2{\cdot}5 \qquad\qquad x = 3162{\cdot}3$

10. $x^2 - bx - c = 0$ roots $\alpha, \beta \Rightarrow \alpha + \beta = b$ **1**

$\qquad\qquad\qquad\qquad\qquad\qquad \alpha\beta = -c$ **2**

$\quad x^2 - 2bx + c = 0$ roots $\alpha, \gamma \Rightarrow \alpha + \gamma = 2b$ **3**

$\qquad\qquad\qquad\qquad\qquad\qquad \alpha\gamma = 2c$ **4**

divide: $\mathbf{4} \div \mathbf{2} \Rightarrow \dfrac{\gamma}{\beta} = -2 \Rightarrow \gamma = -2\beta$

then: $\left.\begin{array}{l}\mathbf{1} \Rightarrow \alpha + \beta = b \\ \mathbf{3} \Rightarrow \alpha - 2\beta = 2b\end{array}\right\} \Rightarrow 3\alpha = 4b, \alpha = \dfrac{4b}{3}$

$\therefore \dfrac{4b}{3} + \beta = b \ (using\ \mathbf{1}) \Rightarrow \beta = -\dfrac{b}{3}$

Finally: $\mathbf{2} \Rightarrow -\dfrac{4b}{3}\cdot\dfrac{b}{3} = -c \Rightarrow 4b^2 = 9c.$

ANSWERS TO WORKSHEET 2

1. $f(x) = 6x - 9 - x^2 = -(x^2 - 6x + 9) = -(x - 3)^2$

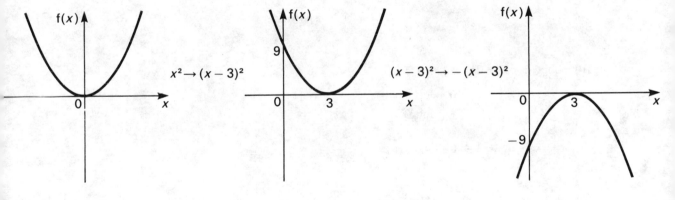

2. $x^2 - 6x + 4 = 0 \quad \Rightarrow \alpha + \beta = 6, \alpha\beta = 4$

$$\dfrac{\alpha}{\beta + 1} + \dfrac{\beta}{\alpha + 1} = \dfrac{\alpha(\alpha + 1) + \beta(\beta + 1)}{(\beta + 1)(\alpha + 1)} = \dfrac{\alpha^2 + \alpha + \beta^2 + \beta}{\alpha\beta + \alpha + \beta + 1}$$

$$= \dfrac{(\alpha + \beta)^2 - 2\alpha\beta + (\alpha + \beta)}{\alpha\beta + (\alpha + \beta) + 1}$$

Substituting: $\Rightarrow \dfrac{6^2 - 8 + 6}{4 + 6 + 1} = \dfrac{34}{11} = 3\cdot1$

3. A → B: time taken, $t_1 = \dfrac{d}{u + 5}$ B → A: time taken, $t_2 = \dfrac{d}{y - 5}$

Average speed for whole journey, $v = \dfrac{2d}{\dfrac{d}{u + 5} + \dfrac{d}{u - 5}}$ *total distance*

total time

$$\therefore v = \dfrac{2d}{\dfrac{d(u - 5) + d(u + 5)}{(u + 5)(u - 5)}} = \dfrac{2d(u + 5)(u - 5)}{2du} = \dfrac{u^2 - 25}{u}$$

> Popular mistake:
> average speed
>
> $$v = \dfrac{(u + 5) + (u - 5)}{2}$$
>
> $$= \dfrac{2u}{2} = u$$
>
> Explain why this is wrong.

4. $\left.\begin{array}{l} axy = 1 \Rightarrow ax = \dfrac{1}{y} \\[2ex] x + \dfrac{1}{y} = b \Rightarrow x + \dfrac{1}{y} = b \end{array}\right\} \Rightarrow x + ax = b \Rightarrow x = \dfrac{b}{a + 1}$ and $y = \dfrac{a + 1}{ab}$

$\dfrac{2}{x} + y = c$ Substitute for x and y: $\Rightarrow \dfrac{2(a + 1)}{b} + \dfrac{(a + 1)}{ab} = c$

$$(a + 1)\dfrac{(2a + 1)}{ab} = c$$

$$\therefore (a + 1)(2a + 1) = abc$$

5. $\log_3 10 = \log_3(2 \times 5) = \log_3 2 + \log_3 5$

$$= \log_3 \dfrac{6}{3} + \dfrac{\log_6 5}{\log_6 3}$$

$$= \log_3 6 - \log_3 3 + \dfrac{\log_6 5}{\log_3 3 / \log_3 6}$$

$$= m - 1 + \dfrac{n}{1/m} = m - 1 + mn$$

6. $3x^2 = 1 + \dfrac{5}{x^2}$

$\Rightarrow 3x^4 - x^2 - 5 = 0$ $\Rightarrow x^2 = \dfrac{1 \pm \sqrt{1 + 60}}{6}$

$\Rightarrow x^2 = 1 \cdot 47$

or $x^2 = -1 \cdot 14$ *Impossible value for x^2*

$\therefore x = \pm\sqrt{1 \cdot 47} = \pm 1 \cdot 21$

7. $\sqrt{288} - \sqrt{27} + 2\sqrt{243} - \sqrt{32} = \sqrt{144}\sqrt{2} - \sqrt{9}\sqrt{3} + 2\sqrt{81}\sqrt{3} - \sqrt{16}\sqrt{2}$
$$= 12\sqrt{2} - 3\sqrt{3} + 18\sqrt{3} - 4\sqrt{2}$$
$$= 8\sqrt{2} + 15\sqrt{3}$$

8. $\dfrac{4}{3^{x-2}} = 3.2^x \quad \Rightarrow 4.3^{2-x} = 3.2^x \quad \Rightarrow 4.3^{1-x} = 2^x \qquad \textit{divide both sides by } 3$

taking log of both sides: $\Rightarrow \log(4.3^{1-x}) = \log(2^x)$
$$\therefore \log4 + \log3^{1-x} = \log2^x$$
$$\therefore \log4 + (1-x)\log3 = x\log2$$
$$\Rightarrow \log4 + \log3 = x(\log2 + \log3)$$
$$\Rightarrow \frac{\log12}{\log6} = x$$
$$\therefore x = 1\cdot39$$

9. $\dfrac{3}{\sqrt{2}-1} - \dfrac{3}{\sqrt{2}+1} = \dfrac{3(\sqrt{2}+1) - 3(\sqrt{2}-1)}{(\sqrt{2}-1)(\sqrt{2}+1)} = 6$

10. $81^{1/2} \times 27^{2/3} \times 6^{-2} = \dfrac{9 \times 3}{36} = \dfrac{3}{4}$

ANSWERS TO WORKSHEET 3

1. $7x = 3x^2 \Rightarrow x(3x - 7) = 0 \Rightarrow x = 0, x = \frac{7}{3} \qquad \textit{two solutions!}$

2. $5x^2 - 18x = 8 \Rightarrow (5x + 2)(x - 4) = 0 \Rightarrow x = 4 \qquad \because x \text{ has to be an integer}$

3. $9^x - 4.3^x + 3 = 0 \Rightarrow (3^x)^2 - 4.3^x + 3 = 0 \Rightarrow (3^x - 1)(3^x - 3) = 0$
$\therefore 3^x = 1 \quad \text{or} \quad 3^x = 3 \Rightarrow x = 0, x = 1$

4.
$\Rightarrow f(x) > 0 \quad \text{for} \quad x < -2 \quad \text{and} \quad 1 < x < 3$

5. $\dfrac{x^2 + 3}{(x + 2)^2(x - 1)} \equiv \dfrac{A}{x + 2} + \dfrac{B}{(x + 2)^2} + \dfrac{C}{x - 1}$
$$x^2 + 3 \equiv A(x + 2)(x - 1) + B(x - 1) + C(x + 2)^2$$
$x = 1 \Rightarrow C = \frac{4}{9}$
$x = -2 \Rightarrow B = -\frac{7}{3}$
c.f. $x^2 \Rightarrow A = \frac{5}{9}$

$\therefore f(x) \equiv \dfrac{5}{9(x + 2)} - \dfrac{7}{3(x + 2)^2} + \dfrac{4}{9(x - 1)}$

6. $a - b = (a^{1/2} - b^{1/2})(a^{1/2} + b^{1/2})$

7. $p = q^m$ and $q = p^n \Rightarrow p = (p^n)^m = p^{nm}$ $\therefore mn = 1$

8. $x^2 - y^2 = 5$ and $x^2 + xy + 3y^2 = 8$

Substitute: $x^2 = y^2 + 5 \Rightarrow y^2 + 5 + xy + 3y^2 = 8 \Rightarrow x = \dfrac{3 - 4y^2}{y}$

Squaring and substituting again: $\Rightarrow (y^2 + 5)y^2 = (3 - 4y^2)^2$

$\Rightarrow 15y^4 - 29y^2 + 9 = 0$ $\therefore y^2 = \dfrac{29 \pm \sqrt{29^2 - 540}}{30}$

$\Rightarrow y = \pm 1 \cdot 2$ or ± 1.6

$y = \pm 1.2 \Rightarrow x = \pm 2 \cdot 5$ $y = \pm 0 \cdot 6 \Rightarrow x = \pm 2 \cdot 3$

There are eight solutions or the curves intersect eight times.

> Prove by drawing!

9. $2x^2 + 7x - 3 = 0 \Rightarrow \alpha + \beta = -\frac{7}{2}, \alpha\beta = -\frac{3}{2}$

If new equation is $Ax^2 + Bx + C = 0$:

$$\left.\begin{array}{l} \dfrac{B}{A} = -\left\{\alpha^2 + \dfrac{1}{\beta} + \beta^2 + \dfrac{1}{\alpha}\right\} = -\left\{(\alpha + \beta)^2 - 2\alpha\beta + \dfrac{\alpha + \beta}{\alpha\beta}\right\} = -\dfrac{211}{12} \\[3mm] \dfrac{C}{A} = \left(\alpha^2 + \dfrac{1}{\beta}\right)\left(\beta^2 + \dfrac{1}{\alpha}\right) = \alpha^2\beta^2 + \alpha + \beta + \dfrac{1}{\alpha\beta} = \dfrac{9}{4} - \dfrac{7}{2} - \dfrac{2}{3} = -\dfrac{23}{12} \end{array}\right\} \Rightarrow 12x^2 - 211x - 23 = 0$$

10. $1 - 5\log_{10}p = \log_{10}10 - \log_{10}p^5 = \log_{10}\left(\dfrac{10}{p^5}\right)$

ANSWERS TO WORKSHEET 4

1. $\dfrac{2x^2 + 3x - 2}{4x - x^2 - 3} = \dfrac{2(2x - 1)(x + 2)}{(x - 3)(1 - x)} \Rightarrow$

Hence $f(x) > 0$ for $1 < x < 3$ and $-2 < x < \frac{1}{2}$.

2. $\alpha + k\alpha = -\dfrac{b}{a}, k\alpha^2 = \dfrac{c}{a} \Rightarrow \alpha^2(1 + k)^2 = \dfrac{b^2}{a^2}$ and $\alpha^2 = \dfrac{c}{ka}$

$\therefore \dfrac{c}{ka}(1 + k)^2 = \dfrac{b^2}{a^2} \Rightarrow ac(1 + k)^2 = kb^2$

3. $y = x - \dfrac{1}{x}$ $\therefore y^2 = x^2 + \dfrac{1}{x^2} - 2 \Rightarrow x^2 + \dfrac{1}{x^2} = y^2 + 2$ *divide throughout by* x^2

$x^4 + 2x^3 - 5x^2 - 2x + 1 = 0 \Rightarrow x^2 + 2x - 5 - \dfrac{2}{x} + \dfrac{1}{x^2} = 0$

$\Rightarrow x^2 + \dfrac{1}{x^2} + 2\left(x - \dfrac{1}{x}\right) - 5 = 0 \Rightarrow y^2 + 2 + 2y - 5 = 0$

> The idea followed from the first part and noticing the pattern of the coefficients in this equation.

$\Rightarrow y^2 + 2y - 3 = 0 \Rightarrow y = -3$ or 1

$\therefore x - \dfrac{1}{x} = -3 \Rightarrow x^2 + 3x - 1 = 0 \Rightarrow x = -3 \cdot 3, 0 \cdot 3$

and $x - \dfrac{1}{x} = 1 \Rightarrow x^2 - x - 1 = 0 \Rightarrow x = -0 \cdot 6, 1 \cdot 6$

4. $x^2 - 3x - 10)x^4$

$$x^4 - 3x^3 - 10x^2$$
$$3x^3 + 10x^2$$
$$3x^3 - 9x^2 - 30x$$
$$19x^2 + 30x$$
$$19x^2 - 57x - 190$$
$$87x + 190$$

$(x^2 + 3x + 19$

$\therefore f(x) = x^2 + 3x + 19 + \dfrac{87x + 190}{(x-5)(x+2)}$

$$\dfrac{87x + 190}{(x-5)(x+2)} \equiv \dfrac{A}{x-5} + \dfrac{B}{x+2}$$

$87x + 190 \equiv A(x+2) + B(x-5) \quad x = -2 \Rightarrow B = -\frac{16}{7}$

$$x = 5 \Rightarrow A = \frac{625}{7}$$

$\therefore f(x) = x^2 + 3x + 19 + \dfrac{625}{7(x-5)} - \dfrac{16}{7(x+2)}$

5. $2x^2 + 8x + 7 \equiv 2(x+2)^2 - 1$

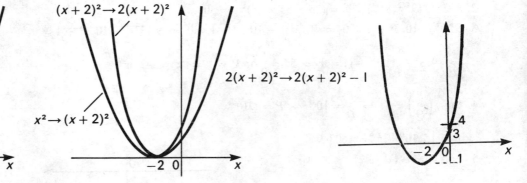

6. $\dfrac{3^{n-2} \times 9^n}{27^{n/3} \times 81^{n/2}} = \dfrac{3^n \times 3^{-2} \times 9^n}{\sqrt[3]{27^n} \times \sqrt{81^n}} = \dfrac{3^n \times 3^{-2} \times 9^n}{3^n \times 9^n} = \dfrac{1}{9}$

7. $x^3 + \dfrac{8}{x^3} = 9 \Rightarrow x^6 - 9x^3 + 8 = 0 \Rightarrow (x^3 - 1)(x^3 - 8) = 0$

$\therefore x^3 = 1 \quad \text{or} \quad x^3 = 8 \Rightarrow x = 1, 2$

8. $\sqrt{7} - \sqrt{6} = (\sqrt{7} - \sqrt{6})\dfrac{(\sqrt{7} + \sqrt{6})}{(\sqrt{7} + \sqrt{6})} = \dfrac{7 - 6}{\sqrt{7} + \sqrt{6}} = \dfrac{1}{\sqrt{7} + \sqrt{6}}$

9. $\left.\begin{array}{r} 3x - 2y + z = 2 \\ x + 2y + z = 8 \\ 5x - 3y + z = 2 \end{array}\right\}$ $\begin{array}{l} - \Rightarrow 2x - 4y = -6 \\ - \Rightarrow -4x + 5y = 6 \end{array}\Big\} \Rightarrow -3y = -6 \Rightarrow y = 2, x = 1, z = 3$

10. $2x^2 + 6x - 5 = 0$ has roots $\alpha, \beta \Rightarrow \alpha + \beta = -3, \alpha\beta = -\dfrac{5}{2}$

For new equation:

$$\frac{b}{a} = -(\alpha^3 + \beta^3) = -(\alpha + \beta)(\alpha^2 - \alpha\beta + \beta^2)$$

$$= -(\alpha + \beta)\{(\alpha + \beta)^2 - 3\alpha\beta\}$$

$$\therefore \frac{b}{a} = --3\left(9 + \frac{15}{2}\right) = \frac{99}{2}$$

$$\frac{c}{a} = \alpha^3\beta^3 = -\frac{125}{8}$$

$\therefore$ new equation is $\quad x^2 + \frac{99}{2}x - \frac{125}{8} = 0$

$$\Rightarrow 8x^2 + 396x - 125 = 0$$

ANSWERS TO WORKSHEET 5

1. $f(x) = x^3 - 7x - 6$ Using the factor theorem $f(-1) = 0$.
   $\therefore f(x) = (x + 1)(x^2 - x - 6) = (x + 1)(x - 3)(x + 2)$

See note on page 338.

2. $\{125^{2/3}(9^{1/2}.8^{1/3})^2\}^{1/2} = (25 \times 3^2 \times 2^2)^{1/2} = 30$

3. $9^{x+1} - 10.3^x + 1 = 0 \Rightarrow 9.(3^2)^x - 10.3^x + 1 = 0 \Rightarrow 9.(3^x)^2 - 10.3^x + 1 = 0$

   $\Rightarrow (9.3^x - 1)(3^x - 1) = 0 \Rightarrow 3^x = \frac{1}{9}$ or $3^x = 1 \Rightarrow x = -2$ or 0

4. $\log_{10}\left(\frac{P}{Q}\right) = \lambda t \Rightarrow \frac{P}{Q} = 10^{\lambda t} \Rightarrow P = Q10^{\lambda t}$

   $P = 15.10^{0.7 \times 2.9} = 1607{\cdot}3$

5. $hgf(x) = -(x^2 + 2)$

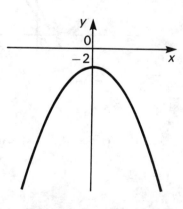

6.

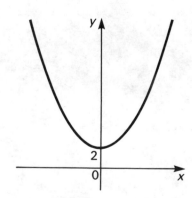

7. $\dfrac{4-x}{6+x-x^2} = \dfrac{4-x}{(3-x)(2+x)}$

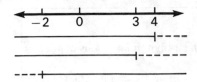

∴ positive for $-2 < x < 3$ and $x > 4$

For $x = 3$, $x = -2$ function $\to \infty$

8. $x + \dfrac{1}{y} = 6 \quad \therefore xy + 1 = 6y$

$\left.\begin{array}{l} \\ \\ \\ y + \dfrac{2}{x} = 1 \qquad xy + 2 = x \end{array}\right\}$ $- \Rightarrow -1 = 6y - x$

> $x, y \in \mathbb{R}$ tells us that the answers have to be real; elements of $\mathbb{R}$, the set of real numbers.

Substitute $x = 6y + 1$ in $x + \dfrac{1}{y} = 6$

$\Rightarrow 6y + 1 + \dfrac{1}{y} = 6 \Rightarrow 6y^2 - 5y + 1 = 0 \Rightarrow \left.\begin{array}{l} y = \frac{1}{3} \\ x = 3 \end{array}\right\}$ or $\left.\begin{array}{l} y = \frac{1}{2} \\ x = 4 \end{array}\right\}$

9. $x^2 + 2 \equiv (Ax + B)(2x + 1) + C(x^2 + 2x + 3)$

$x = -\frac{1}{2} \quad \Rightarrow \quad C = 1$
c.f. $x^2 \quad\quad \Rightarrow \quad 1 = 2A + C \quad \Rightarrow \quad A = 0$
c.f. consts $\quad \Rightarrow \quad 2 = B + 3C \quad \Rightarrow \quad B = -1$

$\therefore \dfrac{x^2 + 2}{(x^2 + 2x + 3)(2x + 1)} \equiv \dfrac{1}{2x + 1} - \dfrac{1}{x^2 + 2x + 3}$

10. $x = t^2, \; y = t^3 \quad \Rightarrow \quad y^2 = x^2$

> $y^2 = x^3$ is known as the semi-cubical parabola and $x = t^2$, $y = t^3$ is the parametric form of the equation. (Parameters are defined on page 298.)

x	0	1	2	3	4	5
y	0	± 1	$\pm 2 \cdot 8$	$\pm 5 \cdot 2$	± 8	$\pm 11 \cdot 2$

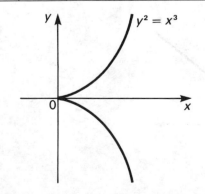

rotation about 0,
90° anticlockwise

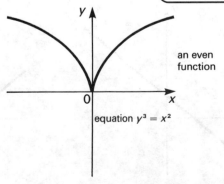

an even function

equation $y^3 = x^2$

The factor theorem:

The remainder theorem states that if $P(x)$, a polynomial in x, is divided by $(x - a)$ then the remainder is $P(a)$.

If $P(a) = 0$, $P(x)$ divides exactly by $(x - a)$ and $x - a$ is a factor of $P(x)$.

In Question 1: $P(x) = x^3 - 7x - 6$

 $P(-1) = -1 + 7 - 6 = 0$

 $\therefore (x + 1)$ is a factor.

ANSWERS TO WORKSHEET 6

1. For real district roots $b^2 - 4ac > 0$ $\Rightarrow$ $\lambda^2 - 400 > 0$
   $\Rightarrow$ $\lambda < -20$ or $\lambda > 20$

2. (a) $f(a) = 3a^5 - 4a + 2$ $\quad$ $f(-a) = -3a^5 + 4a + 2 \neq f(a)$ or $-f(a)$
      $\therefore$ neither

   (b) $f(a) = \dfrac{3a}{a^3 - 4a^5}$ $\quad$ $f(-a) = \dfrac{-3a}{-a^3 + 4a^5} = \dfrac{3a}{a^3 - 4a^5} = f(a)$
      $\therefore$ even

   (c) $f(a) = |a^3|$ $\quad$ $f(-a) = |-a^3| = |a^3| = f(a)$ $\quad$ $\therefore$ even

   (d) $f(a) = 2a^3 - a$ $\quad$ $f(-a) = -2a^3 + a = -f(a)$ $\quad$ $\therefore$ odd

   (e) $f(a) = \dfrac{a^4 - 1}{a^2}$ $\quad$ $f(-a) = \dfrac{a^4 - 1}{a^2} = f(a)$ $\quad$ $\therefore$ even

3. $2x^2 + \mu x + 2 = 0$ $\quad$ Roots are α, 3α.

   $\left.\begin{array}{l} \therefore 4\alpha = -\dfrac{\mu}{3} \\[2mm] \text{and } 3\alpha^2 = \dfrac{2}{3} \end{array}\right\}$ $\Rightarrow$ $\dfrac{\mu^2}{16.9} = \dfrac{2}{9}$ $\quad$ $\mu^2 = 32$ $\quad$ $\mu = \pm 4\sqrt{2}$

4. (a)

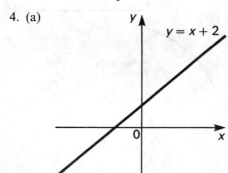

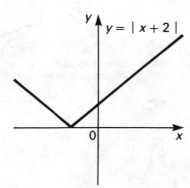

(b)

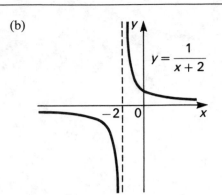

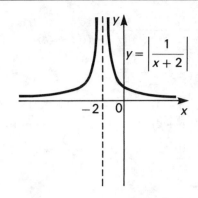

5. $p + q = \dfrac{1}{(p + \sqrt[3]{r})^2} \Rightarrow p + \sqrt[3]{r} = \dfrac{1}{\sqrt{(p + q)}} \Rightarrow \sqrt[3]{r} = \dfrac{1}{\sqrt{(p + q)}} - p$

$\therefore r = \left\{ \dfrac{1}{\sqrt{p + q}} - p \right\}^3$

6. $R = f(2) = 2^3 + 2 . 2^2 - 2a + 7 = 23 - 2a$
   But $23 - 2a = 1$ $\therefore a = 11$

7. $p^{-x}q^{2x} = r^{x-2} \Rightarrow \log(p^{-x}q^{2x}) - \log r^{x-2}$
   $\Rightarrow \log p^{-x} + \log q^{2x} = \log r^{x-2} \Rightarrow -x\log p + 2x\log q = (x - 2)\log r$

   $\Rightarrow 2\log r = x(\log r + \log p - 2\log q)$

   $\Rightarrow x = \dfrac{\log(r^2)}{\log\left(\dfrac{rp}{q^2}\right)}$

8. (a) $\sin 3x$ Complete cycle when $3x = 360°$ i.e. $x = 120°$
      $\therefore$ period $120°$
   (b) $\cos 2x$ Complete cycle when $2x = 360°$ i.e. $x = 180°$
      $\therefore$ period $180°$
   (c) $\tan x$ Complete cycle when $x = 180°$ i.e. $x = 180°$
      $\therefore$ period $180°$

9. $x^2 - 5x + 2 = 0$ $\alpha + \beta = 5, \alpha\beta = 2$

   For new equation: $\dfrac{b}{a} = -(p\alpha + q\beta + q\alpha + p\beta) = -(p + q)(\alpha + \beta)$

   $= -5(p + q)$

   and $\dfrac{c}{a} = (p\alpha + q\beta)(q\alpha + p\beta) = pq(\alpha^2 + \beta^2) + (p^2 + q^2)\alpha\beta$

   $= 21pq + 2(p^2 + q^2)$
   $\therefore$ the equation is: $x^2 - 5(p + q)x + 21pq + 2(p^2 + q^2) = 0$

10. $\dfrac{1}{1 + \sqrt{2} - \sqrt{3}} = \dfrac{1}{\{1 + (\sqrt{2} - \sqrt{3})\}} \dfrac{\{1 - (\sqrt{2} - \sqrt{3})\}}{\{1 - (\sqrt{2} - \sqrt{3})\}}$

$= \dfrac{1 - \sqrt{2} - \sqrt{3}}{1 - (2 + 3 - 2\sqrt{6})} = \dfrac{1 - \sqrt{2} - \sqrt{3}}{2\sqrt{6} - 4}$

$= \dfrac{(1 - \sqrt{2} - \sqrt{3})}{(2\sqrt{6} - 4)} \dfrac{(2\sqrt{6} + 4)}{(2\sqrt{6} + 4)} = \dfrac{2\sqrt{6} - 2\sqrt{12} - 2\sqrt{18} + 4 - 4\sqrt{2} - 4\sqrt{3}}{24 - 16}$

$= \dfrac{4 + 2\sqrt{6} - 8\sqrt{3} - 10\sqrt{2}}{8} = \dfrac{2 + \sqrt{6} - 4\sqrt{3} - 5\sqrt{2}}{4}$

ANSWER TO WORKSHEET 7

1. $pV^{\gamma} = c \quad \Rightarrow \quad \log p + \gamma \log V = \log c \Rightarrow \gamma = \dfrac{\log c - \log p}{\log V} = \dfrac{\log c/p}{\log V}$

   $\therefore \gamma = 1 \cdot 39 \quad$ *Physicists should recognise this.*

2. $x^2 - x + k = 0 \quad$ Real distinct roots if $1 > 4k \Rightarrow k < \frac{1}{4}$

3. $gfh(x) = gf(2x) = g(5^{2x}) = \log_{10} 5^{2x}$

   $3 = \log_{10} 5^{2x} \Rightarrow 2x = \dfrac{3}{\log_{10} 5} \Rightarrow x = \dfrac{1 \cdot 5}{\log_{10} 5} = 2 \cdot 1$

4. $y = kx$ is the line through the origin, of slope k. k must be such that graphs intersect three times (3 roots).

   $\therefore 0 < k < 4 \cdot 1$

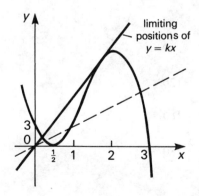

5. $7 - 12x - 3x^2 = -3\left(x^2 + 4x - \dfrac{7}{3}\right) = -3\left\{(x + 2)^2 - \dfrac{19}{3}\right\}$

   $x^2 \to (x + 2)^2 \quad$ translation 2 units to left $(-\text{ve } x)$

   $(x + 2)^2 \to (x + 2)^2 - \dfrac{19}{3} \quad$ translation $\dfrac{19}{3}$ units down $(-\text{ve } y)$

   $(x + 2)^2 - \dfrac{19}{3} \to 3\left\{(x + 2)^2 - \dfrac{19}{3}\right\} \quad$ scaling (stretching) by factor of 3 in y-direction

$$3\left\{(x+2)^2 - \frac{19}{3}\right\} \rightarrow -3\left\{(x+2)^2 - \frac{19}{3}\right\} \quad \text{reflection in } x \text{ axis}$$

6. $\dfrac{x+1}{x-2} < 2 \Rightarrow \dfrac{(x-2)^2(x+1)}{x-2} < 2(x-2)^2 \quad$ *must multiply inequalities by a positive number, hence* $(x-2)^2$

$$\Rightarrow (x-2)(x+1) - 2(x-2)^2 < 0$$

$$\Rightarrow (x-2)(5-x) < 0 \Rightarrow x < 2 \text{ or } x > 5$$

7. $f(x) = (x+1)^2 \quad$ domain $x > 0$
range $f(x) > 1$

$f^{-1}(x) = \sqrt{x} - 1 \quad$ domain $x > 0$
range $f^{-1}(x) > 0$

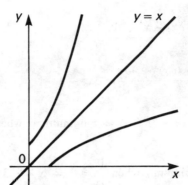

8. $\dfrac{x}{(x-1)^3} \equiv \dfrac{A}{(x-1)^3} + \dfrac{B}{(x-1)^2} + \dfrac{C}{x-1}$

$$\Rightarrow x \equiv A + B(x-1) + C(x-1)^2$$

$x = 1 \Rightarrow A = 1$
c.f. $x^2 \Rightarrow C = 0$
c.f. $x \Rightarrow 1 = B - 2C \Rightarrow B = 1$

$$\therefore \dfrac{x}{(x-1)^3} \equiv \dfrac{1}{(x-1)^3} + \dfrac{1}{(x-1)^2}$$

9. $\dfrac{\sqrt{128} - \sqrt{32} + \sqrt{8}}{\sqrt{3}(\sqrt{81} + \sqrt{27})} = \dfrac{8\sqrt{2} - 4\sqrt{2} + 2\sqrt{2}}{9\sqrt{3} + 9} = \dfrac{2\sqrt{2}}{3\sqrt{3} + 3}$

$$= \dfrac{2\sqrt{2}}{(3\sqrt{3} + 3)} \cdot \dfrac{(3\sqrt{3} - 3)}{(3\sqrt{3} - 3)} = \dfrac{\sqrt{6} - \sqrt{2}}{3}$$

10. $f(x) = x^2 + x - 2 = (x+2)(x-1)$

$$g(x) = \dfrac{1}{(x+2)(x-1)}$$

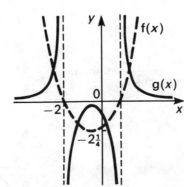

ANSWERS TO WORKSHEET 8

1. (a) $3.2x(x^2 + 3)^2(1 - x)^5 - 5(1 - x)^4(x^2 + 3)^2$

   $= (x^2 + 3)^2(1 - x)^4(6x - 11x^2 - 15)$

   (b) $\dfrac{2.2x(x^2 + 3)(1 - x)^5 + 5(1 - x)^4(x^2 + 3)^2}{(1 - x)^{10}}$

   $= \dfrac{(x^2 + 3)(x^2 + 4x + 15)}{(1 - x)^6}$

2. $\dfrac{\delta y}{\delta x} = \dfrac{(x + \delta x)^3 - 4(x + \delta x) - x^3 + 4x}{\delta x}$

   $= \dfrac{3x^2\delta x + 3x(\delta x)^2 + (\delta x)^3 - 4\delta x}{\delta x} = 3x^2 - 4$

3. (a) $y = x^2 + 6x + 13 = (x + 3)^2 + 4 \Rightarrow$ minimum y when $x = -3$
   and $y = 4$

   (b) $\dfrac{dy}{dx} = 2x + 6 \Rightarrow$ minimum y when $\dfrac{dy}{dx} = 0 \Rightarrow x = -3$ and
   $y = 9 - 18 + 13 = 4$

4. $y = x^3 + 3x^2 - 9x - 3 \Rightarrow x = 0, y = -3$

   $\dfrac{dy}{dx} = 3x^2 + 6x - 9$

   $\dfrac{dy}{dx} = 0 \Rightarrow x^2 + 2x - 3 = 0$ $\Rightarrow$

   $\Rightarrow x = -3, y = 24$
   $\quad\; x = 1, \quad y = -8$

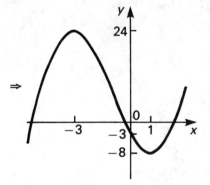

5. $gh(x) = \dfrac{1}{x} + 2 \Rightarrow \dfrac{dy}{dx} = -\dfrac{1}{x^2} < 0$ for all x

   Inverse $= \dfrac{1}{x - 2} \Rightarrow \dfrac{dy}{dx} = -\dfrac{1}{(x - 2)^2} < 0$ for all x

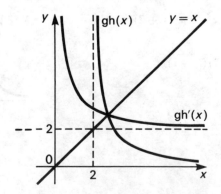

6. $A = x(100 - x) \Rightarrow \dfrac{dA}{dx} = 100 - 2x$

For maximum values $\dfrac{dA}{dx} = 0 \Rightarrow x = 50$

$A = 50^2 = 2500\,\text{m}^2$ *a square is a rectangle*

7. $V = \dfrac{\pi h^2}{3}(3r - h)$ $\dfrac{dV}{dh} = \pi(2hr - h^2)$

$\dfrac{dV}{dh} = \dfrac{dV}{dt}\dfrac{dt}{dh} \Rightarrow \pi(2hr - h^2) = 5\dfrac{dt}{dh} \Rightarrow \dfrac{dh}{dt} = \dfrac{5000}{\pi.75} = 21{\cdot}2\,\text{cm m}^{-1}$

8. $P = 2l + 2b \Rightarrow \dfrac{dP}{db} = 2$ (l is constant)

$\therefore \dfrac{\delta P}{\delta b} \approx 2 \Rightarrow \delta P \approx 2 \times db$

A small change in P is two times a small change in b.

now $\delta b = 2$ $\therefore \delta P = 2 \times 2 = 4\,\text{mm}.$

> In these questions errors are treated as small changes and hence are equivalent to δy, δx etc. in the basic calculus. There will be more questions of this type.

9. $\dfrac{dy}{dx} = \dfrac{[3x^2(x^5 + 1)^5 + 25x^7(x^5 + 1)^4](x + 2)(x - 3) - (2x - 1)x^3(x^5 + 1)^5}{(x + 2)^2(x - 3)^2}$

$= \dfrac{x^2(x^5 + 1)^4}{(x^2 - x - 6)^2}(x^7 - 2x^6 - 18x^5 + 25x^3 - 24x^2 - 152x - 18)$

> A test in basic algebra!?

10. $v = 15 + \dfrac{10}{t} \Rightarrow a = \dfrac{dv}{dt} = -\dfrac{10}{t^2}$

$t = 3 \Rightarrow a = -\dfrac{10}{9}\,\text{m s}^{-2}$

ANSWERS TO WORKSHEET 9

1. $f(x) = (x - 3)^2,\ x > 3 \Rightarrow f^{-1}(x) = \sqrt{x} + 3$ $\dfrac{d(f^{-1}(x))}{dx} = \dfrac{1}{2\sqrt{x}}$

2. $3x^2 + 5x - 2 = 0$ Mean $= \dfrac{\alpha + \beta}{2} = \dfrac{-5/3}{2} = -\dfrac{5}{6}$

3. $x = \dfrac{t^3}{3} - \dfrac{5t^2}{2} + 6t$

$v = \dfrac{dx}{dt} = t^2 - 5t + 6$ $v = 0 \Rightarrow t = 2,\ t = 3 \Rightarrow x = 4\tfrac{2}{3},\ 4\tfrac{1}{2}$

$a = \dfrac{dv}{dt} = 2t - 5$ $a = 0 \Rightarrow t = 2\tfrac{1}{2} \Rightarrow x = \dfrac{55}{12}$

Particle leaves O and accelerates for $2\frac{1}{2}$ seconds when $\dfrac{55}{12}$ m from O.

Retards to stop $4\frac{2}{3} = \dfrac{56}{12}$ m from O.

Returns to stop $4\frac{1}{2} = \dfrac{54}{12}$ m from O.

Accelerates from that point going away from O.

4. $A = \pi r^2 \Rightarrow \dfrac{dA}{dr} = 2\pi r \Rightarrow \delta A \approx 2\pi r \delta r$

If r changes by $0.5\% \Rightarrow \delta r = 0.5\%$ of $r = \dfrac{5r}{1000}$

% change in $A = \dfrac{\delta A}{A} \times 100 = \dfrac{2\pi r \delta r}{\pi r^2} \times 100 = \dfrac{2\pi r}{\pi r^2} \cdot \dfrac{5r}{1000} \times 100 = 1$

$\therefore$ change in A is 1%.

5. $\dfrac{1}{x(x-1)(x+1)} = \dfrac{1}{x^3 - x}$ $\dfrac{dy}{dx} = -\dfrac{(3x^2 - 1)}{(x^3 - x)^2}$

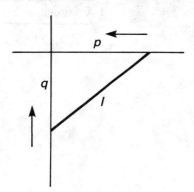

6. $l^2 = p^2 + q^2 \Rightarrow 2l\dfrac{dl}{dt} = 2p\dfrac{dl}{dt} + 2q\dfrac{dq}{dt}$

$\left.\begin{array}{l} \dfrac{dp}{dt} = -40, p = 1 \\[3em] \dfrac{dq}{dt} = -50, q = \frac{1}{2} \end{array}\right\} \Rightarrow \sqrt{1^2 + \frac{1}{2}^2}\,\dfrac{dl}{dt} = -40 - 25 = -65$

$\therefore \dfrac{dl}{dt} = -\dfrac{65}{\sqrt{\frac{5}{4}}} = -58.1\ \text{mph}$

the minus signs $\therefore$ both p and q are decreasing

7. $\dfrac{12}{x+1} > x + 2 \Rightarrow 12(x+1) > (x+1)^2(x+2)$

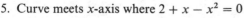

$\Rightarrow (x+1)\{(x+1)(x+2) - 12\} < 0$

$\Rightarrow (x+1)(x+5)(x-2) < 0$

$\Rightarrow x < -5 \quad \text{or} \quad -1 < x < 2$

8. $y = \dfrac{(x^3-1)^{1/3}}{(1-x)^{1/2}} \quad \dfrac{dy}{dx} = \dfrac{\frac{1}{3}.3x^2(x^3-1)^{-2/3}(1-x)^{1/2} + \frac{1}{2}(1-x)^{-1/2}(x^3-1)^{1/3}}{(1-x)}$

$\therefore \dfrac{dy}{dx} = \dfrac{x^2(1-x)^{1/2}}{(x^3-1)^{2/3}(1-x)} + \dfrac{(x^3-1)^{1/2}}{2(1-x)^{3/2}} = \dfrac{2x^2 - x^3 - 1}{2(1-x)^{3/2}(x^3-1)^{2/3}}$

9. $\left.\begin{array}{ll} z = (1+y^2)^{1/2} & \dfrac{dz}{dy} = y(1+y^2)^{-1/2} \\[2mm] y = (x+2)^5 & \dfrac{dy}{dx} = 5(x+2)^4 \end{array}\right\} \Rightarrow \dfrac{dz}{dx} = \dfrac{dz}{dy}.\dfrac{dy}{dx} = \dfrac{y}{(1+y^2)^{1/2}}5(x+2)^4$

$x = -1, y = 1 \Rightarrow \dfrac{dz}{dx} = \dfrac{5}{\sqrt{2}} = \dfrac{5\sqrt{2}}{2}$

10. $8x^3 + 26x^2 - 24x = 0 \Rightarrow x(4x-3)(2x+8) = 0 \Rightarrow x = 0, \frac{3}{4}, -4$

ANSWERS TO WORKSHEET 10

1. $\dfrac{dh}{dt} = 2 \quad V = \dfrac{\pi}{3}r^2h = \dfrac{4\pi h^3}{27} \left(\because \dfrac{r}{h} = \dfrac{10}{15}\right)$

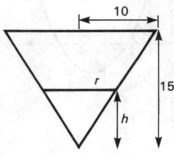

$\dfrac{dV}{dh} = \dfrac{4\pi h^2}{9}$

$\dfrac{dV}{dt} = \dfrac{dV}{dh}.\dfrac{dh}{dt} = \dfrac{4}{9}.\pi.3^2.2 = 8\pi \text{ cm s}^{-1}$

2. $\displaystyle\int_0^4 \dfrac{2x}{\sqrt{x^2+9}}\,dx = \left[2\sqrt{x^2+9}\right]_0^4 = 10 - 6 = 4$

3. $\text{MV} = \dfrac{1}{4-1}\displaystyle\int_1^4 (x^2+x+1)\,dx = \dfrac{1}{3}\left[\dfrac{x^3}{3} + \dfrac{x^2}{2} + x\right]_1^4 = 10\tfrac{1}{2}$

4. $\displaystyle\int(x^2+1)(x^3+3x)^5\,dx = \int\dfrac{1}{3}(3x^2+3)(x^2+3x)^5\,dx$

$= \dfrac{1}{18}(x^2+3x)^6 + A$

5. Curve meets x-axis where $2 + x - x^2 = 0$

$(2-x)(1+x) = 0 \Rightarrow x = -1 \quad \text{or} \quad 2$

$A = \displaystyle\int_{-1}^2 y\,dx = \int_{-1}^2 (2+x-x^2)\,dx = \left[2x + \dfrac{x^2}{2} - \dfrac{x^3}{3}\right]_{-1}^2 = 4\tfrac{1}{2}$

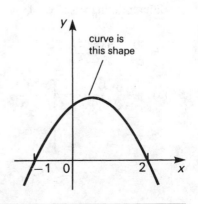

curve is this shape

6. $\left.\begin{array}{l} 8 = a + b \\ 17 = 4a + b \end{array}\right\} \Rightarrow a = 3, b = 5 \Rightarrow \dfrac{dy}{dx} = 3x + 5$

Integrating: $\quad y = \dfrac{3x^2}{2} + 5x + A$

Curve passes through $(2, 18)$ $\quad \therefore 18 = 6 + 10 + A \Rightarrow A = 2$

Equation of curve is $y = \dfrac{3}{2}x^2 + 5x + 2$

7. $y = x^2 - 7x + 10 = (x - 2)(x - 5)$

$$A = \int_1^2 y\,dx - \int_2^3 y\,dx \quad -ve \ sign \ \because \ negative \ area$$

$$= \left[\frac{x^3}{3} - \frac{7x^2}{2} + 10x\right]_1^2 - \left[\frac{x^3}{3} - \frac{7x^2}{2} + 10x\right]_2^3$$

$$= \frac{11}{6} - \frac{-7}{6}$$

$$= 3 \text{ square units}$$

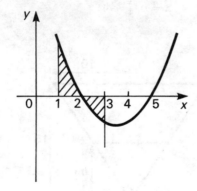

The hint suggests a danger. It is necessary to check where the curve lies.

$\frac{2}{3}$ *is the answer to* $\displaystyle\int_1^3 y\,dx$

8. $2x^2 + 5xy - 3y^2 = 8$

differentiating w.r.t. x: $\quad 4x + 5y + 5x\dfrac{dy}{dx} - 6y\dfrac{dy}{dx} = 0$

$$\Rightarrow \frac{dy}{dx} = \frac{4x + 5y}{6y - 5x}$$

This is also known as differentiating implicitly with respect to x.

9. (a) $\displaystyle\int \frac{(x + 3)^2}{\sqrt{x}}\,dx = \int \frac{x^2 + 6x + 9}{x^{1/2}}\,dx$

$$= \int (x^{3/2} + 6x^{1/2} + 9x^{-1/2})\,dx$$

$$= \frac{2}{5}x^{5/2} + 4x^{3/2} + 18x^{1/2} + A$$

(b) $\int (x+1)(x-1)(x+2)\,dx = \int (x^3 + 2x^2 - x - 2)\,dx$

$$= \frac{x^4}{4} + \frac{2x^3}{3} - \frac{x^2}{2} - 2x + A$$

> Two examples to remind you always to look for the easy way first!

10. $v = 3t^2 - 6t$

Integrating to find s: $\quad s = t^3 - 3t^2 + A$

distance in the 5th second $= s_5 - s_4$

$$= (5^3 - 3.5^2 + A) - (4^3 - 3.4^2 + A)$$

$$= 34\,\text{ft}$$

> $s_5 = distance\ after\ 5\ seconds$
>
> $s_4 = distance\ after\ 4\ seconds$

ANSWERS TO WORKSHEET II

1. $MV = \dfrac{1}{5-1}\displaystyle\int_1^5 (2x-6)\,dx$

$$= \frac{1}{4}\left[x^2 - 6x\right]_1^5$$

$$= \frac{1}{4}(-5) - \frac{1}{4}(-5) = 0$$

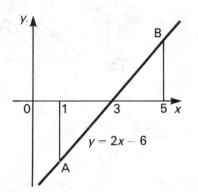

$y = 2x - 6$

> The sketch confirms the answer: the mean value of the function between A and B is 0, its value varies uniformly from -4 to 4.

2. $\displaystyle\int_0^2 (x-2)(x^2-4x)^3\,dx = \left[\frac{1}{8}(x^2-4x)^4\right]_0^2$

$$= \frac{1}{8}(-4)^4$$

$$= 32$$

3. $\dfrac{dV}{dt} = 2 \quad V = 36x^3 \quad A = 72x^2 \qquad$ *Two stages: using $\dfrac{dV}{dt}$ to find $\dfrac{dx}{dt}$*

$\dfrac{dV}{dt} = \dfrac{dV}{dx}\cdot\dfrac{dx}{dt} \Rightarrow 2 = 108.3^2.\dfrac{dx}{dt} \qquad$ *then using $\dfrac{dx}{dt}$ to find $\dfrac{dA}{dt}$*

$$\Rightarrow \frac{dx}{dt} = \frac{2}{108.9}$$

$$\frac{dA}{dt} = \frac{dA}{dx}\cdot\frac{dx}{dt} = 144.3.\frac{2}{108.9} = \frac{8}{9}\,\text{m}^2\,\text{s}^{-1}$$

4. $\displaystyle\int \frac{x}{(5x^2+1)^2}\,dx \qquad$ *Top is (differential of $5x^2+1$) $\div$ 10.*

$$\therefore I = -\frac{1}{10}(5x^2+1)^{-1} = -\frac{1}{10(5x^2+1)}$$

5. $\displaystyle\int_4^9 (x^{-1/2} + x^{1/2})\,dx = \left[2x^{1/2} + \frac{2}{3}x^{3/2} \right]_4^9 = 14^{2/3}$

6. Curves intersect: $x^2 = 2 - x^2 \Rightarrow x = \pm 1$

   $\therefore$ intersect at $(1, 1)$

   Area required is:

   (area under $2 - x^2$) $-$ (area under x^2)

   $\therefore A = \displaystyle\int_0^1 (2 - x^2)\,dx - \int_0^1 x^2\,dx$

   $= \left[2x - \dfrac{x^3}{3} \right]_0^1 - \left[\dfrac{x^3}{3} \right]_0^1$

   $= \dfrac{4}{3}$ square units

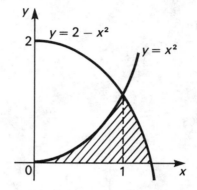

The sketch is essential: without it you won't know what is happening; with it the problem is straightforward.

7. BOA is part rotated.

   $\delta V = \pi y^2\,\delta x$

   where δv is the volume of a fine strip, considered to be a cylinder of radius y and height δx

   $\dfrac{\delta V}{\delta x} = \pi y^2$

   $\delta x \to 0 \quad \dfrac{dV}{dx} = \pi y^2$

   $\therefore \displaystyle\int \frac{dV}{dx}\,dx = \int \pi y^2\,dx$

   $\therefore V = \pi \displaystyle\int y^2\,dx$

   $\therefore V = \pi \displaystyle\int_0^4 \{25 - (x - 5)^2\}\,dx$

   $= \pi \displaystyle\int_0^4 (-x^2 + 10x)\,dx$

   $= \pi \left[-\dfrac{x^3}{3} + 5x^2 \right]_0^4 = 58\frac{2}{3}$ cubic units

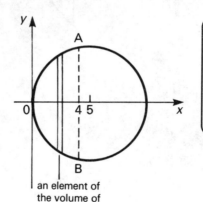

$y^2 + (x - 5)^2 = 25$ is a circle with centre at $(5, 0)$ and radius 5; although not needed the full curve has been drawn. More on circles later.

an element of the volume of thickness δx

You would normally start the question with this, the formula for the volume of revolution.

8. $a = 2t + 1$

$v = t^2 + t + A \quad t = 0, v = 3 \quad \therefore A = 3$

$s = \dfrac{t^3}{3} + \dfrac{t^2}{2} + 3t + B$

Distance in 2nd second $= s_2 - s_1 = \dfrac{8}{3} + 2 + 6 - \dfrac{1}{3} - \dfrac{1}{2} - 3 = \dfrac{41}{6}$ m

9. $A = \displaystyle\int_0^1 x\,\mathrm{d}y \qquad$ *limits are values of y note interchange of x and y*

The sketch is essential.

$y = (x-1)^3 \implies y^{1/2} = x - 1$

$\implies x = y^{1/3} + 1$

$\therefore A = \displaystyle\int_0^1 (y^{1/3} + 1)\,\mathrm{d}y$

$= \left[\dfrac{3}{4} y^{4/3} + y \right]_0^1$

$= 1.75$ square units

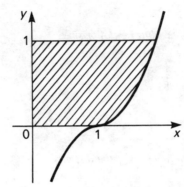

10. Equation of line: $y = \dfrac{r}{h}x \quad \therefore$ slope $= \dfrac{r}{h}$

$V = \pi \displaystyle\int_0^h y^2\,\mathrm{d}x = \pi \displaystyle\int_0^h \dfrac{r^2 x^2}{h^2}\,\mathrm{d}x$

$\implies V = \pi \left[\dfrac{r^2 x^2}{3h^2} \right]_0^h = \dfrac{\pi r^2 h}{3}$

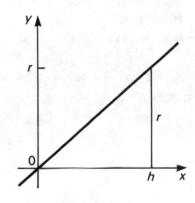

The cone is formed by rotating the straight line through 360° about the x-axis.

ANSWERS TO WORKSHEET 12

1. $\sin\dfrac{\theta}{4} = \dfrac{1}{2}$

$\implies \dfrac{\theta}{4} = 30°, 150°$

$\therefore \theta = 120°$

2. $\dfrac{\mathrm{d}(x\sin x)}{\mathrm{d}x} = \sin x + x\cos x \qquad$ *differential of a product*

Condition: x must be in radians

3. $2\cos^2 x = \cos 2x + 1$

It is an even function.

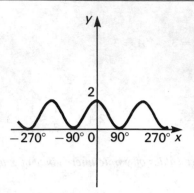

4. $\displaystyle\int_0^{\pi/6} \sin^5 x \cos x \, dx$ *cosx is the differential of sinx*

$\therefore I = \left[\dfrac{1}{6}\sin^6 x\right]_0^{\pi/6} = \dfrac{1}{6}\cdot\dfrac{1}{64} = \dfrac{1}{384}$

5. $x = a\sin kt$

$v = ak\cos kt$

$a = -ak^2\sin kt = -k^2 x$ *a function of the distance*

6. $\sin 5\theta + \sin 3\theta + \sin\theta = \sin 3\theta + 2\sin 3\theta\cos 2\theta$

$\qquad\qquad\qquad = \sin 3\theta\{1 + 2(2\cos^2\theta - 1)\}$

$\qquad\qquad\qquad = \sin 3\theta(4\cos^2\theta - 1)$

7. $\sin 3\theta(4\cos^2\theta - 1) = \sin 3\theta(2\cos\theta - 1)(2\cos\theta + 1) = 0$

$\quad\Rightarrow \sin 3\theta = 0 \;\Rightarrow\; \theta = 0, \pi, 2\pi, 3\pi$

$\quad$ or $\cos\theta = \dfrac{1}{2} \;\Rightarrow\; \theta = \dfrac{\pi}{3}, \dfrac{5\pi}{3}$

$\quad$ or $\cos\theta = -\dfrac{1}{2} \;\Rightarrow\; \theta = \dfrac{2\pi}{3}, \dfrac{4\pi}{3}$

8. $AB^2 = 4^2 + 5^2 - 2.4.5\cos 80°$ *cos rule needed*

$\therefore AB = 5\cdot 8$ miles

Bearing of A from B is θ.

First find A.

$\sin A = \dfrac{4}{5\cdot 8}\sin 80°$ *sine rule*

$\Rightarrow A = 42\cdot 8°$

$\Rightarrow$ bearing of A from B is $30° + 42\cdot 8° = 72\cdot 8°$.

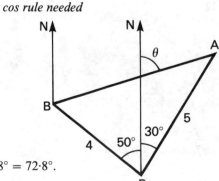

Since speed is in knots these are nautical miles.
1 n.m. $\approx$ 2025 yards
1 m $\;= 1760$ yards

9. $\tan 2\theta = -1$

$$\Rightarrow 2\theta = \frac{3\pi}{3}, \frac{7\pi}{4}, \frac{11\pi}{4}, \frac{15\pi}{4}$$

$$\Rightarrow \theta = \frac{3\pi}{8}, \frac{7\pi}{8}, \frac{11\pi}{8}, \frac{15\pi}{8}$$

General solution: $\theta = n\pi + \dfrac{3\pi}{8}$

10. $CD = 50 \tan 40° = 42'$

$BD = 42 \tan 62° = 79' \Rightarrow AB = (50^2 + 79^2)^{1/2} = 93\cdot 5$

$DE \times 93\cdot 5 = 50 \times 79 \Rightarrow DE = 42\cdot 2$ *using area of* Δ

$C\hat{E}D = \tan^{-1}\dfrac{42}{42\cdot 2} = 45°$

> Maximum elevation is $C\hat{E}D$ where $DE \perp AB$ and $CE \perp AB$ $\therefore$ we need to find DE and CD.

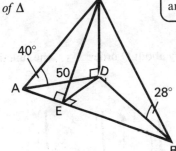

ANSWERS TO WORKSHEET 13

1. $\cos 2x + 3\cos x - 1 = 0$ *good idea to remove multiple angle, $2x$*

$$\Rightarrow 2\cos^2 x + 3\cos x - 2 = 0$$

$$\Rightarrow (2\cos x - 1)(\cos x + 2) = 0$$

$$\Rightarrow \cos x = \frac{1}{2} \quad \text{general solution: } x = 2n\pi \pm \frac{\pi}{3} \Rightarrow x = \frac{\pi}{3}, \frac{5\pi}{3}$$

or $\cos x = -2$ *no solutions*

2. $\displaystyle\int_0^{\pi/2} \sin^5 x\, dx = \int_0^{\pi/2} \sin x \sin^4 x\, dx$

$$\Rightarrow \int_0^{\pi/2} \sin x\,(1 - \cos^2 x)^2\, dx \quad \textit{making use of the fact that differential of } \cos x \textit{ is } \sin x$$

$$\Rightarrow \int_0^{\pi/2} \sin x - 2\sin x \cos^2 x + \sin x \cos^4 x\, dx$$

$$= \left[-\cos x + \frac{3}{2}\cos^2 x - \frac{1}{5}\cos^5 x \right]_0^{\pi/2}$$

> Study this solution carefully; it is most useful.

$$= -1 + \frac{2}{3} - \frac{1}{5} = -\frac{8}{15}$$

3. $\dfrac{d}{d\theta}(\tan\theta) = \dfrac{d}{d\theta}\left(\dfrac{\sin\theta}{\cos\theta}\right)$

$\qquad = \dfrac{\cos^2\theta + \sin^2\theta}{\cos^2\theta}$

$\qquad = \sec^2\theta$

4. $\displaystyle\int \dfrac{2}{\sqrt{9-4x^2}}\,dx = \int \dfrac{2}{3\sqrt{\left\{1-\left(\dfrac{2x}{3}\right)\right\}^2}}\,dx$

$\qquad I = \sin^{-1}\left(\dfrac{2x}{3}\right) + A$

5. Rotational symmetry about O order 2 $\quad\therefore$ the function is odd. Period 60°.

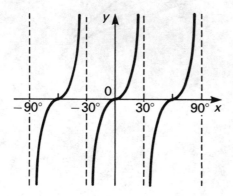

6. Description: an even function of period $\dfrac{\pi}{2}$. *dotted sections show negative values of* $\cos 2x$

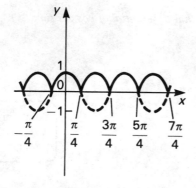

7. $\displaystyle\int_0^1 \frac{1}{2 + 2x + x^2}\,dx$

$\displaystyle = \int_0^1 \frac{1}{1 + (1 + x)^2}\,dx = \Big[\; \tan^{-1}(1 + x)\;\Big]_0^1$

$= \tan^{-1}2 - \tan^{-1}1$

$= 0{\cdot}3\,\text{radians}$

8. Let $5\sin x + 12\cos x \equiv R\sin(x + \alpha)$

$\Rightarrow 5 = R\cos\alpha,\; 12 = R\sin\alpha$

$\Rightarrow R = 13,\; \alpha = \tan^{-1}\dfrac{12}{5} = 1{\cdot}2\,\text{radians}$

$\therefore \sin(x + 1{\cdot}2) = \dfrac{5}{13}$

$\therefore x = 1{\cdot}2 + 0{\cdot}4,\; 2{\cdot}7 \quad \Rightarrow x = -0{\cdot}8,\; 1{\cdot}5\,\text{radians}.$

9. $\dfrac{\sqrt{\sin\theta}\,\cos\theta}{\sin\dfrac{\theta}{2}\cos\dfrac{\theta}{2}} = \dfrac{\sqrt{\sin\theta}\,\cos\theta}{\dfrac{1}{2}\sin\theta} = \dfrac{2\cos\theta}{\sqrt{\sin\theta}}$

> Always look carefully to see if the function will simplify.

$\dfrac{d}{d\theta}\left(\dfrac{2\cos\theta}{\sqrt{\sin\theta}}\right) = \dfrac{-2\sin\theta\sqrt{\sin\theta} - 2.\frac{1}{2}(\sin\theta)^{-1/2}\cos\theta}{\sin\theta}$

$= \dfrac{-2\sin^2\theta - \cos\theta}{\sin^{3/2}\theta}$

10. $f(x) = \dfrac{3}{2} + \sin x + \dfrac{1}{2}\left(1 - 2\sin^2\dfrac{x}{2}\right) = \dfrac{3}{2} + \sin x + \dfrac{1}{2}\cos x$

> Necessary to make the variable angles either x
> or $\dfrac{x}{2}$.

Let $\sin x + \dfrac{1}{2}\cos x \equiv R\sin(x + \alpha)$

$\Rightarrow R = \sqrt{1^2 + (\tfrac{1}{2})^2} = \dfrac{\sqrt{5}}{2}$

$\therefore \text{maximum value of } f(x) = \dfrac{3}{2} + \dfrac{\sqrt{5}}{2} = \dfrac{3 + \sqrt{5}}{2}$

ANSWERS TO WORKSHEET 14

1. $\displaystyle\int \frac{3}{2x^2 + 12x + 20}\,dx = \int \frac{3}{2(1 + (x + 3)^2)}\,dx$

$= \dfrac{3}{2}\tan^{-1}(x + 3) + A$

2. $x = 5\sin 2x \quad \Rightarrow \dfrac{x}{5} = \sin 2x \quad \therefore \textit{there is no value in plotting for } x > 5$

Scales: $2\,\text{cm} = 1$ unit on Ox $\quad \therefore$ *then* $\dfrac{x}{5} > 1$ *i.e. no more solutions*

$\qquad\qquad 4\,\text{cm} = 1$ unit on Oy

Solutions: $x = 0,\ 1{\cdot}45,\ 3{\cdot}58,\ 4{\cdot}22$ radians

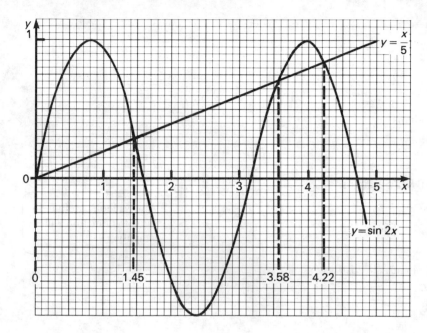

3. $\sin^2 x + \sin x \cos y + \cos^2 y = 1$

$$2\sin x \cos x + \cos x \cos y - \sin x \sin y \frac{dy}{dx} - 2\cos y \sin y \frac{dy}{dx} = 0$$

$$\Rightarrow \frac{dy}{dx} = -\frac{\cos x(2\sin x + \cos y)}{\sin y(\sin x + 2\cos y)} \qquad \textit{implicit differentiation again}$$

4. $\displaystyle\int \cos^2(2x+1)dx = \int \frac{1}{2}\Big\{\cos(4x+2) + 1\Big\}dx \qquad \textit{using } \cos^2 x = \tfrac{1}{2}(\cos 2x + 1)$

$$= \frac{1}{8}\sin(4x+2) + \frac{x}{2} + A$$

> You will meet this frequently in integration questions.

5. $2\tan^2 x + \sec x + 1 = 0$
$\Rightarrow 2(\sec^2 x - 1) + \sec x + 1 = 0$
$\Rightarrow (2\sec x - 1)(\sec + 1) = 0$
$\Rightarrow \sec x = \tfrac{1}{2}$ – *no solutions*
or $\sec x = -1 \Rightarrow \cos x = -1$
General solution is $x = 2n\pi \pm \pi$

> $\sec^2 x = 1 + \tan^2 x$

6. $\displaystyle\int \frac{1}{\sqrt{(3 + 2x - x^2)}}\,\mathrm{d}x = \int \frac{1}{\sqrt{4 - (1 - x)^2}}\,\mathrm{d}x$ $- x^2$ *suggests* $\sin^{-1}$

$$= \int \frac{1}{2\sqrt{1 - \left(\dfrac{1 - x}{2}\right)^2}}\,\mathrm{d}x$$

$$= -\sin^{-1}\left(\frac{1 - x}{2}\right) + A$$

7. $\displaystyle\int \cos^3 x\,\mathrm{d}x = \int \cos x \cos^2 x\,\mathrm{d}x$

$$= \int (\cos x - \cos x \sin^2 x)\,\mathrm{d}x$$

$$= \sin x - \frac{1}{3}\sin^3 x + A$$

8. $7\sin 2x + 24\cos 2x \equiv 25\sin(2x + \alpha)$

$\alpha = \tan^{-1}\dfrac{24}{7}$

$\therefore$ maximum value $= 25 + 3 = 28$ $\because$ *maximum value of sin is 1*

9. $\cos 50° - \tan 40° \sin 50° = \cos 50° - \dfrac{\sin 40° \sin 50°}{\cos 40°}$

$$= \frac{\cos 50° \cos 40° - \sin 50° \sin 40°}{\cos 40°}$$

$$= \frac{\cos(50° + 40°)}{\cos 40°}$$

$$= 0$$

10. $\tan 30° = \dfrac{2\tan 15°}{1 - \tan^2 15°}$

$\therefore \dfrac{1}{\sqrt{3}} = \dfrac{2\tan 15°}{1 - \tan^2 15°}$

> Only a slight hint given. This first line is the really hard part – just thinking of it.

$\Rightarrow \tan^2 15° + 2\sqrt{3}\tan 15° - 1 = 0$ *quadratic in* $\tan\theta$

$\Rightarrow \tan 15° = \dfrac{-2\sqrt{3} \pm \sqrt{12 + 4}}{2}$ *using quadratic formula*

$\qquad = -\sqrt{3} \pm 2$

$\therefore \tan 15° = 2 - \sqrt{3}$ $\because$ *tan 15° is positive*

ANSWERS TO WORKSHEET 15

1. $1 \equiv A(2 + x) + B(1 - x)$

   $x = 1 \Rightarrow A = \frac{1}{3}, \; x = -2 \Rightarrow B = \frac{1}{3}$

$$\therefore \frac{1}{(1 - x)(2 + x)} = \frac{1}{3}(1 - x)^{-1} + \frac{1}{3}(2 + x)^{-1}$$

$$= \frac{1}{3}\left[1 + (-1)(-x) + \frac{(-1)(-2)(-x)^2}{2} \right.$$

$$\left. + \frac{(-1)(-2)(-3)(-x)^3}{3!} + \cdots \right]$$

$$+ \frac{2^{-1}}{3}\left[1 + (-1)\left(\frac{x}{2}\right) + \frac{(-1)(-2)}{2}\left(\frac{x}{2}\right)^2 \right.$$

$$\left. + \frac{(-1)(-2)(-3)}{3!}\left(\frac{x}{2}\right)^3 + \cdots \right]$$

$$= \frac{1}{2} + \frac{x}{4} + \frac{3x^2}{8} + \frac{5}{16}x^3 + \cdots$$

$$\frac{1}{3}(2 + x)^{-1}$$

$$= \frac{2^{-1}}{3}\left(1 + \frac{x}{2}\right)^{-1}$$

$$= \frac{1}{6}\left(1 + \frac{x}{2}\right)^{-1}$$

2. GP with $a = 2, r = -\frac{1}{3}$

$$\therefore S_\infty = \frac{2}{1 - -\frac{1}{3}} = \frac{3}{2}$$

3. Term in $x^3 y^4$ is:

$$\binom{7}{4}(3x)^3(2y)^4 = 15\,120x^2y^4$$

4. $\displaystyle\int_0^1 \frac{2x}{\sqrt{1 - x^2}}\,dx = \left[-2\sqrt{1 - x^2} \right]_0^1$ *bottom is square root and top is differential of the inside*

   $$= 2$$

5. $7.2^x = \dfrac{5}{3^{x-1}}$

   $\therefore \ln(7.2^x) = \ln\left(\dfrac{5}{3^{x-1}}\right)$ *taking ln of both sides*

   $\therefore \ln 7 + x\ln 2 = \ln 5 - (x - 1)\ln 3$

   $$x = \frac{\ln 5 + \ln 3 - \ln 7}{\ln 2 + \ln 3}$$

   $$= \frac{\ln\left(\dfrac{15}{7}\right)}{\ln 6} = 0 \cdot 43$$

6. $S = \log2 + \log2^2 + \log2^3 + \cdots + \log2^{50}$

   $\quad = \log2 + 2\log2 + 3\log2 + \cdots + 50\log2$

   $\quad = \log2(1 + 2 + 3 + \cdots + 50)$

   $\quad = \log2 \times \dfrac{50}{2}(1 + 50) \qquad using\ S_n = \dfrac{n}{2}(a + l)$

   $\quad = 383\cdot8$

7. $(1 + 2x)^{30}$

   $T(x^{10}) = T_{11} = \dbinom{30}{10}(2x)^{10}$

   $\qquad\qquad = 3\cdot08 \times 10^{10} \times x^{10}$

> The question is answered at this point.

8. $\left(2x - \dfrac{1}{x^2}\right)^{21}$

   Term independent of x is $\dbinom{21}{14}(2x)^{14}\left(\dfrac{-1}{x^2}\right)^7$

> This is the important part: selecting the correct term.

   $\quad = -1\,905\,131\,520$

9. $x^{2/3} + 3x^{1/3} - 2 = 0 \qquad quadratic\ in\ x^{1/3}$

   $x^{1/3} = \dfrac{-3 \pm \sqrt{9 + 8}}{2} = \dfrac{-3 \pm \sqrt{17}}{2}$

   $x \quad = 0\cdot18\ \text{or}\ -45\cdot2$

10. T reflected in M_1 to give $I_1 \quad TI_1 = 2a$

    I_1 reflected in M_2, to give $I_2 \quad I_1M_2 = M_2I_2 = 3a \Rightarrow I_2T = 4a$

    I_2 reflected in M_1 to give $I_3 \quad I_2M_1 = M_1I_3 = 5a \Rightarrow I_3T = 6a$

    $\Rightarrow$ Successive distances are $1 \times 2a, 2 \times 2a, 3 \times 2a, \cdots$

    $\therefore$ distance of 12th image is $12 \times 2a = 24a$

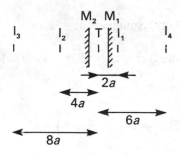

ANSWERS TO WORKSHEET 16

1. $2x^2 + 12x + k = 2\left\{(x + 3)^2 + \dfrac{k}{2} - 9\right\}$

   The minimum value is when $x = -3$ and is $2\left(\dfrac{k}{2} - 9\right)$.

   For the function to be +ve $\dfrac{k}{2} - 9 > 0 \quad \Rightarrow k > 18$

2. $y = \tan^2\theta - 2\tan\theta$

$\dfrac{dy}{d\tan\theta} = 2\tan\theta - 2$ *differentiating w.r.t. tanθ and not θ*

> This makes the solution much easier.

Minimum when $\tan\theta = 1$

and then $y = 1 - 2 = -1$

3. $x^2 + 3x + c = 0$

$$x = \frac{-3 \pm \sqrt{9 - 4c}}{2}$$

$$= -\frac{3}{2} \pm \frac{3}{2}\left(1 - \frac{4c}{9}\right)^{1/2}$$

$$\therefore x = -\frac{3}{2} \pm \frac{3}{2}\left\{1 + \frac{1}{2}\left(-\frac{4c}{9}\right) + \left(\frac{1}{2}\right)\left(-\frac{1}{2}\right)\left(-\frac{4c}{9}\right)^2 \frac{1}{2} + \cdots\right\}$$

$$= -\frac{3}{2} \pm \left\{\frac{3}{2} - \frac{c}{3} - \frac{c^2}{27}\cdots\right\}$$

$$\therefore x = -\frac{c}{3} - \frac{c^2}{27}\cdots \quad \text{or} \quad x = -3 + \frac{c}{3} + \frac{c^2}{27}\cdots$$

4. Let the numbers be $\dfrac{a}{r}$, a, ar

Product $= a^3 = 1728 \Rightarrow a = 12$ **Note** This selection of terms
$\Rightarrow r$ not appearing on this line

Sum $= 12\left(\dfrac{1}{r} + 1 + r\right) = 42$

$\Rightarrow 2r^2 - 5r + 2 = 0 \quad \Rightarrow r = \dfrac{1}{2}$ or 2

> Either value is good $\because$ same three terms are generated.

$\therefore$ the terms are 6, 12, 24

5. $0\cdot\dot{1} = 0\cdot11111\cdots$

$= 0\cdot1 + 0\cdot01 + 0\cdot001 + \cdots$

$= 0\cdot1 + 0\cdot1.0\cdot1 + 0\cdot1.(0\cdot1)^2 + 0\cdot1.(0\cdot1)^3 + \ldots$ *infinite GP, $a = 0\cdot1$, $r = 0\cdot1$*

$S = \dfrac{0\cdot1}{1 - 0\cdot1} = \dfrac{1}{9} \quad \therefore 0\cdot\dot{1} = \dfrac{1}{9}$

6. $\sqrt{0\cdot98} = (1 - 0\cdot02)^{1/2}$

$$= 1 + \left(\frac{1}{2}\right)(-0\cdot02) + \left(\frac{1}{2}\right)\left(-\frac{1}{2}\right)\left(\frac{-0\cdot02}{2}\right)^2$$

$$= 1 - 0\cdot01 - 0\cdot000\,05 \quad \textit{further terms unnecessary}$$

$$= 0\cdot990$$

7. $\dfrac{1}{(1 + x)(1 + x + x^2)} \equiv \dfrac{A}{1 + x} + \dfrac{Bx + C}{1 + x + x^2}$

$$\therefore 1 \equiv A(1 + x + x^2) + (Bx + C)(1 + x)$$

$$\Rightarrow f(x) = \frac{1}{1 + x} - \frac{x}{1 + x + x^2}$$

$$= (1 + x)^{-1} - x(1 + \overline{x + x^2})^{-1}$$

$$= 1 - x + x^2 - x^3 + \cdots$$

$$- x\left(1 + (-1)(x + x^2) + \frac{(-1)(-2)}{2}(x + x^2)^2\right.$$

$$\left. + \frac{(-1)(-2)(-3)}{3!}(x + x^2)^3 \cdots\right)$$

$$= (1 - x + x^2 - x^3 + \cdots) - x(1 - x - x^2 + x^2 \cdots)$$

$$= 1 - 2x + 2x^2 - x^3 + \cdots$$

> Only work out the
> necessary terms – as
> shown.

8. Nine means $\therefore d = \dfrac{10 - -5}{10} = 1\cdot5$

Nine means are $8\cdot5, 7, 5\cdot5, 4, 2\cdot5, 1, -0\cdot5, -2, -3\cdot5$

9. $\text{ghf}(x) = \sqrt{2x + 1}$

$$(1 + 2x)^{1/2} = 1 + x - \frac{x^2}{2} + \frac{x^3}{2}$$

10. $(2a + 5b)^{12}$

$$T_8 = \binom{12}{5}(2a)^7(5b)^5, \ T_9 = \binom{12}{4}(2a)^8(5b)^4$$

$$\therefore \frac{12!}{5!7!} \cdot 2^7 a^7 5^5 b^5 = \frac{12!}{4!8!} \cdot 2^8 a^8 5^4 b^4$$

$$\Rightarrow b = \frac{a}{4}$$

$$\Rightarrow a : b = 4 : 1$$

ANSWERS TO WORKSHEET 17

1. $y = e^x \sin x \qquad \dfrac{dy}{dx} = e^x \cos x + e^x \sin x$

   $\dfrac{d^2 y}{dx^2} = -e^x \sin x + e^x \cos x + e^x \cos x + e^x \sin x$

   $\qquad = 2e^x \cos x = 2\left(\dfrac{dy}{dx} - e^x \sin x\right)$

   $\therefore \dfrac{d^2 y}{dx^2} = 2\dfrac{dy}{dx} - 2y$

2. $y = \log_{10}(2x + 1) = \dfrac{\ln(2x + 1)}{\ln 10}$

   $\therefore \dfrac{dy}{dx} = \dfrac{1}{\ln 10(2x + 1)}$

3. $h(x) = (e^x)^2 = e^{2x} \qquad k(x) = e^{x^2}$

   They are not the same $\because 2x \neq x^2$

   $h^{-1}(x) = \dfrac{1}{2}\ln x = \ln\sqrt{x}$

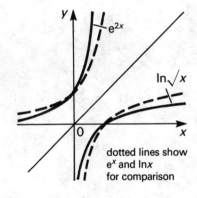

dotted lines show
e^x and $\ln x$
for comparison

4. $A = \displaystyle\int_{-2}^{1} e^{-2x}\, dx = \left[-\dfrac{1}{2}e^{-2x}\right]_{-2}^{1} = -\dfrac{1}{2}(e^{-2} - e^{+4})$

   $\therefore A = \dfrac{1}{2}(e^4 - e^{-2}) = 27\cdot2$ square units

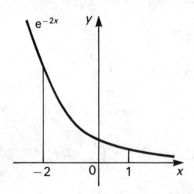

5. $\int_0^1 x^2 e^x \, dx = \left[x^2 e^x \right]_0^1 - \int_0^1 2x e^x \, dx$ *by parts;* $x^2 = du, e^x = v$

$= e - \left\{ \left[2x e^x \right]_0^1 - \int_0^1 2e^x \, dx \right\}$ *by parts again*

$= e - 2e + \left[2e^x \right]_0^1$

$= e - 2$

6. $e^x(e^x + 1) = 2$

$\Rightarrow e^{2x} + e^x - 2 = 0$ *quadratic in* e^x

$\Rightarrow (e^x + 2)(e^x - 1) = 0$

$\Rightarrow e^x = -2$ *no solutions*

and $e^x = 1 \quad \Rightarrow x = 0$

7. $\left. \begin{array}{l} e^x = y \quad \therefore x = \ln y \\ e^y = z \quad \therefore y = \ln z \end{array} \right\} x = \ln(\ln z)$

8. $I = \int e^x \sin x \, dx$ *by parts;* $e^x = du, \sin x = v$

$= e^x \sin x - \int e^x \cos x \, dx$ *by parts again;* $e^x = du, \cos x = v$

$= e^x \sin x - \{ e^x \cos x - \int -e^x \sin x \, dx \}$

$= e^x \sin x - e^x \cos x - \int e^x \sin x \, dx$

$= e^x \sin x - e^x \cos x - I \qquad \because I = \int e^x \sin x \, dx$

$\therefore 2I = e^x \sin x - e^x \cos x$

$I = \frac{e^x}{2}(\sin x - \cos x)$

> The integrand (the bit you are integrating) contains e^x and $\sin x$, two functions which differentiate indefinitely. The technique therefore is to apply 'by parts' twice until the integrand reappears and then manipulate as in the example. This is an important technique with applications at higher levels e.g. reduction formulae.

9. In the new equation $ax^2 + bx + c = 0$:

$\frac{b}{a} = -\left\{ \alpha^3 + \beta^3 + \frac{\alpha + \beta}{\alpha\beta} \right\}$

$= -\left\{ (\alpha + \beta)[(\alpha + \beta)^2 - 3\alpha\beta] + \frac{\alpha + \beta}{\alpha\beta} \right\} = -\frac{51}{2}$

$\frac{c}{a} = \alpha^3 \beta^3 + \frac{1}{\alpha\beta} + \alpha^2 + \beta^2$

$= \alpha^3 \beta^3 + \frac{1}{\alpha\beta} + (\alpha + \beta)^2 - 2\alpha\beta = \frac{63}{8}$

$\therefore$ the equation is $8x^2 - 204x + 63 = 0$

10. $y = a^x$

$\therefore \log^a y = x$

$\therefore \dfrac{\ln y}{\ln a} = x$

$\ln y = x \ln a$

$y = e^{x \ln a}$

ANSWERS TO WORKSHEET 18

1. $A = \displaystyle\int_2^3 \ln x \, dx = \int_2^3 1 . \ln x \, dx$ *by parts; du = 1v = lnx*

$= \Big[x \ln x \Big]_2^3 - \displaystyle\int_2^3 x . \dfrac{1}{x} dx$

$= 3\ln3 - 2\ln2 - \Big[x \Big]_2^3$

$= \ln27 - \ln4 - 1 = \ln\dfrac{27}{4} - 1 = 0{\cdot}9$ square units

2. $\displaystyle\int \dfrac{3}{\sqrt{5 - x^2}} dx = \int \dfrac{3}{\sqrt{5}\sqrt{1 - \left(\dfrac{x}{\sqrt{5}}\right)^2}} dx$

$= \dfrac{3}{\sqrt{5}} \sin^{-1}\left(\dfrac{x}{\sqrt{5}}\right) + A$

3.

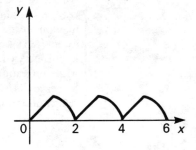

4.

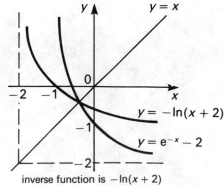

$y = x$

$y = -\ln(x + 2)$

$y = e^{-x} - 2$

inverse function is $-\ln(x + 2)$

5. $y = e^{2x}\ln(1 + x)$

$$\frac{dy}{dx} = 2e^{2x}\ln(1 + x) + \frac{e^{2x}}{1 + x}$$

$$\Rightarrow \frac{dy}{dx} - 2y = \frac{e^x}{1 + x}$$

6. $y = 3e^x + x^2$ $\qquad z = 2\ln(2x^3 + x)$

$$\frac{dy}{dt} = (3e^x + 2x)\frac{dx}{dt} \quad \frac{dz}{dt} = \frac{2(6x^2 + 1)}{(2x^3 + x)}\frac{dx}{dt}$$

$$7 = \frac{2 \times 7}{3} \cdot \frac{dx}{dt}$$

$$\Rightarrow \frac{dy}{dt} = (3e + 2) \cdot \frac{3}{2} = \frac{3e}{2} + 3$$

7. $\displaystyle\int_1^4 \frac{3x + 1}{3x^2 + 2x}dx = \int \frac{1}{2} \cdot \frac{6x + 2}{3x^2 + 2x}dx$

$$= \frac{1}{2}\ln(3x^2 + 2x) + A$$

8. Minimum value of e^x in domain $x > 0$ is $e^0 = 1$

$\therefore 2x - k > 0$ when $x = 0$

$\Rightarrow k < 0$

9. $\displaystyle\int \frac{2x + 1}{1 + x^2}dx = \int\left(\frac{2x}{1 + x^2} + \frac{1}{1 + x^2}\right)dx$

$$= \ln(1 + x^2) + \tan^{-1}x + A$$

10. $\displaystyle\int_0^{\pi/2} \sin3x\cos2x\,dx = \int_0^{\pi/2} \frac{1}{2}(\sin5x + \sin x)\,dx$

$\quad using \ \sin C + \sin D = 2\sin\dfrac{(C + D)}{2}\cos\dfrac{(C - D)}{2}$

$$= \left[-\frac{1}{10}\cos5x - \frac{1}{2}\cos x\right]_0^{\pi/2}$$

$$= (0) - \left(-\frac{1}{10} - \frac{1}{2}\right)$$

$$= \frac{3}{5}$$

PURE MATHS FOR A LEVEL

ANSWERS TO WORKSHEET 19

1.
$$\begin{pmatrix} 2 \\ 3 \\ -1 \end{pmatrix} \cdot \begin{pmatrix} 5 \\ -2 \\ 3 \end{pmatrix} = \sqrt{(2^2 + 3^2 + (-1)^2)} \cdot \sqrt{5^2 + (-2)^2 + 3^2} \cdot \cos\theta \qquad \textit{using scalar product}$$

$$\Rightarrow \cos\theta = \frac{1}{\sqrt{14}\sqrt{38}} \qquad \therefore \theta = 87\cdot5°$$

2. $5(1 - \sec x) = \tan^2 x$

$\Rightarrow \sec^2 x + 5\sec x - 6 = 0$ $\qquad\qquad$ $\boxed{\because \sec^2 x = 1 + \tan^2 x}$

$(\sec x + 6)(\sec x - 1) = 0$

$\Rightarrow \sec x = -6 \Rightarrow \cos x = -\dfrac{1}{6} \Rightarrow x = 99\cdot6°$

and $\sec x = 1 \quad \Rightarrow \cos x = 1 \quad \Rightarrow x = 0$

3.
$$\mathbf{r} = \begin{pmatrix} 1 \\ 0 \\ 2 \end{pmatrix} + \lambda \begin{pmatrix} 2 \\ 3 \\ -1 \end{pmatrix} \text{ and } \mathbf{r} = \begin{pmatrix} 3 \\ 1 \\ -2 \end{pmatrix} + \mu \begin{pmatrix} 1 \\ 2 \\ 8 \end{pmatrix}$$

The direction vectors of the lines are $\begin{pmatrix} 2 \\ 3 \\ -1 \end{pmatrix}$ and $\begin{pmatrix} 1 \\ 2 \\ 8 \end{pmatrix}$.

$\therefore$ the angle between the lines is the angle between these vectors.

$$\theta = \cos^{-1} \frac{\begin{pmatrix} 2 \\ 3 \\ -1 \end{pmatrix} \cdot \begin{pmatrix} 1 \\ 2 \\ 8 \end{pmatrix}}{\sqrt{14}\sqrt{69}} = 91\cdot8°$$

4. The lines intersect if $\left.\begin{array}{c} \lambda = 2 - \mu \\ 2\lambda = 1 + \mu \end{array}\right\} \Rightarrow \lambda = 1, \mu = 1$

and $4 - \lambda = 1 + 2\mu \qquad$ *substituting $\lambda = 1, \mu = 1$ verifies this*

$\therefore$ the lines intersect.

Position vector of the intersection point:

$r = \begin{pmatrix} 1 \\ 2 \\ 3 \end{pmatrix} \qquad$ *substituting for λ in equation above*

5. $\displaystyle\int_{\pi/6}^{\pi/3}\left(\frac{\cos x}{\sin x}+\frac{\sin x}{\cos x}\right)dx = \Big[\ln\sin x - \ln\cos x\Big]_{\pi/6}^{\pi/3}$

$$= \Big[\ln\tan x\Big]_{\pi/6}^{\pi/3} = \ln\sqrt{3} - \ln\left(\frac{1}{\sqrt{3}}\right)$$

$$= \ln\sqrt{3} - \ln 1 + \ln\sqrt{3}$$

$$= \ln 3 = 1\cdot 1$$

6. M and N are midpoints of AB and AC.

$$\mathbf{BC} = \mathbf{BA} + \mathbf{AC}$$

$$\mathbf{MN} = \mathbf{MA} + \mathbf{AN} = \frac{1}{2}\mathbf{BA} + \frac{1}{2}\mathbf{AC}$$

$$\therefore \mathbf{MN} = \frac{1}{2}(\mathbf{BA} + \mathbf{AC}) = \frac{1}{2}\mathbf{BC}$$

$$\Rightarrow \mathbf{MN} = \frac{1}{2}\mathbf{BC} \text{ and } \mathbf{MN}\|\mathbf{BC} \qquad \text{the midpoint theorem}$$

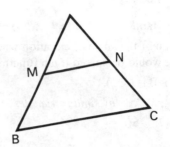

7. $\mathbf{r} - \begin{pmatrix}4\\1\\-2\end{pmatrix}\cdot\begin{pmatrix}2\\-1\\-1\end{pmatrix} = 0$

$$\Rightarrow \mathbf{r}\cdot\begin{pmatrix}2\\-1\\-1\end{pmatrix} = 9 \qquad \text{the equation of the plane}$$

8. $\sqrt{(1 - x - 12x^2)}$

$$= (1 - 4x)^{1/2}(1 + 3x)^{1/2}$$

$$= \left\{1 - 2x - 2x^2 - 4x^3\cdots\right\}\left\{1 + \frac{3}{2}x - \frac{9}{8}x^2 + \frac{27}{16}x^3\cdots\right\}$$

$$= 1 - \frac{x}{2} - \frac{49}{8}x^2 - \frac{49}{16}x^3\cdots$$

$\left.\begin{array}{l}(1 - 4x)^{1/2} \text{ is valid for } |x| < \frac{1}{4}\\(1 + 3x)^{1/2} \text{ is valid for } |x| < \frac{1}{3}\end{array}\right\}$ $\therefore$ series is valid for $|x| < \frac{1}{4}$

9. $\mathbf{r} = t^2\mathbf{i} + 2t\mathbf{j} + 3\mathbf{k}$

$$\mathbf{v} = \frac{d\mathbf{r}}{dt} = 2t\mathbf{i} + 2\mathbf{j} \qquad \text{particle is moving in plane } \| \mathbf{i}, \mathbf{j} \text{ plane}$$

$$\mathbf{a} = \frac{d\mathbf{v}}{dt} = 2\mathbf{i} \qquad \text{particle accelerating only in } \mathbf{i} \text{ direction}$$

10. $\left.\begin{array}{l}2x + 3y - z = 0\\3x - 6y - 5z = 7\\4x - 9y + z = 18\end{array}\right\}$ $\begin{array}{l}\Rightarrow \quad 7x - 7z = 7 \quad \Rightarrow \quad x - z = 1\\\Rightarrow \quad 10x - 2z = 18 \Rightarrow 5x - z = 9\\\Rightarrow \quad x = 2, z = 1, y = -1\end{array}$

ANSWERS TO WORKSHEET 20

1. First multiple is 702, last is 798.

   i.e. $703 + (n-1)3 = 798 \quad \Rightarrow n = 33$

   $\therefore S = \dfrac{33}{2}(702 + 798) = 24\,750$

> Work out n carefully:
> this is the best way.

2. $\tan\beta = \dfrac{h}{d}$ and $\tan\alpha = \dfrac{h}{2d}$

   $\therefore \tan\alpha = \tfrac{1}{2}\tan\beta$

   It is the tan of the angle of elevation which is halved.
   The angle would be halved if tan function were linear.

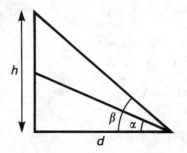

3. A is $(1, 4)$, B is $(3, 1)$.

   $\therefore$ P is $(2\tfrac{1}{3}, 2)$ *by similar triangles*

   and Q is $(7, -5)$

   Position vector of P is $\dfrac{7}{3}\mathbf{j} + 2\mathbf{j}$ or $\begin{pmatrix} \tfrac{7}{3} \\ 2 \end{pmatrix}$

   and position vector of Q is $\begin{pmatrix} 7 \\ -5 \end{pmatrix}$

> **Remember**
> $BQ = 2AB$
> $AQ:QB = 3:2$ i.e. 3
> units from A to Q and 2
> from Q back to B.

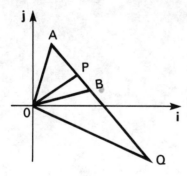

   Vector $\mathbf{PQ} = \begin{pmatrix} 7 - \tfrac{7}{3} \\ -5 - 2 \end{pmatrix} = \begin{pmatrix} \tfrac{14}{3} \\ -7 \end{pmatrix}$

4. $P(x) = 2x^4 + 3x^3 - 4x^2 - 3x + 2$

   $P(1) = 0 \quad \therefore P(x) = (x-1)(2x^3 + 5x^2 + x - 2)$

   $P(-1) = 0 \quad \therefore P(x) = (x-1)(x+1)(2x^2 + 3x - 2)$

   $\therefore P(x) = (x-1)(x+1)(x+2)(2x-1)$

> Use the factor theorem:
> if $P(a) = 0$ then $x - a$ is
> a factor. Notation:
> $P(x) =$ polynomial in x

5. $y = e^{-t}(\cos 2t + \sin 2t)$

   $\dfrac{dy}{dt} = -e^{-t}(\cos 2t + \sin 2t) + e^{-t}(-2\sin 2t + 2\cos 2t)$

   $= e^{-t}\cos 2t - 3e^{-2}\sin t$

$$\frac{d^2y}{dt^2} = -e^{-t}\cos2t - 2e^{-t}\sin2t + 3e^{-t}\sin2t - 3e^{-t}2\cos2t$$

$$= -7e^{-t}\cos2t + e^{-t}\sin2t$$

Then $\dfrac{d^2y}{dt^2} + 2\dfrac{dy}{dt} + 5y$

$$= e^{-t}(-7\cos2t + \sin2t + 2\cos2t - 6\sin2t + 5\cos2t + 5\sin2t) = 0$$

6. The lines intersect if $\left.\begin{array}{l} 1 - \lambda = \mu \\ 2\lambda = 5 + \mu \end{array}\right\} \Rightarrow \lambda = 2, \mu = -1$

$1 + \lambda = 1 - 2\mu \quad \Rightarrow$ satisfied by $\lambda = 2, \mu = -1$

$\therefore$ they intersect

Position vector of the point of intersection is $\begin{pmatrix} -1 \\ 4 \\ 3 \end{pmatrix}$

Lines are $\mathbf{r} = \begin{pmatrix} 1 \\ 0 \\ 1 \end{pmatrix} + \lambda \begin{pmatrix} -1 \\ 2 \\ 1 \end{pmatrix}$ and $\mathbf{r} = \begin{pmatrix} 0 \\ 5 \\ 1 \end{pmatrix} + \mu \begin{pmatrix} 1 \\ 1 \\ -2 \end{pmatrix}$

$\cos\theta = \dfrac{\begin{pmatrix} -1 \\ 2 \\ 1 \end{pmatrix} \cdot \begin{pmatrix} 1 \\ 1 \\ -2 \end{pmatrix}}{\sqrt{6}\sqrt{6}} = -\dfrac{1}{6} \quad \therefore \theta = 80\cdot4°$

7. $\displaystyle\int \dfrac{dx}{7 + 4x + x^2}\, dx \quad$ *form suggests* $\tan^{-1}$

$$\int \dfrac{dx}{3 + (2 + x)^2} = \int \dfrac{1}{3} \dfrac{dx}{\left\{1 + \left(\dfrac{2+x}{\sqrt{3}}\right)^2\right\}}$$

$$= \dfrac{1}{\sqrt{3}}\tan^{-1}\left(\dfrac{2+x}{\sqrt{3}}\right) + A$$

8. $12(x^2 + x + 1) > 17x + 14$

$\Rightarrow 12x^2 - 5x - 2 > 0 \quad \Rightarrow (4x + 1)(3x - 2) > 0$

$\Rightarrow$ true for $x < -\frac{1}{4}$ or $x > \frac{2}{3}$

9. $12\sin x - 5\cos x \equiv R\sin(x - \alpha) = 13$

$\Rightarrow R = 13$ and $\alpha = \tan^{-1}\frac{5}{12} = 0\cdot4$ rad

Then $x - 0\cdot4 = \sin^{-1} = \frac{\pi}{2}$ $x = 1\cdot97$ rad

General solution is $x = n\pi + (-1)^n 1\cdot97$

10. $\mathbf{v} = 2t\mathbf{i} + 3t^2\mathbf{j} + \mathbf{k}$

$\mathbf{s} = (t^2 + A)\mathbf{i} + (t^3 + B)\mathbf{j} + (t + C)\mathbf{k}$

At $t = 0$: $\mathbf{s} = 2\mathbf{i} + \mathbf{j} + 3\mathbf{k} \quad \Rightarrow A = 1, B = 1, C = 3$

$\therefore \mathbf{s} = (t^2 + 2)\mathbf{i} + (t^3 + 1)\mathbf{j} + (t + 3)\mathbf{k}$

ANSWERS TO WORKSHEET 21

1. $x^4 - 5x^2 - 36 = 0 \implies (x^2 - 9)(x^2 + 4) = 0$

$\implies x^2 - 9 = 0 \implies x = \pm 3$

and $\implies x^2 + 4 = 0 \implies x = \pm 2i$

$\therefore$ the four roots are ± 3 and $\pm 2i$.

2. $\dfrac{1}{1 + 2i} + \dfrac{3}{3 - i} = \dfrac{3 - i + 3 + 6i}{5 + 5i} = \dfrac{(6 + 5i)(1 - i)}{5(1 + i)(1 - i)} = \dfrac{11 - i}{10}$

3. $z_1 = 1 + i, z_2 = 1 + \sqrt{3}i$

$z_1 z_2 = (1 + i)(1 + \sqrt{3}i) = 1 - \sqrt{3} + i(1 + \sqrt{3})$

$\dfrac{z_1}{z_2} = \dfrac{(1 + i)}{(1 + \sqrt{3}i)} \dfrac{(1 - \sqrt{3}i)}{(1 - \sqrt{3}i)} = \dfrac{1 + \sqrt{3} + i(1 - \sqrt{3})}{4}$

z_1 is $\left(\sqrt{1^2 + 1^2}, \tan^{-1} \dfrac{1}{1} \right) = (\sqrt{2}, \frac{\pi}{4})$

z_2 is $(2, \frac{\pi}{3})$

$z_1 z_2$ is $\left(\sqrt{(1 - \sqrt{3})^2 + (1 + \sqrt{3})^2}, \tan^{-1} \left(\dfrac{1 + \sqrt{3}}{1 - \sqrt{3}} \right) \right) = (2\sqrt{2}, -1 \cdot 3)$

$\dfrac{z_1}{z_2}$ is $\left(\dfrac{2\sqrt{2}}{4}, -0 \cdot 3 \right)$ *mod is $\frac{1}{4}$ of mod of $z_1 z_2$ and*

                                      arg = complement arg $z_1 z_2$, by inspection

4. $V = \dfrac{1}{3}\pi r^2 h \implies 300\pi = \dfrac{1}{3}\pi r^2 h$ and $\dfrac{dr}{dt} = 2$

$\therefore r^2 h = 900 \implies$ when $h = 9$ then $r = 10$

differentiating $\implies 2rh\dfrac{dr}{dt} + r^2 \dfrac{dh}{dt} = 0$

$\therefore 2.10.9.2 + 100\dfrac{dh}{dt} = 0 \implies \dfrac{dh}{dt} = -3 \cdot 6 \,\text{cm s}^{-1}$ *height is decreasing*

5. $\displaystyle\int_{\pi/6}^{\pi/3} \dfrac{\cos\theta - \sin\theta}{\cos\theta + \sin\theta} d\theta = \left[\ln(\cos\theta + \sin\theta) \right]_{\pi/6}^{\pi/3}$

$= \ln\dfrac{1 + \sqrt{3}}{2} - \ln\dfrac{\sqrt{3} + 1}{2}$

$= 0$

6. $\mathbf{r} = \begin{pmatrix} 1 \\ 3 \\ 2 \end{pmatrix} + \lambda \begin{pmatrix} 5 \\ 1 \\ 3 \end{pmatrix}$

A is $(6, 4, 5)$ $\therefore 1 + 5\lambda = 6 \implies \lambda = 1$

Substituting $\lambda = 1$ in $\mathbf{r}$ $\Rightarrow$ $\mathbf{r} = \begin{pmatrix} 6 \\ 4 \\ 5 \end{pmatrix}$ $\quad \therefore$ A is on the line.

B is (11, 3, 9) $\quad \therefore 1 + 5\lambda = 11 \quad \Rightarrow \lambda = 2$

Substituting $\lambda = 2$ in $\mathbf{r}$ $\Rightarrow$ $\mathbf{r} = \begin{pmatrix} 11 \\ 5 \\ 8 \end{pmatrix}$ $\quad \therefore$ B not on the line.

AB is $\begin{pmatrix} 11 - 6 \\ 3 - 4 \\ 9 - 5 \end{pmatrix} = \begin{pmatrix} 5 \\ -1 \\ 4 \end{pmatrix}$

Angle between AB and line is angle between $\begin{pmatrix} 5 \\ -1 \\ 4 \end{pmatrix}$ and $\begin{pmatrix} 5 \\ 1 \\ 3 \end{pmatrix}$.

$\theta = \cos^{-1} \dfrac{\begin{pmatrix} 5 \\ -1 \\ 4 \end{pmatrix} \cdot \begin{pmatrix} 5 \\ 1 \\ 3 \end{pmatrix}}{\sqrt{42}\sqrt{35}} = 20 \cdot 1°$

For C: $x_C - x_B = x_B - x_A \Rightarrow x_C - 11 = 11 - 6 \quad \therefore x_C = 16$
Similarly $y_C = 2$ and $z_C = 13 \quad \therefore$ C is (16, 2, 13)

7.

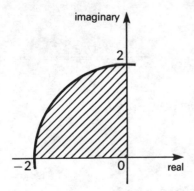

8. $\displaystyle\int_1^2 \dfrac{(2x - 1)^2}{x}\,\mathrm{d}x = \int_1^2 \dfrac{4x^2 - 4x + 1}{x}\,\mathrm{d}x$

$\displaystyle\int_1^2 \left(4x - 4 + \dfrac{1}{x}\right)\mathrm{d}x = \left[2x^2 - 4x + \ln x\right]_1^2 = 2 + \ln 2$

9. $\ln(2+x) = \ln2\left(1 + \frac{x}{2}\right) = \ln2 + \ln\left(1 + \frac{x}{2}\right)$ *need to make ln(1 + ?)*

$= \ln2 + \frac{x}{2} - \frac{1}{2}\left(\frac{x}{2}\right)^2 + \frac{1}{3}\left(\frac{x}{2}\right)^3 \cdots = \ln2 + \frac{x}{2} - \frac{x^2}{8} + \frac{x^3}{24} \cdots$

Valid for $-1 < \frac{x}{2} < 1 \Rightarrow -2 < x < 2$.

10. $\dfrac{i^5 + 1}{i^3} = \dfrac{(i+1)}{-i}\cdot\dfrac{i}{i} = \dfrac{i^2 + i}{-i^2} = -1 + i$

ANSWERS TO WORKSHEET 22

1. $\dfrac{(3-2i)}{(2+3i)}\dfrac{(2-3i)}{(2-3i)} = \dfrac{-13i}{4+9} = -i \Rightarrow a = 0, b = -1$

   $|z| = 1 \quad \arg z = 270°$.

2. Area required = OABC

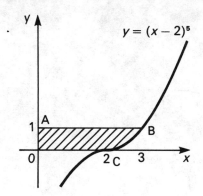

$A = \displaystyle\int_0^1 x\,dy = \int_0^1 (y^{1/5} + 2)\,dy$ *area between curve and y-axis is $\int x\,dy$*

$\therefore A = \left[\dfrac{5}{6}y^{6/5} + 2y\right]_0^1 = \dfrac{5}{6} + 2 = 2\tfrac{5}{6}$ square units

3. $e^{ix} = 1 + ix + \dfrac{(ix)^2}{2!} + \dfrac{(ix)^3}{3!} + \dfrac{(ix)^4}{4!} + \cdots$ *using series for e^x, page 242*

   $= 1 + ix - \dfrac{x^2}{2!} - \dfrac{ix^3}{3!} + \dfrac{x^4}{4!} + \dfrac{ix^5}{5!}\cdots$

   $= \left(1 - \dfrac{x^2}{2!} + \dfrac{x^4}{4!} - \cdots\right) + i\left(x - \dfrac{x^3}{3!} + \dfrac{x^5}{5!}\cdots\right)$ *separating real and imaginary*

$\therefore \, e^{ix} = \cos x + i \sin x$ *using series for sinx, cosx page 213*

$e^{-ix} \Rightarrow \cos x - i \sin x$

Adding: $\Rightarrow e^{ix} + e^{-ix} = 2\cos x \Rightarrow \cos x = \dfrac{e^{ix} + e^{-ix}}{1} \Rightarrow$

Subtracting: $\Rightarrow e^{ix} - e^{-ix} = 2i\sin x \Rightarrow \sin x = \dfrac{e^{ix} - e^{-ix}}{2i}$

> cosx and sinx defined in terms of e^x. Not in basic A level but useful in that they help to illustrate the unification of the subject.

4. $A = \pi ab$ Differentiating: $\Rightarrow 0 = \pi a \cdot \dfrac{db}{dt} + \pi b \cdot \dfrac{da}{dt}$

$\therefore \dfrac{da}{dt} = -\dfrac{a}{b} \cdot \dfrac{db}{dt}$

> A very easy question. Don't let the wording put you off.

5. If the roots are α, β, γ then:

$(x - \alpha)(x - \beta)(x - \gamma) = 0$

$\Rightarrow x^3 - (\alpha + \beta + \gamma)x^2 + (\alpha\beta + \alpha\gamma + \beta\gamma)x - \alpha\beta\gamma = 0$

c.f. with $x^3 + bx^2 + cx + d = 0$ $b = -(\alpha + \beta + \gamma)$

$c = \alpha\beta + \alpha\gamma + \beta\gamma$

$d = -\alpha\beta\gamma$

> c.f. these results with those for a quadratic: another illustration that the subject can always be developed further.

6. Let $z = x + iy$, then

$(x + iy)(x - iy) + 3(x + iy) = 56 + 12i$

$\Rightarrow x^2 + y^2 + 3x + i \cdot 3y = 56 + 12i$

c.f. imaginary part: $3y = 12 \Rightarrow y = 4$

and $x^2 + 3x - 40 = 0 \Rightarrow x = -8$ or 5 *comparing the real parts and substituting for y.*

$\therefore z$ is $-8 + 4i$ or $5 + 4i$

> z has to be written as 'real + imaginary' before you can progress – the usual opening for questions of this type.

7. $y = 10 - 12x + 6x^2 - x^3$

$\Rightarrow \dfrac{dy}{dx} = -12 + 12x - 3x^2 = -3(2 - x)^2 < 0$ for all x.

$\therefore$ the gradient is always negative – a decreasing function.

8. $\displaystyle\int_0^{\pi/2} e^x \cos x \, dx = \left[e^x \sin x \right]_0^{\pi/2} - \int_0^{\pi/2} e^x \sin x \, dx$

$= \left[e^x \sin x \right]_0^{\pi/2} - \left\{ \left[-e^x \cos x \right]_0^{\pi/2} + \int_0^{\pi/2} e^x \cos x \, dx \right\}$

$\Rightarrow 2I = e^{\pi/2} - 1 \quad \therefore I = \dfrac{1}{2}(e^{\pi/2} - 1)$

9. $(1 + ax)^{-1} - 2(2 - x)^{-1} = (1 + ax)^{-1} - 2 \cdot 2^{-1} \left(1 - \dfrac{x}{2}\right)^{-1}$

$$= (1 - ax + a^2 x^2 \cdots) - \left(1 + \dfrac{x}{2} + \dfrac{x^2}{4} + \cdots\right)$$

The term in x^2 is: $\left(a^2 - \dfrac{1}{4}\right) x^2 = 0 \implies a = \pm \dfrac{1}{2}$.

> A popular type of question i.e. where terms of two expansions are combined or compared.

10. $y = 4\cos^3\theta - 2\cos^2\theta - \cos\theta$

$$\dfrac{dy}{d\cos\theta} = 12\cos^2\theta - 4\cos\theta - 1 = (6\cos\theta + 1)(2\cos\theta - 1)$$

$$\dfrac{dy}{d\cos\theta} = 0 \text{ for } \cos\theta = -\tfrac{1}{6} \text{ and } \cos\theta = \tfrac{1}{2}$$

> Not a common question but a type you should be aware of.

ANSWERS TO WORKSHEET 23

1. $\displaystyle\int y \, dy = \int 2x \, dx$ *separating the variables*

$$\therefore \dfrac{y^2}{2} = x^2 + A \quad x = 1, y = 1 \implies A = -\dfrac{1}{2}$$

$\therefore$ the solution is $y^2 = 2x^2 - 1$

2. Let $x = 3\sin\theta \implies dx = 3\cos\theta \, d\theta$

$$I = \int_0^{\pi/2} 3\cos\theta \sqrt{9 - 9\sin^2\theta} \, d\theta = 0 \, 9\cos^2\theta \, d\theta$$

$$= 9 \int_0^{\pi/2} \dfrac{1}{2} (\cos 2\theta + 1) \, d\theta = 9 \left[\dfrac{1}{4}\sin 2\theta + \dfrac{1}{2}\theta\right]_0^{\pi/2}$$

$$= \dfrac{9\pi}{4}$$

> substitution suggested by $\sqrt{c - x^2}$
> c = constant and remembering to change the limits

3. $\dfrac{dy}{dx} = e^y \sin x \implies \displaystyle\int e^{-y} \, dy = \int \sin x \, dx$

$\implies -e^{-y} = -\cos x + A \quad x = 0, y = 0 \implies A = 0$

$\therefore e^{-y} = \cos x \implies e^y = \sec x$

$\therefore y = \ln \sec x$

4. $4z - 3z\bar{z} = -7 - 4i$

Let $z = x + iy \implies 4(x + iy) - 3(x^2 + y^2) = -7 - 4i$

c.f. imaginary parts: $4y = -4 \quad y = -1$

c.f. real parts and substituting: $4x - 3x^2 - 3 = -7$

$3x^2 - 4x - 4 = 0 \Rightarrow x = -\dfrac{2}{3}$ or $x = 2$

$\therefore z$ is $-\dfrac{2}{3} - i$ or $2 - i$

5. $I = \displaystyle\int \dfrac{x^2}{\sqrt{1 - x^2}}\,dx \quad x = \sin\theta \Rightarrow \int dx = \int \cos\theta\,d\theta$

$\therefore I = \displaystyle\int \dfrac{\cos\theta \sin^2\theta}{(\sqrt{(1 - \sin^2\theta)})}\,d\theta = \int \sin^2\theta\,d\theta$

$\therefore I = \dfrac{1}{2}\displaystyle\int (1 - \cos2\theta)\,d\theta = \dfrac{\theta}{2} - \dfrac{1}{4}\sin2\theta + A$

$\therefore I = \dfrac{1}{2}\sin^{-1}x - \dfrac{1}{2}\cdot x\sqrt{1 - x^2} + A$

> Substitute back to original variable in indefinite integrals

6. $\dfrac{dv}{dt} = k(1 + v^2) \Rightarrow \displaystyle\int \dfrac{dv}{1 + v^2} = \int k\,dt$

$\therefore \tan^{-1}v = kt + A \quad t = 0, v = 1 \Rightarrow A = \dfrac{\pi}{4}(\tan^{-1}1)$

$\therefore \tan^{-1}v = kt + \dfrac{\pi}{4} \Rightarrow v = \tan(kt + \dfrac{\pi}{4})$

> constant of proportionality – long name for such as a in $y = ax$, $y = ax^2$ etc.

7. The vector $\begin{pmatrix} 2 \\ 5 \\ 1 \end{pmatrix}$ is perpendicular to first plane and $\begin{pmatrix} a \\ b \\ c \end{pmatrix}$ is perpendicular to second plane.

> A test in understanding of the equation of a plane.

If planes are $\perp$ then $\begin{pmatrix} 2 \\ 5 \\ 1 \end{pmatrix} \perp \begin{pmatrix} a \\ b \\ c \end{pmatrix}$

$\therefore \begin{pmatrix} 2 \\ 5 \\ 1 \end{pmatrix} \cdot \begin{pmatrix} a \\ b \\ c \end{pmatrix} = 0 \Rightarrow 2a + 5b + c = 0$

8. $\displaystyle\int_1^2 x^2 e^x\,dx = \left[x^2 e^x \right]_1^2 - \int_1^2 2x e^x\,dx \quad by\ parts\ v = x^2,\ du = e^x$

$= \left[x^2 e^x \right]_1^2 - \left\{ \left[2x e^x \right]_1^2 - \int_1^2 2e^x\,dx \right\}$

$= 4e^2 - e - 4e^2 + 2e + \left[2e^x \right]_1^2$

$= 2e^2 - e = 12$ to nearest whole number.

9. $\int \dfrac{V}{e^{V^2}}\,dV = \int \ln(2t + \varepsilon)\,dt$ *separating the variables*

$\therefore \int Ve^{-V^2}\,dV = \int \ln(2t + \varepsilon)\,dt$

$\Rightarrow -\dfrac{1}{2}e^{-V^2} = t\ln(2t + \varepsilon) - \int \dfrac{2t}{2t + \varepsilon}\,dt$ *by parts using* $\ln(2t + \varepsilon) = 1 \times \ln(2t + \varepsilon)$

$= t\ln(2t + \varepsilon) - \int\left(1 - \dfrac{\varepsilon}{2t + \varepsilon}\right)dt$

$\therefore -\dfrac{1}{2}e^{-V^2} = t\ln(2t + \varepsilon) - t + \dfrac{\varepsilon}{2}\ln(2t + \varepsilon) + A$

$\Rightarrow (2t + \varepsilon)\ln(2t + \varepsilon) - 2t + e^{-V^2} = c$

> You will have to learn not to be put off by complicated looking answers. With care this question is quite straightforward.

10. $a = -2$: three means $\therefore ar^4 = -162$.

$\Rightarrow \dfrac{ar^4}{a} = r^4 = -\dfrac{162}{-2} \Rightarrow r = \pm 3$

$\therefore$ the means are $6, -18, 54$ or $-6, -18, -54$

ANSWERS TO WORKSHEET 24

1. $V = \pi \displaystyle\int_0^2 x^2 e^{2x}\,dx$ *using* $V = \pi\int y^2\,dx$

$= \pi\left[\dfrac{x^2 e^{2x}}{2}\right]_0^2 - \pi\displaystyle\int_0^2 \dfrac{2xe^{2x}}{2}\,dx$ *by parts* $v = x^2,\ du = e^{2x}$

$= 2\pi e^4 - \pi\left\{\left[\dfrac{xe^{2x}}{2}\right]_0^2 - \displaystyle\int_0^2 \dfrac{e^{2x}}{2}\,dx\right\}$

$= 2\pi e^4 - \pi e^4 + \dfrac{e^4}{4} - \dfrac{1}{4} = e^4\left(\pi + \dfrac{1}{4}\right) - \dfrac{1}{4}$

2. $(1 + ax)^{-3} = 1 - 3ax + 6a^2x^2\cdots$

$\Rightarrow -3a = 6a^2 \Rightarrow a = -\tfrac{1}{2}$ (or 0)

3. $(x^2y + xy - 12y)\dfrac{dy}{dx} = 1$

$\Rightarrow \displaystyle\int y\,dy = \int \dfrac{1}{x^2 + x - 12}\,dx = \int \dfrac{1}{(x + 4)(x - 3)}\,dx$

$\Rightarrow \dfrac{y^2}{2} = \displaystyle\int\left(\dfrac{1}{7(x - 3)} - \dfrac{1}{7(x + 4)}\right)dx$

$\Rightarrow \dfrac{y^2}{2} = \dfrac{1}{7}\ln\left(\dfrac{x - 3}{x + 4}\right) + A$

$$\Rightarrow \frac{y^2}{2} = \frac{1}{7}\ln\left(\frac{x-3}{x+4}\right) + \frac{1}{7}\ln B$$

$$\Rightarrow 7y^2 = 2\ln B\left(\frac{x-3}{x+4}\right)$$

*constant written in form of log so that
it can be combined as on this line.*

4. $I = \displaystyle\int_2^6 x^2\sqrt{12 - x^2 - 4x}\,dx$ *suggests $\sqrt{c - x^2}$ type*

$$= \int_2^6 x^2\sqrt{16 - (x^2 - 4x + 4)}\,dx = \int_2^6 x^2\sqrt{16 - (x-2)^2}\,dx$$

Let $\dfrac{x-2}{4} = \sin\theta \Rightarrow \displaystyle\int dx = \int \cos\theta\,d\theta$

$$\therefore I = \int_0^{\pi/2} 4(2 + 4\sin\theta)^2\sqrt{1 - \sin^2\theta}\,\cos\theta\,d\theta$$

$$= \int_0^{\pi/2} 16(1 + 4\sin\theta + 4\sin^2\theta)\cos^2\theta\,d\theta$$

$$= 16\int_0^{\pi/2} (\cos^2\theta + 4\sin\theta\cos^2\theta + \sin^2 2\theta)\,d\theta$$

$$= 16\left[\frac{1}{4}\sin2\theta + \frac{\theta}{2} - \frac{4}{3}\cos^3\theta + \frac{\theta}{2} - \frac{1}{8}\sin4\theta\right]_0^{\pi/2}$$

$$= 16\left(\frac{\pi}{4} + \frac{\pi}{4}\right) - 16\left(\frac{-4}{3}\right)$$

$$= 8\pi + \frac{64}{3}$$

A long solution – a test in stamina. They won't come any worse than this one.

5. The roots of the equation are α and $\dfrac{1}{\alpha}$.

Then $\alpha . \dfrac{1}{\alpha} = 1 = \dfrac{r}{p} \Rightarrow p = r$

6. $\dfrac{dx}{dt} = x^2 e^{3t} \Rightarrow \displaystyle\int \frac{dx}{x^2} = \int e^{3t}\,dt$

$$\Rightarrow -\frac{1}{x} = \frac{1}{3}e^{3t} + A$$

Substituting $x = 1$, $t = 1 \Rightarrow A = -1 - \frac{1}{3}e^3$

$$\Rightarrow 1 - \frac{1}{x} = \frac{1}{3}(e^{3t} - e^3) \Rightarrow 3(x-1) = x(e^{3t} - e^3)$$

$$\therefore x = \frac{3}{3 - e^{3t} + e^3}$$

when $t = 0$, $x = \dfrac{3}{2 + e^3} = 0\cdot 14$

7. $\left(2x^3 - \dfrac{1}{x}\right)^{20}$

Required term is $\dbinom{20}{n}(2x^3)^n\left(-\dfrac{1}{x}\right)^{20-n}$

where $3n = 20 - n$ $\quad \therefore x$ cancel out

$\Rightarrow n = 5$

$\therefore$ the required term is $\dfrac{20!}{5!15!}2^5(-1)^{15} = -496\,128$

8. $z_1 = 24 - 7i$ and $z_2 = -5 + 12i$

$$\therefore z_1 = \left(\sqrt{24^2 + 7^2},\ \tan^{-1}\dfrac{-7}{24}\right) = (25,\ -16\cdot 3°)$$

$\Rightarrow z_1 = 25(\cos(-16\cdot 3°) + i\sin(-16\cdot 3°)) = 25(\cos 16\cdot 3° - i\sin 16\cdot 3°)$

Similarly $z_2 = 13(-\cos 54\cdot 5° + i\sin 54\cdot 5°)$ from $z_2 = 13(\cos 125\cdot 5° + i\sin 125\cdot 5°)$

$z_1 z_2 = (325,\ (125\cdot 5° - 16\cdot 3°)) = 325(\cos 119\cdot 2° + i\sin 119\cdot 2°)$

or $z_1 z_2 = 325(-\cos 60\cdot 8° + i\sin 60\cdot 8°)$

9. $y = \ln(\ln \sin^2 x)$

$$\frac{dy}{dx} = \frac{1}{\ln \sin^2 x}\cdot\frac{1}{\sin^2 x}\cdot 2\sin x \cos x$$

$$= \frac{2\cot x}{\ln \sin^2 x}$$

10. Lines intersect.

$\therefore 1 + 2 \times 2 = 2 + 3a \Rightarrow a = 1$

$2 + 2 \times -1 = 0 + 3b \Rightarrow b = 0$

$3 + 2 \times 2 = 1 + 3c \Rightarrow c = 2$

ANSWERS TO WORKSHEET 25

1. $xy = 16 \quad \therefore y + x\cdot\dfrac{dy}{dx} = 0 \quad \therefore \dfrac{dy}{dx} = \dfrac{-y}{x}$

$x = 2,\ y = 8 \Rightarrow$ equation of normal is $y - 8 = \dfrac{2}{8}(x - 2)$

or $4y = x + 30$

2. $AC^2 = AB^2 - BC^2$ *Pythagoras' theorem*

$AB^2 = 1^2 + 3^2 = 10$ $(x_1 - x_2)^2 + (y_1 - y_2)^2$

$BC = \dfrac{12 + 12 - 11}{5} = \dfrac{13}{5}$ $d = \dfrac{ax_1 + by_1 + c}{\sqrt{a^2 + b^2}}$

$\therefore AC = \sqrt{10 - \dfrac{169}{25}} = 1 \cdot 8$

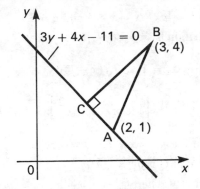

3. Suppose line cuts parabola in (x_1, y_1) and (x_2, y_2).

The midpoint is $\left(\dfrac{x_1 + x_2}{2}, \dfrac{y_1 + y_2}{2} \right)$

> An obvious but important line, as you will see later.

Solving the equations $\Rightarrow (3x - 1)^2 = 6(x + 2)$

$\Rightarrow 9x^2 - 12x - 11 = 0$

x_1 and x_2 are the roots of this equation which is a messy one to solve but we want $x_1 + x_2$, i.e. the sum of roots.

$\therefore$ x-coordinate of the midpoint is $\dfrac{1}{2} \cdot \dfrac{12}{9} = \dfrac{2}{3}$

> Be aware of this situation; if only the sum of the roots is required don't waste time finding the roots.

and y coordinate of the midpoint is $3x - 2 = 3 \cdot \dfrac{2}{3} - 2 = 0$

$\therefore$ the midpoint is $\left(\dfrac{2}{3}, 0 \right)$

4. $|z - i| \leqslant 2$

If $z = x + iy \Rightarrow x^2 + (y - 1)^2 \leqslant 4$

This is a circle centre $(0, 1)$, radius 2.

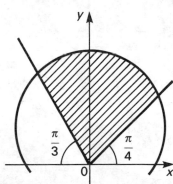

5. Line perpendicular to $y = -\dfrac{5}{4}x + \dfrac{1}{2}$ $\therefore$ gradient is $\dfrac{4}{5}$ and it passes through $(0, 4)$.

$\therefore$ the equation is $y = \dfrac{4}{5}x + 4 \Rightarrow 5y = 4x + 20$

6. c.f. with $y^2 = 4ax$ $x \to x - 1$ and $a = 3 - 1 = 2$

   $\therefore$ the equation is $y^2 = 8(x - 1)$

   $$\text{Area} = \int_1^5 y\,dx = \int_1^5 \sqrt{8}\sqrt{(x-1)}\,dx$$

   $$= \left[\sqrt{8}(x-1)^{3/2} \cdot \frac{2}{3}\right]_1^5 = 8\sqrt{8} = 16\sqrt{2} \text{ square units}$$

7. Tangent at P is $py = x + ap^2$

   and tangent at Q is $qy = x + aq^2$

   They meet at R where $y_R = a(p + q)$, $x_R = apq$

   Since the tangents are perpendicular to each other: $\dfrac{1}{p} \times \dfrac{1}{q} = -1$

   $\therefore pq = -1 \Rightarrow x_R = -a$

   $\therefore x_R$ is constant in value, $-a$, and the locus of R is $x = -a$, a straight line

8. $\dfrac{3 - 5x - 2x^2}{6 - 11x + 4x^2} = \dfrac{(3 + x)(1 - 2x)}{(4x - 3)(x - 2)}$

   $\therefore f(x) > 0$ for $-3 < x < \frac{1}{2}$ or $\frac{3}{4} < x < 2$.

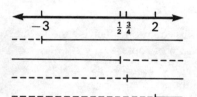

9. $y = \sin 2x$

   $y + \delta y = \sin 2(x + \delta x)$

   $\Rightarrow \delta y = \sin 2(x + \delta x) - \sin 2x = 2\cos(2x + \delta x)\sin\delta x$

   $\delta x + 0 \Rightarrow \dfrac{\delta y}{\delta x} = \dfrac{dy}{dx} = 2\cos 2x$

10. $\ln\left(\dfrac{1 + x}{1 - x}\right) = \ln(1 + x) - \ln(1 - x)$

    $$= \left(x - \frac{x^2}{2} + \frac{x^3}{3} - \frac{x^4}{4}\cdots\right) - \left(-x - \frac{x^2}{2} - \frac{x^3}{3}\cdots\right)$$

    $$= 2\left(x + \frac{x^3}{3} + \frac{x^5}{5} + \cdots\right)$$

ANSWERS TO WORKSHEET 26

1. M is midpoint of BC $\therefore$ M is $(2, 1)$

   Equation of AM: $\dfrac{y - 1}{x - 2} = \dfrac{4 - 1}{-1 - 2}$

   $\Rightarrow y + x = 3$

> The median is the line from the vertex to the midpoint of opposite side.

G is $x_A + \dfrac{2}{3}(x_M - x_A) = -1 + 2 = 1$, and $y_G = 2$

i.e. G is $(1, 2)$.

The equation of BG: $\dfrac{y - 2}{x - 1} = \dfrac{5 - 2}{3 - 1} \Rightarrow 2y = 3x + 1$

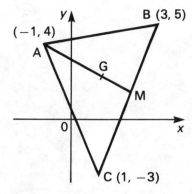

> The centroid is the centre of gravity of a triangle and it is the point where all three medians meet; $\frac{2}{3}$ way along any one from vertex to the opposite side.

2. It is a semi-cubical parabola.

$y^2 = x^3 \Rightarrow 2y\dfrac{dy}{dx} = 3x^2.$

At $(1, 1)$ $\dfrac{dy}{dx} = \dfrac{3}{2}.$

$\Rightarrow$ equation of tangent: $y - 1 = \dfrac{3}{2}(x - 1)$ i.e. $2y + 1 = 3x$

Substituting $y = \dfrac{3x - 1}{2}$ in $y^2 = x^3 \Rightarrow 4x^3 - 9x^2 + 6x - 1 = 0$

This has three roots but we know that two are 1 (twice).

$\therefore (x - 1)^2(4x - 1) = 0 \Rightarrow x = \frac{1}{4}, y = -\frac{1}{8}$

$\therefore$ it cuts the curve at $(\frac{1}{4}, -\frac{1}{8})$

3. $v\dfrac{dv}{dx} = c(1 + v^2)$

$\Rightarrow \displaystyle\int \dfrac{v\,dv}{1 + v^2} = \int c\,dx$

$\therefore \dfrac{1}{2}\ln(1 + v^2) = cx + A$

When $x = 0, v = 0 \Rightarrow A = 0$

$\therefore \ln(1 + v^2) = 2cx$

$1 + v^2 = e^{2cx}$

$v = \sqrt{(e^{2cx} - 1)}$

> **Remember:**
>
> acceleration may be written as $\dfrac{d^2x}{dt^2}$ or $\dfrac{dv}{dt}$ or $v\dfrac{dv}{dx}$. In this case the variables are v and x $\therefore$ use $v\dfrac{dv}{dx}$.

4. $(x - 4)^2 + m^2x^2 = 4$ *curve is a circle*

     $\therefore (m^2 + 1)x^2 - 8x + 12 = 0$

If the line is a tangent this equation has equal roots.

     $\therefore (-8)^2 = 4 \cdot (m^2 + 1) \cdot 12$ $b^2 = 4ac$

     $\Rightarrow m = \pm\dfrac{1}{\sqrt{3}} = \pm\dfrac{\sqrt{3}}{3}$

5. $x^2 + 2y^2 = 9 \Rightarrow 2x + 4y\dfrac{dy}{dx} = 0$ *curve is an ellipse*

At $(1, 2)\ \dfrac{dy}{dx} = -\dfrac{1}{4}$ $\Rightarrow$ gradient of normal is 4

and equation is $\dfrac{y - 2}{x - 1} = 4$ $\Rightarrow y + 2 = 4x$

Meets the curve again when $x^2 + 2(4x - 2)^2 = 9$ *substituting from linear in quadratic*

     $\Rightarrow 33x^2 - 32x - 1 = 0$

One known root of this is $x = 1$.

     $\therefore \Rightarrow (x - 1)(33x + 1) = 0$

The other root is $x = -\frac{1}{33}$.

It meets the curve again at $(-\frac{1}{33}, -\frac{70}{33})$.

6. $y = 5x$ has slope 5, $2y + 6x = 3$ has slope -3.

Then $\tan\theta = \dfrac{5 - -3}{1 + 5 \times -3} = \dfrac{8}{-14}$

     $\therefore \theta = 29 \cdot 7°$ *supplement of 150·3°*

7.

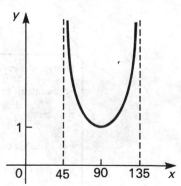

8.

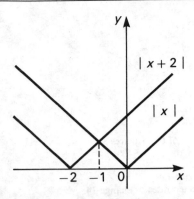

from graph:
$$|x| = |x + 2| \text{ for } x > -1$$

9. $x^2 + y^2 - 2x - 4y - 20 = 0 \Rightarrow$ circle centre $(1, 2)$, radius $= 5$.

If $3x + 4y + c = 0$ is a tangent it is 5 units from $(1, 2)$.

$$\therefore \frac{3 + 8 + c}{\sqrt{3^2 + 4^2}} = 5 \quad \text{using } d = \frac{ax_1 + by_1 + c}{\sqrt{a^2 + b^2}}$$

$$\Rightarrow \quad c = 25 - 11 = 14$$

Also the distance may be $-5 \Rightarrow c = -36$.

Not the only method, but the easiest.

10. (a) $z^2 = (3^2, \frac{\pi}{3})$ i.e. $9(\cos\frac{\pi}{3} + i\sin\frac{\pi}{3})$ or $\frac{9}{2} + i\frac{9\sqrt{3}}{2}$

(b) $\frac{z}{\bar{z}} = \left(\frac{3}{3}, \frac{\pi}{3}\right)$ i.e. $\cos\frac{\pi}{3} + i\sin\frac{\pi}{3}$ or $\frac{1}{2} + i\frac{\sqrt{3}}{2}$.

Index